Contractual Procedures in the Construction Industry

Third edition

ALLAN ASHWORTH

M.Sc., ARICS

Longman

Addison Wesley Longman
Addison Wesley Longman Limited,
Edinburgh Gate, Harlow,
Essex CM20 2JE, England
and associated companies throughout the world

© Addison Wesley Longman Limited 1985, 1996

First published 1985
Second edition 1991
Third edition 1996

British Library Cataloguing in Publication Data
A catalogue entry for this title is available from the British Library

ISBN 0-582-28875-4

Library of Congress Cataloging-in-Publication Data
A catalog entry for this title is available from the Library of Congress

Set by 4 in Times New Roman 10^1/$_2$/12^1/$_2$
Produced through Longman Malaysia, VVP

To Margaret, Amanda, and Caroline

Contents

Preface to the third edition

The aim of this book is to provide a knowledge of the nature, purpose and legal requirements of contractual procedures that are used in the construction industry. This knowledge can then be applied across the various types of project and procurement arrangements encountered in the industry. This book has been written for people in the construction industry. It has been prepared largely to meet the needs of students on undergraduate and higher technician courses across the different disciplines that are found in the industry. It also provides a good basis for anyone wishing to gain an understanding of the contractual procedures that are used in the industry.

The construction industry at the present time (the mid-1990s) is in a state of disarray. Output continues to decline, unemployment at all levels is rising, people are leaving the industry, the number of bankrupt builders is increasing and professional practices are having to regroup. Recent reports that property is no longer seen as a good investment in the United Kingdom, are also helping to prolong for the construction industry its worst depression in activities this century. However, it is at times like this that the industry becomes more responsive, efficient and innovative. It seeks out ways of encouraging people and organizations to desire the provision of new buildings. Consequently there is now a better use of technology, design and quality have improved and ways of reducing costs whilst maintaining quality are being achieved. The process of change, whilst evolutionary and gradual, has gathered apace as we move towards the end of the twentieth century.

There is also a sense that 'there is nothing new under the sun'. History somehow wants to repeat itself. The industry long ago was comprised of different tradesmen. Now these are known as subcontractors. The architect was responsible for their management and co-ordination. Today, many a project manager does a similar task. The different trade contractors recouped their costs for the work done. Today, we seem to want to see the merits in some form of cost plus arrangements. Our contractual procedures are being influenced by other industries in the UK and from countries abroad in Europe, USA and Japan. The dissatisfaction with our current arrangements is to some extent influenced by changes in society at large. In some cases it is also due to a lack of research and a better understanding of the procedures involved.

It is against this background that the third edition of *Contractual Procedures in the Construction Industry* has been written. The book is arranged in seven sections, each having a common theme. The largest of these sections includes a commentary on the JCT Standard Form of Building Contract (1980 edition). This continues to remain the most popular form at the present time. This commentary has attempted to group the clauses on the basis of common-theme chapters for ease of use and future reference purposes. A separate section deals with the different conditions appropriate to both nominated and domestic subcontract works. The family of JCT forms are likely to remain the most important contract conditions among architects, builders and surveyors.

The first section of the book provides a brief summary of the principles of contract law. Discerning students will wish to read more widely around this topic. They will therefore need, from time to time, to make reference to one or more of the standard legal texts dealing with the principles of law. However, it is anticipated that students studying contractual procedures for the first time may already have a good understanding of that subject, or are studying it concurrently with a study of contractual procedures. A new chapter on the settlement of disputes has been added to this part. This includes the existing chapter on arbitration with the addition of new material on litigation and alternative dispute resolution (ADR). The final section of the book provides a thumbnail sketch of some of the relevant interesting and important case law.

Other sections of the book provide a brief comparison with other contractual methods and forms that are also used in the construction industry. A further section describes the different parties and organizations that are normally involved in one way or another with construction projects. A new chapter has been included on site communications, and their impact on contractual procedures.

A section that has continued to grow with subsequent editions of the book, is that which deals with procurement. Interestingly this was almost a new word when the book was first written! The publication in 1994, of *Constructing the Team*, the Latham Report, has huge implications for contractual procedures in the construction industry. This report has generated almost enough material for a chapter of its own, entitled Procurement issues. Whilst there appears to be a desire to standardize practices and procedures, it appears that only a proposed construction bill through Parliament will have any real impact in this direction. As chapters in the book note, since Banwell's report in 1967, contractual procedures have become more divergent, which was contrary to the advice given at that time.

Allan Ashworth
York 1995

Acknowledgements

In preparing this third edition, I would like to express my thanks to my colleagues with whom I have exchanged ideas. I would like particularly in this respect to mention Mr Ian Bell, ARICS, of Nene College of Higher Education. Finally I would like to thank my wife and family for their continued support and patience during these times.

We are indebted to the copyright holder RIBA Publications Ltd for their kind permission in allowing us to reproduce extracts from the JCT Standard Form of Building Contract.

Table of relevant statutes
(Acts of Parliament)

A complete list of statutes can be found in *Halsbury's Statutes of England* (fourth edition).

Administration of Justice (Appeals) 1934
Arbitration Acts, 1934, 1950, 1975, 1979
Architects (Registration) Acts, 1931, 1938
Architects Registration (Amendment) Act 1969

Bankruptcy Acts, 1869, 1914
Building Act 1984
Building Societies Act 1986

Civil Jurisdiction and Judgments Act 1982
Companies Acts, 1948, 1985, 1989
Consumer Credit Act 1974
Consumer Protection Act 1987
Contracts (Applicable Law) Act 1990
Copyright, Design and Patents Act 1988
County Court Act 1984
Courts and Legal Services Act 1990

Defective Premises Act 1972

Employer's Liability (Compulsory Insurance) Act 1969
Employment Protection Acts, 1975, 1978
Environmental Protection Act 1990
European Communities Act 1972

Factories Acts, 1937, 1961
Fair Trading Act 1973
Finance Acts, 1970, 1971, 1972, 1975, 1980, 1985, 1989
Financial Services Act 1986

Health and Safety at Work Act 1974
Highways Acts, 1959, 1980
Housing Acts, 1936, 1957, 1959, 1961, 1974, 1985

Income and Corporation Taxes Act 1988
Industrial Training Act 1964
Insolvency Act 1986

Landlord and Tenant Act 1927
Latent Damage Act 1986
Law of Property Act, 1925, 1989
Limitation Acts, 1939, 1963, 1980
Local Government Acts, 1933, 1972, 1988
London Building Acts, 1894, 1930, 1939

Magistrates' Court Act 1980
Misrepresentation Act 1967

National Heritage Act 1983
National Insurance Act 1962

Official Secrets Acts, 1911, 1939

Partnership Act 1890
Patents Acts, 1949, 1977
Planning and Compensation Act 1991
Planning (Listed Buildings and Conservation) Act 1990
Prevention of Corruption Acts 1889–1916
Public Health Acts, 1848, 1875, 1908, 1936, 1961
Public Utilities Street Works Act 1950

Race Relations Act 1976
Restrictive Practices Act 1976
Rights of Light Act 1959

Sale of Goods Acts, 1893, 1979

Town and Country Planning Acts, 1947, 1968, 1971, 1990
Trade Descriptions Act 1968

Unfair Contract Terms Act 1977

War Damage Acts, 1943, 1965

Part 1

Contract law

Chapter 1

The English legal system

There are many individuals within the construction industry who will, at some time in their careers, become professionally involved in either litigation or arbitration. The laws which are applied in the construction industry are both of a general and a specialist nature. They are general in the sense that they embrace the tenets of law appropriate to all legal decisions; and are special since the interpretation of construction contracts and documents requires a particular knowledge and understanding of the construction industry. It should be noted, however, that the interpretation and application of law will not be contrary to or in opposition to the established legal principles and precedents found elsewhere. It is appropriate at this stage to consider briefly the framework of the English legal system.

The nature of law

Law, in its legal sense, may be distinguished from scientific law or the law of nature and from the rules of morality. In the first case, scientific laws are not man-made and are not therefore subject to change. In the case of morality it is less easy to draw a distinction between legal rules and moral precepts. It may be argued, for example, that the legal rules follow naturally from a correct moral concept. The difference between the two is, perhaps, that obedience to law is enforced by the state whereas morals are largely a matter of conscience and conduct. The laws of a country are, however, to some extent an expression of its current morality, since laws can generally only be enforced by a common consensus. Law, therefore, may be appropriately defined as a body of rules for the guidance of human conduct but which may be enforced by the authorities concerned.

Classification of law

Law is an enormous subject and some specialization is therefore essential. A complete classification system would require a very detailed chart. Essentially the basic division in the English legal system is the distinction between criminal and civil law. Usually, the distinction will be obvious. It is the difference between being prosecuted for a criminal offence and being sued for a civil wrong. If the aim of the person bringing the case is to punish the defendant then it will probably be a criminal case. However, if the aim is to obtain some form of compensation or other benefit then it will generally be a civil case.

Alternative methods of classification are to subdivide the offences that are committed against persons, property or the state under these headings. Laws may also be classified as either public or private. Public law is primarily concerned with the state itself. Private law is that part of the English legal system which is concerned with the rights and obligations of the individuals.

Sources of English law

Every legal system has its roots, the original sources from which authority is drawn. The sources of English law can be categorized in the following ways.

Custom

In the development of the English legal system the common law was derived from the different laws associated with the different parts of the country. These were adapted to form a national law common to the whole country. Since the difference between the regions stemmed from their different customary laws, it is no exaggeration to say that custom was the principal original source of the common law. The term 'custom' has three generally accepted meanings:
1.   General custom – accepted by the country at large.
2.   Mercantile custom – principles established on an international basis.
3.   Local custom – applicable only to certain areas within a country. The following conditions must be complied with before a local custom will be recognized as law:
      (a) The custom must have existed from 'time immemorial'. The date for this has been fixed as 1189.
      (b) The custom must be limited to a particular locality.
      (c) The custom must have existed continuously.
      (d) The custom must be a reasonable condition in the eyes of the law.
      (e) The custom must have been exercised openly.
      (f) The custom must be consistent with, and not in conflict with, existing laws.

In some countries the writings of legal authors can form an important source of law. In England, however, because of tradition, such writings have in the past been treated with comparatively little respect. They are, therefore, rarely cited in the courts. This general rule has always been subject to certain exceptions and there are therefore 'books of authority' which are almost treated as equal to precedents. Many of these books are very old, and in some cases date back to the twelfth century.

Legislation

The majority of new laws are made in a documentary form by way of an Act of Parliament. Statute has always been a source of English law and by the nineteenth century it rivalled decided cases as a source. If statute and common law clash, then the former will always prevail, since the courts cannot question the validity of any Act. The acceptance by the courts of Parliament's supremacy is entirely a matter for history. Today it is the most important new source of law because:

1. The complex nature of commercial and industrial life has necessitated legislation to create the appropriate organizations and legal framework.
2. Modern developments such as drugs and the motor car have necessitated legislation to prevent their abuse.
3. There are frequent changes in the attitudes of modern society, such as that relating to females, and the law must thus keep in step with society.

Before a legislative measure can become law it must undergo an extensive process.

1. The measure is first drafted by civil servants who present it to the House of Commons or the House of Lords as a 'Bill'.
2. The various clauses of the Bill will already have been accepted and agreed by the appropriate government department prior to its presentation.
3. Before the Bill can become an Act of Parliament it must undergo five stages in each house:
    (a) First reading – the Bill is introduced to the House.
    (b) Second reading – a general debate takes place upon the general principles of the measure.
    (c) Committee stage – each clause of the Bill is examined in detail.
    (d) Report stage – the House is brought up to date with the changes that have been made.
    (e) Third reading – only matters of detail are allowed to be made at this stage.

The length of time which is necessary for the Bill to pass through these various stages depends upon the nature and length of the Bill and how politically controversial it is. Once the Bill has been approved and accepted by each House, it then needs the Royal Assent for it to become law.

A public Bill is legislation which affects the public at large and applies throughout England and Wales. It should be noted at this point that Scottish law, although similar, is different from English law. A private Bill is legislation affecting only a limited section of the population, for example, in a particular locality. A Private Member's Bill is a public Bill introduced by a back-bench Member of Parliament as distinct from a public Bill which is introduced by the government in power.

Delegated legislation arises when a subordinate body makes laws under specific powers from Parliament. These can take the form of:

(a)   Orders in Council;
(b)   Statutory Instruments;
(c)   By-laws.

Whilst these are essential to the smooth running of the nation, the growth of delegated legislation can be criticized, because law making is transferred from the elected representatives to the minister, which is in effect the civil servants. The validity of delegated legislation can be challenged in the courts as being *ultra vires*, i.e. beyond the powers of the party making it, and thus making it void. The judicial safeguard depends on the parent legislation, i.e. the Act giving the powers. Often this is extremely wide and such a restraint may therefore be almost ineffectual.

All legislation requires interpreting. The object of interpretation is to ascertain Parliament's will as expressed in the Act. The courts are thus at least in theory concerned with what is stated and not with what it believes Parliament intended. A large proportion of cases reported to the House of Lords and the High Court involve questions of statutory interpretation and in many of these the legislature's intention is impossible to ascertain because it never considered the question before the court. The judge must then do what he thinks Parliament would have done had they considered the question.

Since Britain's entry into the European Community on 1 January 1973 it has been bound by Community law. All existing and future Community law which is self-executing is immediately incorporated into English law. A self-executing law therefore takes immediate effect and does not require action by the United Kingdom legislature.

Case law

Case law is often referred to as judicial precedent. It is the result of the decisions made by judges who have laid down legal principles derived from circumstances of the particular disputes coming before them. Importance is attached to this form of law in order that some form of consistency in application in practice can be achieved. The doctrine of judicial precedent is known as *stare decisis*, which literally means 'to stand upon decisions'. In practice, therefore, a judge, when trying a case must always look back to see how previous judges dealt with similar cases. In looking back the judge will expect to discover those principles of law which are relevant to the case now being decided. The decision made will therefore seek to be in accordance with the already established principles of law and may in turn develop those principles further. One fact which should be noted is that the importance of case law is governed by the status of the court which decided the case. The cases decided in a higher court will take precedence over the judgments in a lower court.

The main advantages claimed for judicial precedent are:

1.   Certainty – because judges must follow previous decisions, a barrister can usually advise a client on the outcome of a case.

2.   Flexibility – it is claimed that case law can be extended to meet new situations thereby allowing the law to adjust to new social conditions.

A direct result of the application of case law is that these matters must be properly reported and published and should be readily available for all future users. Consequently there is now available within the English legal system an enormous collection of law reports stretching back over many centuries. Within the construction professions a number of different firms and organizations now collate and publish law reports which are relevant to this industry. Computerized systems are also available to allow for rapid access and retrieval from such reports.

It is not the entire decision of a judge that creates a binding precedent. When a judgment is delivered, the judge will give the reason for the decision. This is known as *ratio decidendi*, and is a vital part of case law. It is the principle which is binding on subsequent cases that have similar facts in the same branch of law. The second aspect of judgments, *obiter dicta*, are things said 'by the way', and these do not have to be followed. Although the facts of a case appear similar to a binding precedent, a judge may consider that there is some aspect or fact which is not covered by the *ratio decidendi* of the earlier case. The judge will therefore 'distinguish' the present case from the earlier one which created the precedent.

A higher court may also consider that the *ratio decidendi* set in a lower court is not the correct law which should be followed. When another case is argued on similar facts, the higher court will overrule the previous precedent and set a new precedent to be followed in future cases. Such a decision does not affect the parties in the earlier case, unlike a decision that is reversed on appeal.

Finally a superior court may consider that there is some doubt as to the standing of a previous principle, and it may disapprove but not expressly overrule the earlier precedent.

Examples

The following are some examples of how the above sources of English law are appropriate to the construction industry:

Custom   – Right to light
         – Right of way
Legislation – Highways Act 1980
         – Town and Country Planning Act 1990
         – Local Government Act 1988
         – Control of Pollution Act 1974
         (See also Table of Statutes)
Cases   – *Hadley* v. *Baxendale* 1854
         – *Sutcliffe* v. *Thackrah and Others* 1974
         – *Dawber Williamson Roofing* v. *Humberside County Council* 1979

European Union Law

A completely new source of English law was created when Parliament passed the European Communities Act 1972. Section 2(1) of the Act provides that:

> All such rights, powers, liabilities, obligations and restrictions from time to time created or arising by or under the Treaties, and all such remedies and procedures from time to time provided for by or under the Treaties, as in accordance with the treaties are without further enactment to be given legal effect or used in the United Kingdom shall be recognized and available in law, and be inforced, allowed and followed accordingly ...

The effect of this section is that all United Kingdom courts have to recognize European Union law, whether it comes directly from treaties or other Community legislation. As soon as the 1972 Act became law, some aspects of English law were changed to bring them into line with European Union law.

There are several institutions to implement the work of the European Union. These include the European Parliament, the Council of Ministers, the Commission and the European Court of Justice.

The courts

There are a number of different courts in which civil actions may be tried. Cases are first heard in either the High Court or the County Court, and should an appeal be necessary, then the matter is brought to the Court of Appeal. Where the matter is still not resolved then it is brought to the House of Lords. Technical cases may be heard in the official referee's court. A further alternative is to allow the dispute to be settled through arbitration or alternative dispute resolution procedures. (See Chapter 5)

County Court

There are approximately 340 districts in England and Wales in which a County Court is held at least once a month. These are divided into 60 circuits, each with its own judge. A County Court can hear almost all types of civil cases. Its jurisdiction is limited to actions in contract and tort up to sums of £5,000; actions for the recovery of land where the net annual value for rating does not exceed £1,000; equity proceedings where the sum involved does not exceed £30,000 and some bankruptcy claims. These sums are kept under review. The main advantages claimed for County Courts are their lower costs and shorter delays before coming to trial. These are also the two similar reasons claimed for arbitration. The court comprises a circuit judge assisted by a registrar who is a solicitor of 7 years' standing. The latter mainly performs administrative tasks but, with the leave of the judge, he may hear actions in which the defendant does not appear, admits liability or where the claim does not exceed £2,000.

In order to reduce litigation coming before the County Court, and enable those with very small claims to bring an action without fear of excessive court costs, a 'small claims' procedure is now available.

The High Court

The High Court hears all the more important civil cases. It is the lower half of the Supreme Court of Judicature and was brought into being under the Judicature Acts 1873–1875. It comprises three divisions which all have equal competence to try any actions, according to the pressure of work, although certain specific matters are reserved for each of them:

1. The Queen's Bench Division (known as QBD) deals with all types of common law work, such as contract and tort. This is the busiest division. Matters concerning the construction industry usually come to this High Court. The division is headed by the Lord Chief Justice and there are about 40–50 lesser judges. These are known as puisne (pronounced 'puny') judges. There are two specialist courts within QBD. The Commercial Court hears major commercial disputes, usually in private, with the judge hearing the case in the more informal role of an arbitrator. The Admiralty Court hears maritime disputes.

2. The Chancery Division deals with such matters as trusts, mortgages, deeds, and land, taxation and partnership disputes. The division, whilst nominally headed by the Lord Chancellor and the Master of the Rolls, is actually run by a Vice-Chancellor, with the help of about ten to twelve lesser judges.

3. The Family Division deals with matters of family disputes such as probate and divorce. This division is headed by a President and three lesser judges.

The High Court normally sits at the Strand in London but there are fifteen other towns to which judges of the High Court travel to hear common law claims.

The Court of Appeal

Once a case has been heard either party may consider an appeal. This means that the case is transferred to the Court of Appeal where three judges usually sit to form a court. The High Court has the right to refuse an appeal. In civil appeals the appellant has 6 weeks from the date of judgment in which to give the Court of Appeal formal notice of appeal. The appellant must specify the exact grounds on which the appeal is based and on which the lower court reached an 'incorrect' decision.

The Civil Division hears appeals on questions of law and of fact, rehearsing the whole of the evidence presented to the court below relying on the notes made at the trial. If the appeal is allowed the court may reverse the decision of the lower court, or amend it, or order a retrial. It can hear appeals about the exercise of discretion; for example, discretion as to costs.

Most appeals are heard by three judges, although some (e.g. appeals from County Court decisions) can be heard by only two judges. Decisions need not be unanimous. The head of the court is the Master of the Rolls, perhaps the most influential appointment in our legal system.

The House of Lords

Appeals from decisions of the Court of Appeal are made to the House of Lords, although leave must first be obtained to do so and this is sparingly given. Permission is only given if the appeal is of general legal importance. The court used to sit in the Chamber of the House of Lords but since 1948 it has usually sat as an Appellate Committee in a committee room in the Palace of Westminster. The normal rule is that a case can only go to the House of Lords after it has been heard by the Court of Appeal, so the case progresses slowly up the judicial hierarchy. In exceptional circumstances it is possible to leap-frog over the Court of Appeal, but this is rarely done. There must be at least three judges for a committee to be quorate, although in practice appeals are heard by five judges.

All of the courts must apply statute law in reaching their decisions and, in general, the lower courts are bound by the decisions of the higher courts. In practice, the law resulting from a case to the House of Lords can only be changed by an Act of Parliament.

Arbitration

Arbitration is an alternative to litigation in the courts, and is widely used for the settlement of disputes which involve technical or commercial elements. The tribunal is chosen by the parties concerned, and the powers of the arbitrator largely depend upon agreement between these parties. Arbitration is more fully explained in Chapter 5.

Fig. 1.1 The court system

The lawyers

Solicitors

There are around 60,000 solicitors in England and Wales. They are the lawyers that the public most frequently meets and as such are the general practitioners of the legal profession. A solicitor's work falls into two main categories of court work and non-court work. The latter accounts for about three-quarters of their business. A solicitor operates in many ways like a businessman, with an office to run, clients to see and correspondence to be answered. Traditionally, property (conveyancing and probate) has been one of the main fee earners.

The Solicitors Act 1974 gave solicitors three monopolies: of conveyancing; probate; and suing and starting court proceedings. The conveyancing monopoly was, however, significantly eroded by the Administration of Justice Act 1985. This allowed for licensed conveyancers to do this work.

The Law Society is the solicitor's professional body and as such it has two roles: firstly, to act as the representative body of solicitors, and secondly, to ensure that proper professional standards are maintained and that defaulting solicitors are disciplined. It lays down the rules on professional conduct, the most important of which prohibits touting for business or unfair attraction of business. Advertising of solicitors' services is now allowed in the press and on the radio, but they must be very careful what they say about themselves. They cannot claim, for example, that they do a better job than another firm of solicitors.

Barristers

There are about 4,000 barristers in England and Wales. They are specialist advocates and the specialist advisers of the legal profession. About 10 per cent of the Bar is made up of Queen's Counsel. Whilst solicitors may appear in the lower courts, barristers have a monopoly over appearing in the higher courts. Some of their work is non-court work, such as advising on difficult points of law or on how a particular case should be conducted.

Barristers cannot form partnerships with other barristers; several barristers will, however, share a set of rooms, known as chambers, and employ clerical staff and a clerk between them. They will not, however, share their earnings in the way that a firm of solicitors would.

Future considerations

Law is sometimes seen as a question of how far you can afford to go rather than how good your case is. Lord Wolf, the current Law Lord, is currently heading a commission to help remedy the huge problems of cost, delay, complexity and inequality in the civil justice system. The key is to recognize that justice is not an abstract quality. It has to be proportionate, within the means of the parties and expeditious. Many people are denied access to the courts because the costs involved are disproportionate to their claims. Lord Wolf is suggesting that in future, judges should become trial managers able to dictate the pace of legal cases. Attitudes must change but the powers to encourage settlement or to strike out unworthy cases must also be provided. Judges should also be able to encourage litigants to look at other ways of settling disputes such as mediation or alternative dispute resolution (see Chapter 5). These procedures encourage early settlement. They should also to be able to give summary judgment, leaving only the core of the dispute to go to trial. The key proposals include:

- small claims court expanded to take claims up to £3,000;
- fast track cases up to £10,000 including personal injury claims with capped costs and fixed hearings;
- new multi-track for cases above £10,000 providing 'hands on' management teams by judges for heaviest cases;
- new post of Head of Civil Justice to run all civil courts as a single system. Post to be filled by a senior judge;
- better use of technology, with laptop computers for all judges and video conference facilities;
- incentives for early settlement including 'plaintiff's offer' and referral to alternative dispute procedures;
- solicitors to inform clients of charges as the bill for legal services mounts.

The consequences at the present time of the current system is that it is often excessive, disproportionate and unpredictable. The delay is frequently unreasonable. In 1994, for example, High Court cases took on average 163 weeks in London just to reach trial. Outside of London it was even longer at 189 weeks. In the County Courts the typical figure was 80 weeks.

The report recommends a three-track civil system with a single entry point, headed by a senior judge in a new post of Head of Civil Justice. A key point of the proposed system is to encourage settlement. Both parties will be able to make offers to settle at any stage, relating to the whole case or just one of the issues involved.

It should also be noted that annually almost 300,000 writs are lodged with the Lord Chancellor's Office, with only a fraction, less than 3 per cent, ever coming to trial.

Some legal jargon

abate	To reduce or make less.
actus reus	The guilty act.
ad valorem	According to the value. For example, stamp duty on sale of land is charged according to the price paid.
affidavit	A written statement to be used as evidence in court proceedings.

ancient lights	Windows which have had an uninterrupted access of light for at least 20 years. Buildings cannot be erected which interfere with this right of light.
attestation	The signature of a witness to the signing of a document by another person.
burden of proof	The obligation of proving the case.
caveat emptor	Let the buyer beware.
certiorari	An order of the High Court to review and quash the decision of the lower court which was based on an irregular procedure.
chattels	All property other than freehold real estate.
consideration	Where a person promises to do something for another it can only be enforced if the other person gave or promised to give something of value in return. Every contract requires consideration.
costs	The expenses relating to legal services.
counterclaim	When a defendant is sued any claim against the plaintiff may be included, even if it arises from a different matter.
custom	An unwritten law dating back to time immemorial.
defendant	A person who is sued or prosecuted, or who has any court proceedings brought against him.
enactment	An Act of Parliament, or part of an Act.
estoppel	A rule which prevents a person denying the truth of a statement or the existence of facts which another person has been led to believe.
ex-parte	An application to the court by one party to the proceedings without the other party being present.
expert witness	One who is able to give an opinion on a subject. This is an exception to the rule that a witness must only tell the facts.
fieri facias	A court order to the sheriff requiring the seizure of a debtor's goods to pay off a creditor's judgment.
frustration	A contract is frustrated if it becomes impossible to perform because of a reason that is beyond the control of the parties. The contract is then cancelled.
good faith	Honesty.
goodwill	The whole advantage, wherever it may be, of the reputation and connection of the firm.
in camera	When evidence is not heard in open court.
injunction	A court order requiring someone to do, or to refrain from doing, something.
judicial review	An application made to the Divisional Court when a lower court or tribunal has behaved incorrectly.
limitation	Court proceedings must begin within a limitation period. Different periods exist for different types of claim.

liquidated sum	A specific sum, or a sum that can be worked out as a matter of arithmetic.
liquidator	A person who winds up a company.
moiety	One-half.
obiter dictum	A statement of opinion by a judge which is not relevant to the case being tried. It is not of such authority as if it had been relevant to the case being tried.
official referee	A layman appointed by the High Court to try complex matters in which he is a specialist.
plaintiff	Person who sues.
plc	A public limited company. Most used to call themselves 'Ltd' but changed this when UK company law was brought into line with EC law in 1981.
pleadings	Formal written documents in a civil action. The plaintiff submits a statement of claim and the defendant a defence.
pre-trial review	Preliminary meeting of parties in a County Court action to consider administrative matters and what agreement can be reached prior to the trial.
quantum meruit	As much as has been earned.
ratio decidendi	The reason for a judicial decision. A statement of legal principle in a *ratio decidendi* is more authoritative than if in an *obiter dictum*.
res ipsa loquitor	The matter speaks for itself.
retrospective legislation	An Act that applies to a period before the Act was passed.
seal	This used to be an impression of a piece of wax to a document. Now a small red sticky label is used instead. The absence of the seal will not invalidate the document, since to constitute a sealing neither wax, wafer, a piece of paper or even an impression is necessary.
sine die	Indefinitely.
special damage	Financial loss that can be proved.
specific performance	When a party to a contract is ordered to carry out their part of the bargain. Only ordered where monetary damages would be an inadequate remedy.
stare decisis	To stand by decided matters. Alternative name for the doctrine of precedent.
statute	An Act of Parliament.
statutory instrument	Subordinate legislation made by the Queen in Council or a minister, in exercise of a power granted by statute.
stay of proceedings	When a court action is stopped by the court.
subpoena	A court order that a person attends court, either to give evidence or to produce documents.

uberrimae fidei	Of utmost good faith.
unenforceable	A contract or other right that cannot be enforced because of a technical defect.
vicarious liability	When one person is responsible for the actions of another because of their relationship.
void	Of no legal effect.
voidable	Capable of being set aside.
with costs	The winner's cost will be paid by the loser.
writ	The document that commences many High Court actions.

Chapter 2

Legal aspects of contracts

A number of Acts of Parliament affect construction contracts, although it is only during this present century that they have begun to play any significant part. Historically the law of contract has evolved by judicial decisions, so that there now exists a body of principles which apply generally to all types of construction contract. These principles have been accepted on the basis of proven cases that have been brought before the courts.

Construction contracts are usually made in writing, using one of the standard forms available. The use of a standard form provides many advantages, and although standard forms are not mandatory in practice their use should be encouraged in all possible circumstances. It is important to remember, however, that the making of a contract does not require any special formality. A binding contract could be made by an exchange of letters between the parties, rather than signing an elaborate printed document. On some occasions a binding contract could be made by a gentlemen's agreement, i.e. by word of mouth. There are, however, many practical reasons why construction contracts for all but the simplest projects should be made using an approved and accepted form of contract.

Definition of a contract

A contract has been defined by Sir William Anson as 'a legally binding agreement made between two or more parties, by which rights are acquired by one or more to acts or forbearances on the part of the other or others'. The essential elements of this definition are as follows:

1. *Legally binding.* Not all agreements are legally binding. In particular there are social or domestic arrangements which are made without any intention of creating legal arrangements.
2. *Two or more parties.* In order to have an agreement there must be at least two parties. In law one cannot make bargains with oneself.
3. *Rights are acquired.* An essential feature of a contract is that legal rights are acquired. One person agrees to complete part of a deal and the other person agrees to do something else in return.
4. *Forbearances.* To forbear is to refrain from doing something. There may

thus be a benefit to one party to have the other party promise not to do something.

Agreement

The whole basis of the law of contract is agreement. Specifically, a contract is an agreement bringing with it obligations which are able to be enforced in the courts if this becomes necessary. Most of the principles of modern contract date from the eighteenth and nineteenth centuries. The concept of a contract at that time was of equals coming together to bargain and reach agreement, which they would wish to be upheld by the courts. Whilst it is still true that individuals come together to form agreements, it should be recognized that many contracts are formed between parties who are not equals in any way, even where the law may pretend that they are. A major criticism of contract law in recent years has been that the wealthy, experienced and legally advised corporations have been able to make bargains with many people who are themselves of limited resources and poorly legally represented. Because of this the law of contract has gradually moved away from a total commitment to enforce, without qualification, any agreement which has the basic elements of a contract. In particular, Parliament has introduced statutes which are often designed to protect relatively weak consumers from businessmen having greater bargaining power. Despite this, the courts are still reluctant to set aside an agreement having all of the elements of a contract and in this respect follow their nineteenth-century predecessors.

The elements of a contract

Capacity

In general every person has full legal powers to enter into whatever contracts they might choose. There are, however, some broad exceptions to this general rule. Infants and minors, that is anyone under the age of 18 years as set out in the Family Law Reform Act 1969, cannot contract other than in certain circumstances, such as, for example, for necessaries or benefits. Persons of an unsound mind, as defined in the Mental Health Act 1959, can never make a valid contract. Other persons of an unsound mind, and those unbalanced by intoxication are treated alike. Their contracts are divided into two types, those for necessary goods (the situation with minors above) and other contracts where the presumption is one of validity. Corporations are legal entities created by a process of law. A company can only contract on matters falling within its objects clause, and since the records of companies are matters of public record available for inspection at Companies House it used to be the case that a company could not have a contract enforced against it if it lay outside its objects clause. The presumption was that those entering into contracts with a

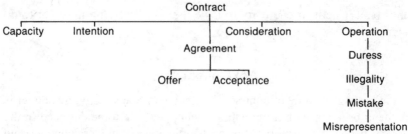

Fig. 2.1 The elements of a contract

company knew or ought to have known the contents of the objects clause. Consequently anyone making an *ultra-vires* (outside-the-powers) contract with a company only had themselves to blame. On entry into the European Community in 1973 this *ultra-vires* doctrine had to be revised, since it is not followed in the other countries of the Community.

Intention to create legal relations

As mentioned earlier, merely because there is an agreement, it cannot be assumed that an enforceable contract exists. English law requires that the parties to a contract actually intended to enter into legal relations. These are relations actionable and enforceable in the courts. If it can be demonstrated that no such intention existed then the courts will not intervene, despite the presence of both agreement and consideration. In commercial agreements the courts presume that the parties do intend to enter into legal relations. (This is different from social, family and other domestic agreements, where the general rule is that the courts presume that there is no intention to enter into legal relations.) These are the general rules and it is also possible to demonstrate the opposite intention.

In contract law we need to know what we have agreed. It is possible for two parties to use words which are susceptible to interpretation in different ways, so that they do not have the same idea in mind when they agree. It is important that both parties have agreement to the same idea (*consensus ad idem*). The classic case to which students should refer is *Raffles* v. *Wichelhaus* (1864).

Offer and acceptance

The basis of the contract is agreement and this is composed of two parts: offer and acceptance. In addition, conditions are generally required by law (in all but the simplest of contracts) to make the offer and acceptance legally binding.

The offer

An offer must be distinguished from a mere attempt to negotiate. An offer, if it is accepted, will become a binding contract. An invitation for contractors to submit tenders is inviting firms to submit offers for doing the work. The invitation often states that the employer is not bound to accept the lowest or any tender or to be responsible for the costs incurred.

An offer may be revoked by the person who made it, at any time before it is accepted. Thus a contractor may submit a successful tender in terms of winning the contract. However, the contractor may choose to revoke this offer prior to formal acceptance.

Tenders for building works do not remain on offer indefinitely. If they are not accepted within a reasonable time the offer may lapse, or be subject to some monetary adjustment should it later be accepted. The building owner may stipulate in the invitation to the tenderers that the offer should remain open for a prescribed period of time.

Offers concerned with building projects are generally made on the basis of detailed terms and conditions. The parties to the contract will be bound by these conditions, as long as they know that such conditions were incorporated in the offer, even though they may never have read them or acquainted themselves with the details.

In many instances with building contracts the offer must follow a stipulated procedure. Such procedures often incorporate delivery of the offer by a certain date and time, in writing, on a special form, and in a particular envelope, and stipulate that the offer must not be disclosed to a third party. Failure to comply with these procedures will result in the offer being rejected.

The acceptance

Once an agreeable offer has been made, there must be an acceptance of it before a contract can be established. The acceptance of the offer must be unconditional and it must be communicated to the person who made the offer. The unconditional terms of acceptance must correspond precisely with the terms of the offer. In practice, of course, the parties may choose to negotiate on the basis of the offer. For example, the building owner may require the project to be completed one month earlier and they may result in the tenderer revising the tender sum. A fresh offer made in this way is known as a counter-offer, and is subject to the conditions now applied.

An offer or acceptance is sometimes made on the basis of 'subject to contract'. In practice the courts tend to view such an expression of no legal effect. No binding contract will come into effect until the formal contract has been agreed.

Form

'Form' means some peculiar solemnity or procedure accompanying the expression of agreement. It is this formality which gives to the agreement its binding character. The formal contract in English law is the contract under seal

– that is, one made by deed. The contract is executed – that is, it is made effective by being signed, sealed and delivered.

1. *Signature.* Doubts have been expressed regarding the necessity for a signature. Some statutes make a signature a necessity.
2. *Sealing.* Today this consists of affixing an adhesive wafer, or in the case of a corporate body an impression in the paper, and the party signs against this and acknowledges it as his seal.
3. *Delivery.* This is not now necessary for legal effectiveness. As soon as the party acknowledges the document as the deed, it is immediately effective.
4. *Witnesses.* These attest by signing the document. They are not usually a legal necessity.

Consideration

Another essential feature of a binding contract, other than a contract made under seal, is that the agreement must be supported by consideration. The most common forms of consideration are payment of money, provision of goods and the performance of work. Consideration has been judicially defined as 'some right, forbearance, detriment, loss or responsibility given, suffered or undertaken by the other in respect of the promise'. In building contracts the consideration of the contractor to carry out the works in accordance with the contract documents is matched by that of the building owner to pay the price. The following rules concerning consideration should be adhered to:

1. Every simple contract requires consideration to make it valid.
2. The consideration must be worth something in the eyes of the law. The courts are not concerned whether the bargain is a good one, but simply that there is a bargain.
3. Each party must get something in return for the promise, other than something already entitled to, otherwise there is no consideration.
4. The consideration must not be such that it conflicts with the established law.
5. The consideration must not relate to some event in the past.

Duress and undue influence

Duress is actual or threatened violence to, or restraint of the person of, a contracting party. If a contract is made under duress it is at once suspect, because consent has not been freely given to the bargain supposedly made. The contract is voidable at the option of the party concerned. Duress is a common law doctrine which relates entirely to the person and has no relation to that person's goods. As such it is a very limited doctrine and is one where cases are rare.

Unenforceable contracts

Contracts may be described as void, or voidable or unenforceable. A void contract creates no legal rights and cannot therefore be sued upon. It may occur because of a mistake as to the nature of the contract, or because it involves the performance of something illegal that is prohibited by a statute. A void contract will also result because of the incapacity of the parties, as in the case of infants. Corporations cannot make contracts beyond their stated powers which are said to be *ultra vires* – 'beyond one's powers'.

A contract is said to be voidable when only one of the parties may take advantage. In cases involving misrepresentation, only the party who has been misled has the right to a void in one of the ways previously described.

Unenforceable contracts are those that are valid, but owing to the neglect of the formalities involved a party seeking to enforce it will be denied a remedy.

Mistake

The law recognizes that, in some circumstances, although a contract has been formed, one or both of the parties are unable to enforce the agreement. The parties are at variance with one another and this precludes the possibility of any agreement. Mistake may be classified as follows:

1. *Identity of subject matter.* This occurs where one party intends to contract with regard to one thing and the other party with regard to another. The parties in this situation cannot be of the same mind and no contract is formed.
2. *Identity of party.* If the identity of either party enters into consideration, this will negate the contract.
3. *Basis of contract.* If two parties enter into a contract on the basis that certain facts exist, and they do not, then the contract is void.
4. *Expressing the contract.* If a written contract fails to express the agreed intentions of the two parties, then it is not enforceable. Courts may, however, express the true intention of the parties and enforce it as amended.

Misrepresentation

Misrepresentation consists in the making of an untrue statement which induces the other party to enter into a contract. The statement must relate to fact rather than opinion. Furthermore, the injured party must have relied on the statement and it must have been a material cause of their entering into the contract. Where such a contract is voidable it may be renounced by the injured party, but until such time it is valid. Misrepresentation may be classified as:

1. *Innocent misrepresentation* – where an untrue statement is made in the belief that it is true.

2.   *Fraudulent misrepresentation* – which consists of an untrue statement made with the knowledge that it is untrue or made recklessly without attempting to assess its validity.
3.   *Negligent misrepresentation* – is a statement made honestly, but without reasonable grounds for belief that it is true. It is really a special case of innocent misrepresentation, for, although the statement is made in the belief that it is true, insufficient care has been taken to check it.

Where misrepresentation occurs the injured party has several options:

1.   The injured party can affirm the contract, when it will then continue for both parties.
2.   The injured party can repudiate the contract and set up misrepresentation as a defence.
3.   An action can be brought for rescission and restitution. Rescission involves cancelling the contract and the restoration of the parties to the state that they were in before the contract was made. Restitution is the return of any money paid or transferred under the terms of the contract.
4.   The injured party can bring an action for damages. The claim for damages is only possible in circumstances of fraudulent misrepresentation.

Disclosure of information

When entering into a contract it is not always necessary to disclose all the facts that are available. A party may observe silence in regard to certain facts, even though it may know that such facts would influence the other party. This is summed up in the maxim, *caveat emptor* – 'let the buyer beware'.

There are, however, circumstances where the non-disclosure of relevant information may affect the validity of the contract. This can occur where the relevant facts surrounding the contract are almost entirely within the knowledge of one of the parties, and the other has no means of discerning the facts. These contracts are said to be *uberrimae fidei*, which interpreted means 'of the utmost good faith'.

Privity of contract

A contract creates something special for the parties who enter into it. The common law rule of privity is that only the persons who are party to the contract can be affected by it. A contract can neither impose obligations nor confer rights upon others who are not privy to it. For example, the clause in the Standard Form of Building Contract which allows the employer to pay money direct to the subcontractor may be used by the employer. It cannot be enforced by the subcontractor, who is not a party to the main contract. The subcontractor may seek to persuade the employer to adopt this course of action but cannot enforce the employer to do so in a court of law.

Express and implied terms

The terms of contract can be classified as either express or implied. Those terms which are written into the contract documents or expressed orally by the parties are described as express terms. Those terms which were not mentioned by the parties at the time that they made the contract are implied terms, so long as they were in the minds of both parties. The courts will, where it becomes necessary, imply into building and engineering contracts a number of implied terms. Although the implied term is one which the parties probably never contemplated when making the contract, the courts justify this by saying that the implication is necessary in order to give business efficacy to the contract. This does not mean, however, that the courts will make a contract more workable or sensible. The courts, for example, will generally imply into a building contract the following terms:

1. The contractor will be given possession of the site within a reasonable time, should nothing be stated in the contract documentation.
2. The employer will not unreasonably prevent the contractor from completing the work.
3. The contractor will carry out the work in a workmanlike manner.

Implied terms which have evolved from decided cases often act as precedents for future events. In the majority of the standard forms of building contract all of these matters are normally express terms, since the contracts themselves are very comprehensive and hope to cover every eventuality.

There are some notable terms which are not normally to be implied into building and engineering contracts, such as, for example, the practicability of the design. However, there will be express or implied terms that the work will comply with the appropriate statutes.

Express terms

An express term is a clear stipulation in the contract which the parties intend should be binding upon them. Traditionally, the common law has divided terms into two categories of conditions and warranties:

1. *Conditions*. These are terms which go to the root of the contract, and for breadth of which the remedies of repudiation or rescission of the contract and damages are allowed.
2. *Warranties*. These are minor terms of the contract, for breach of which the only remedy is damages.

Implied terms

Implied terms are those which, although not expressly stated by the parties by words or conduct, are by law deemed to be part of the contract. Terms may be implied into contracts by custom, statute or the courts:

1. *By custom.* In law this means an established practice or usage in a trade, locality, type of transaction or between parties. If two or more people enter into a contract against a common background of business, it is considered that they intend the trade usage of that business to prevail unless they expressly exclude it.
2. *By statute.* There are many areas in the civil law where Parliament has interfered with the right of parties to regulate their own affairs. This interference mainly occurs where one party has used a dominant bargaining position to abuse this freedom. Thus in the sale of goods, the general principle *caveat* emptor (let the buyer beware) has been greatly modified, particularly in favour of the consumer by the provisions in the Sale of Goods Act 1979. In addition there have been important changes in relation to exemption clauses brought about by the Unfair Contract Terms Act 1977.
3. *By the courts.* The court will imply a term into a contract under the doctrine of the implied term, if it was the presumed intention of the parties that there should have been a particular term, but they have omitted to expressly state it.

Limitations of actions

Generally speaking, litigation is a costly and time-consuming process which becomes more difficult as the time between the disputed events and the litigation increases. Also rights of action cannot be allowed to endure for ever. Parties to a contract must be made to prosecute their causes within a reasonable time. For this reason Parliament has enacted limitation acts which set a time limit on the commencement of litigation. The rules and procedures in respect of limitation of actions are contained in the Limitation Act 1980. The right to bring an action can be discharged in three ways:

1. The parties to a contract might decide to discharge their rights.
2. Through the judgment of a court.
3. Through lapse of time.

If an action is not commenced within a certain time the right to sue is extinguished. Actions in a simple contract (not under seal) and tort become statute barred after 6 years. In the case of contracts under seal, then this period is extended to 12 years. The Act does permit certain extensions to these time limits in very special circumstances, for example, where a person may be unconscious as the result of an accident. If damage is suffered at a later date then this will not affect the limitation period, although an action for negligence may be pursued. The period of limitation can be renewed if the debtor acknowledges the claim or makes a part payment at some time during this period. A number of international conventions, particularly with respect to the law of carriage, lay down shorter limitation periods for action than those specified in the Act. For example, in carriage by air under the Warsaw Rules the period is 2 years.

The Unfair Contract Terms Act 1977

Contractual clauses designed to exonerate a party wholly or partly from liability from breaches of express or implied terms, first appeared in the nineteenth century. The common law did not interfere but took the view that parties forming a contractual relationship were free to make a bargain within the limits of the law. This is still largely the rule today although the growth of large trading organizations has led to an increase in both excluding and restricting clauses to the severe detriment of other parties.

The efforts of the courts to mitigate against the worst effects of objectionable exclusion clauses have been reinforced by the Unfair Contract Terms Act 1977. This Act restricts the extent to which liability can be avoided for breach of contract and negligence. The Act relates only to business liability and transactions between private individuals are not therefore covered. The reasonableness is further extended to situations where parties attempt to exclude liability for a fundamental breach, i.e. where performance is substantially different from that reasonably expected or there is no performance at all of the whole, or any part, of the contractual obligations. The following are subject to the Act's provisions:

1. Making liability or its enforcement subject to restrictive or onerous conditions.
2. Excluding or restricting any right or remedy.
3. Excluding or restricting rules of evidence or procedure.
4. Evasion of the provisions of the Act by a secondary contract is prohibited.

Contra proferentem

Any ambiguity in a clause in a contract will be interpreted against the party who put it forward. It is a general rule of construction of any document that it will be interpreted *contra proferentem*, that is, against the person who prepared the document. As an exclusion clause is invariably drafted by the imposer of it, this is an extremely useful weapon against exclusion clauses. The effect of the rule is to give the party who proposed the ambiguous clause only the lesser of the protections possible. The one who draws up the contract has the choice of words and must choose them to show clearly the intention.

Agency

Agency is a special relationship whereby one person (the agent) agrees on behalf of another (the principal) to conclude a contract between the principal and a third party. Providing that the agent acts only within the scope of the authority conferred upon him, those acts become those of the principal, and he must therefore accept the responsibility for them. The majority of contractual relationships involve some form of agency. For example, the architect in ordering extra work is acting in the capacity of the employer's agent. The contractor may presume, unless anything is known to the contrary, that the carrying out of these extras will result in future payment by the client.

A contract of agency may be established by:

1. *Express authority* – that is, authority that has been directly given to an agent by his principal.

2. *Implied authority* – where because a person is engaged in a particular capacity, others dealing with that person are entitled, perhaps because of trade custom, to infer that that person has the necessary authority to contract within the limits usually associated with that capacity.

3. *Ratification* – that is, where a principal subsequently accepts an act done by the principal's agent, even where this exceeds the agent's authority. This becomes as effective as if the principal originally authorized it.

In contracts of agency a principal cannot delegate to an agent powers which the principal does not already possess. The capacity of the agent is therefore determined by the capacity of the agent's principal.

Chapter 3

Discharge of contracts

A contract is said to be discharged when the parties become released from their general contractual obligations. The discharge of a contract may be brought about in several ways.

Discharge by performance

In these circumstances the party has undertaken to do a certain task and nothing further remains to be done. In general, only the complete and exact performance of the contractual obligations can discharge the contract. In practice, where a contract has been substantially performed, payment can be made with an adjustment for the work that is incomplete.

A building contract is discharged by performance once the contractor has completed all the work, including the making good of defects under the terms of the contract. The architect must have issued all the appropriate certificates and the building owner paid the requisite sums. If, however, undisclosed defects occur beyond this period the building owner can still sue for damages under the statute of limitations. The contract has not been properly performed if there are hidden defects.

Thus, A undertakes to sell to B 1,000 roof tiles. A will be discharged from the contract when he has delivered the tiles, and B when he has paid the price. A question sometimes arises whether performance by another party will discharge the contract. The general rule is that where personal qualifications are a factor of consideration, then that person must perform the contract. Where, however, personal considerations are unimportant it would not matter who supplied the goods.

Discharge under condition

Contracts consist of a large number of stipulations or terms. In many types of contract there are conditions which, although not expressed, are intended because the parties must have contracted with these conditions in mind. It will, however, be obvious that the terms and conditions of a building contract are not of equal importance. Some of the terms are fundamental to the contract, and are so essential that if they are broken the whole purpose of the contract is defeated.

Thus, if a contractor agreed to design and build a building for a specific use, and it is incapable of such a use, the building owner would be able to reject the project and recover the costs from the contractor.

Building contracts frequently contain a number of terms forming a specification. The builder agrees to construct the project in accordance with this specification. If the builder deviates from this in some small way then this will give rise to an action for damages and the contract will not be discharged.

It is, however, well established that subject to an express or implied agreement to the contrary, a party who has received substantial benefit under a contract cannot repudiate it for breach of condition.

Discharge by renunciation

This is effected when one of the parties refuses to perform obligations. Thus, A employs an architect to design and supervise a proposed building project. On completion of the design, A decides not to continue with the project. This is renunciation of the contract and the architect can sue for fees on a *quantum meruit* basis – that is, for as much as has been earned.

Discharge by fresh agreement

A contract can be discharged by a fresh agreement being made between the parties, which is both subsequent to and independent of the original contract. Such a contract may, however, discharge the parties altogether. This is known as a rescission of the original contract. Where one party to a contract is released by a third party from undertaking obligations, then the original contract discharged is termed 'novation'. Any alteration to a contract made with the consent of the parties concerned has the effect of making a new contract.

Frustration

A contract formed between two parties will expressly or impliedly be subject to the condition that it will be capable of performance. If the contract becomes incapable of performance then the parties will be discharged from it. Impossibility of performance is usually called frustration of contract. It occurs whenever the law recognizes that, without default of either party, a contractual obligation has become incapable of execution.

For example, the event causing the impossibility may be due to a natural catastrophe. A agrees to carry out a contract for the repair of a road surface, but prior to starting the work the road subsides to such an extent that it disappears completely down the side of a hill. Impossibility may also occur because a government may introduce a law that makes the contract illegal. For example, A contracts to carry out some insulation work using asbestos. The government subsequently introduce legislation forbidding the use of this material in buildings, thus making the contract impossible to carry out. A contractor cannot, however, claim that a contract is frustrated if by deliberate actions he causes a delay to avoid completion. For example, a contract for the building of a sea wall must be completed prior to winter weather setting in, otherwise practical performance will become impossible. The knowledge that this predictable event will occur, coupled with a deliberate delay, does not result in a frustration of the contract.

Examples of building contracts being frustrated are extremely rare. It should be noted that hardship, inconvenience or loss do not decide whether an occurrence frustrates the contract, because these are accepted risks. The legal effect of frustration is that the contract is discharged and money prepaid in anticipation of performance should be returned. A party receiving benefit from a partly executed contract should reimburse the other party to the value of that benefit.

Determination of contract

There are provisions in all the common forms of contract that allow either party to terminate the contract. There must, of course, be good reasons to support any party who decides to determine, otherwise a breach of contract can occur. Clause 27 of the Standard Form of Building Contract provides circumstances which allow the employer to terminate the contract with the contractor. In one sense they are fairly exceptional happenings, and so they should be, since they provide a final option to the employer. The decision to determine must be taken very carefully and reasonably. It generally occurs because the contractor is failing to take notice of instructions from the architect to remedy an already existing breach of contract. Clause 28 provides for determination because of either a refusal or interference with payments due to the contractor. It may also occur where the works are suspended for an unreasonable length of time. Again the action to determine must be carefully taken, and is a last-resort decision on the part of the contractor. The latter takes this decision when it is felt it is no longer possible to continue, perhaps after a number of delays in payment, to work with the employer. Determination of contract by either party results in two losers and no winners. Although there are provisions in the contract for financial recompense to the aggrieved party, these rarely suffice.

Assignment

It sometimes happens that one party to a contract wishes to dispose of its obligations under it, but the extent to which this is permitted is limited. The other party may have valid reasons why it prefers the obligations to be performed by the original contractor. The rule is that liabilities can only be assigned by novation. This is the formation of a new contract between the party who wishes performance and the new contractor, who is accepted as adequately qualified to perform as the original contractor. Liabilities can only be assigned by consent. By contrast, rights under a contract can usually be assigned without consent of the other party, except where the subject matter involves a personal service. Even, however, in those circumstances where the contract does not involve personal service, but specifically restricts the right to assign the contract or any interest in it to a third party then the assignment of rights will not be permitted.

Chapter 4

Remedies for breach of contract

A breach of contract occurs when one party fails to perform an obligation under the terms of the contract. For example, a breach of contract of the JCT 80 conditions of contract occurs if:

1. The contractor refuses to obey an architect's instruction (clause 4).
2. The employer fails to honour an architect's certificate (clause 28).
3. The contractor refuses to hand over certain antiquities found on the site (clause 34).
4. The contractor fails to proceed regularly and diligently with the works (clause 23).

Defective work is not necessarily in breach of contract, as long as the contractor rectifies it in accordance with an architect's instruction. A breach will occur where the contractor either refuses to remove the defective work or ignores the remedial work required.

A breach of contract may have two principal consequences:

1. Damages.
2. If the breach is sufficiently serious, then determination by the aggrieved party under the terms of the contract. The aggrieved party may decide to terminate the contract with the other, and also sue for damages, or alternatively take only one of these courses of action. Damages may include both the loss resulting from the breach, the loss flowing from the termination and the additional costs of completing the contract.

Damages

There is, with few exceptions, the rule that no one who is not a party to the contract can sue or be sued in respect of it. There may be other remedies, for instance in tort, but these are beyond the scope of this book.

The legal remedy for breach of contract is damages. This consists of the award of a sum of money to the injured party, designed to compensate for the loss sustained. The basis of the award of damages is by way of compensation. The damages awarded are made in an attempt to recompense the actual loss sustained by reason of the breach of contract. The injured party is to be placed, as far as money can do it, in the same situation as if the contract had been performed. It should be clearly understood that not every breach automatically results in damages. In order for damages to be paid, the injured party must be able to prove that a loss resulted from the breach. Furthermore, the innocent party must take all reasonable steps to mitigate any loss. Damages may be classified as follows.

Nominal damages

Where a party can show a breach of contract, but cannot prove any sustained loss as a result, then nominal damages may be awarded. These comprise merely a small sum in recognition that a contractual right has been infringed.

Substantial damages

These damages represent the measure of loss sustained by the injured party. Despite their name they might be quite small.

Remoteness of damage

A breach of contract can, in some circumstances, create a chain of events resulting in considerable damage, and the question may arise whether the injured party or parties can claim for the whole of the damage sustained. In ordinary circumstances, the only damages that can be claimed are those which arise immediately because of the breach. Damage is not considered too remote if the parties at the time the contract was entered into contemplated that it could occur. If the contract specifies the extent of the liability, then no question of consequential damages arise. Defects liability clauses, which require the builder to rectify defects, do not limit the extent of the remedial work, but may also require other work to be put right that has resulted from these defects.

Special damage

Damages resulting from special circumstances are recoverable if they flow from a breach of contract, and that the special circumstances were known to both parties at the time of making the agreement.

Liquidated damages

Each of the standard forms of contract provide for payment of agreed damages by the contractor when completion of work is not within the stipulated time. These payments are known as liquidated damages, and their amount should be recorded on the appendix to the form of a contract. The sum stated should be a genuine estimate of the damage that the building owner may suffer. If, however, the sum stated is excessive and bears no relation to the actual damage, then it may be regarded as a penalty. In these circumstances the courts will not enforce the amount stated in the contract but will assess the damage incurred on an unliquidated basis. Liquidated damages may be estimated on the basis of loss of profit in the case of commercial projects, but they are much more difficult to determine in the case of public works projects such as roads.

In some circumstances a building owner may seek the occupation of a project even though it remains incomplete. This would normally deprive the owner of the right to enforce a claim for liquidated damages.

Unliquidated damages

When no liquidated damages have been detailed in the contract, the employer can still recover damages should the contractor fail to complete on time. The sum awarded in this case is that regarded as compensation for the loss actually sustained by the breach.

Specific performance

Specific performance was introduced by the courts for use in those cases where damages would not be an adequate remedy. In building contracts this remedy is only really available in exceptional circumstances. The courts will enforce a party to do what it has contracted to do, in preference to awarding damages to the aggrieved party. A decree of specific performance will not be granted where the court cannot effectively supervise or enforce the performance.

Injunction

Injunction is a remedy for the enforcement of a negative undertaking. A party is prohibited from carrying out a certain action. It is often awarded by the courts as an effective remedy against nuisance.

Rescission

This is an equitable remedy, which endeavours to place the parties in the pre-contractual position by returning goods or money to the original owners. This means that the parties are no longer bound by the contract. This is granted at the discretion of the court but will not be awarded where:
1.   The injured party was aware of the misrepresentation and carried on with the contract.
2.   The parties cannot be returned to their original position.
3.   Another party has acquired an interest in the goods.
4.   The injured party waited too long before claiming this remedy.

Quantum meruit

A claim for damages is a claim for compensation for loss. Where, under the terms of the contract, one party undertakes its duty for the other, and the other party breaks the contract, the former can sue upon a *quantum meruit* basis – that is, to claim a reasonable price for the work carried out. It is payment for work that has been earned. If the two parties cannot agree, the question of what sum is reasonable is decided by the court. A claim on a *quantum meruit* basis is appropriate where there is an express agreement to pay a reasonable sum upon the completion of some work. In assessing a *quantum meruit* claim the parties may choose to use the various means that are available. For example, it may be based upon the costs of labour and materials plus profit, or the measurement of the work using reasonable rates.

Chapter 5

Settlement of disputes

And God said unto Noah, the Ark shall be finished within seven days. And Noah saith, it shall be so. But it was not so. And the Lord saith, what seemeth to be the trouble this time? And Noah saith, mine subcontractor hath gone bankrupt. The pitch which thou commandest me to use has not arrived. The plumber hath gone on strike. And the glazier departeth on holiday to Majorca, even tho I did offer him double time.

Christopher Taylor, Engineering Manager, Shell UK.

Introduction

Construction contracts in the distant past consisted of a document of about five pages long. They generally concluded with a handshake, but underlying such agreements were an essential set of values of competence, fairness and honesty. Today things are different. We have developed a complex and onerous set of conditions that attempt to cover every eventuality and in so doing create loopholes that the legal professions can feast upon. It has often been suggested that the only individuals to make any money in the construction industry are the lawyers. Precious time and resources are thus drawn away from the main purpose of getting the project built on time, to the right design and construction technology at an agreed price and quality.

Construction contracts need to become less adversarial, more simply constructed and emphasizing the positive needs of the project. Consultants and contractors should be allowed and encouraged to use their best endeavours and to work together as a team (see project partnering, Chapter 11) rather than watching their individual backs all of the time. When a project ends up in a protracted dispute, the project will fail to meet its original goals and expectations. In addition, clients will suffer from high legal fees, delayed completion and occupation and general dissatisfaction. The contractor's profits will diminish and to these will be added additional legal fees. There are no winners under these circumstances.

The reasons why disputes arise

The construction industry is a risky business. It generally does not build many prototypes, with each different project being individual in many respects. Even identical buildings that have been constructed on different sites create their own special circumstances, are subject to the vagaries of different site and weather conditions and use labour that may have different trade practices even from one site to another. Even the identical building constructed on an adjacent site by a different contractor will have different costs and different problems associated with its construction. Disputes are therefore likely to arise under the best circumstances, even where every possibility has been potentially eliminated. However, this is not usually the case, with projects being constructed often more to do with luck than good management and organization by all those involved. Some of the main areas for possible disputes occurring are:

General
- adversarial nature of construction contracts
- poor communication between the parties concerned
- proliferation of forms of contract and warranties
- fragmentation in the industry
- tendering policies and procedures

Clients
- poor briefing
- changes and variation requirements
- changes to standard conditions of contract
- interference in the contractual duties of the contract administrator
- late payments

Consultants
- design inadequacies
- lack of appropriate competence and experience
- late and incomplete information
- lack of co-ordination
- unclear delegation of responsibilities

Contractors
- inadequate site management
- poor planning and programming
- poor standards of workmanship
- disputes with subcontractors
- delayed payments to subcontractors
- co-ordination of subcontractors

Subcontractors
- mismatch of subcontract conditions with main contract
- failure to follow and adopt agreed procedures
- poor standards of workmanship

Manufacturers and suppliers
- failure to define performance or purpose
- failure of performance

Issues for the resolution of disputes

The following are matters that need to be resolved in order to reduce the possibility of future disputes occurring:
- clarification of responsibilities
- need of single point responsibility contracts
- allocation of risk to the parties who are best able to control it
- further investigation of insurance-based alternatives
- need to develop and extend non-adversarial methods of dispute resolution
- partnership sourcing (contractors and consultants working in a consortium)
- quality management and quality assurance

Contractual claims

Contractual claims arise where contractors assess that they are entitled to additional payments over and above that paid within the general terms and conditions of the contract. For example, the contractors may seek reimbursement for some alleged loss that has been suffered for reasons beyond their control. On many occasions the costs incurred lie where they fall and contractors will have recourse to recover them. Thus losses and delays arising from the intervention of third parties who are unconnected with the contract almost invariably fall with the contractor. The fact that a loss has been sustained, without fault on the part of the loser, may merit sympathy, but does not in itself demand compensation. Where a standard form of contract is used, many attempts may be made by contractors to invoke some of the compensatory provisions of the contract in order to secure further payment to cover the losses involved.

The details of such claims will be investigated by the quantity surveyors and a report made to the architect, engineer or other lead consultant. The report should summarize the arguments involved and set out the possible financial effect of each claim. Quantity surveyors frequently end up negotiating with contractors over such issues in an attempt to solve the problems and come to some amicable solution. This is preferable to a lengthy legal dispute. As with many issues in life, contractual claims are rarely the fault of one side only. If the claim cannot be resolved in this way then some form of legal proceedings may be initiated. Particular care therefore needs to be properly exercised in the conduct of the negotiations since they may have an effect upon the outcome of any subsequent legal proceedings.

Litigation

Litigation is a dispute procedure which takes place in the courts. It involves third parties who are trained in the law, usually barristers, and a judge who is appointed by the courts. This method of solving disputes is often expensive and can be a very lengthy process before the matter is resolved. The process is frequently extended to higher courts involving additional expense and time (see Chapter 1). Also since a case needs to be properly prepared prior to the trial, a considerable amount of time can elapse between the commencement of the proceedings and the trial, as noted above.

A typical action is started by the issuing of a writ. This places the matter on the official record. A copy of the writ must be served on the defendant, either by delivering it personally or by other means such as through the offices of a solicitor. The general rule is that the defendants must be made aware of the proceedings against them. The speed of a hearing in most cases depends upon the following:

- availability of competent legal advisers to handle the case, i.e. its preparation and presentation
- expeditious preparation of the case by the parties concerned
- availability of courts and judges to hear the case

The amount of money involved in the case will determine whether it is heard in the County Court or High Court. Where the matter is largely of a technical nature the case may be referred in the first instance to the Official Referees Court. An Official Referee is a circuit judge whose court is used to hearing commercial cases, and hence handles most of the commercial and construction disputes. Under these circumstances a full hearing does not normally take place, but points of principle are established. The outcome of this hearing will determine whether the case then proceeds towards a full trial.

Under some circumstances, the plaintiff may apply to the court for a judgment on the claim (or the defendant for a judgment on the counterclaim), on the ground that there is no sufficient defence. Provided that the court is satisfied that the defendant (or plaintiff) has no defence that warrants a full trial of the issues involved, judgment will be given, together with the costs involved.

Every fact in a dispute that is necessary to establish a claim must be proved to the judge by admissible evidence whether oral, documentary or of other kind. Oral evidence must normally be given from memory by a person who heard or saw what took place. Hearsay evidence is not normally permissible.

In a civil action the facts in the dispute must be proved on a balance of probabilities. This is unlike a criminal case where proof beyond reasonable doubt is required. The burden of proof usually lies upon the party asserting the fact.

Arbitration

Arbitration is an alternative to legal action in the courts, in order to settle an unresolved dispute. No one is compelled to submit a dispute to arbitration unless they have agreed to do so within the terms of the contract. Once a person has agreed to this method of settling a disagreement they cannot then take legal proceedings. If they attempt to do so the courts will stay such proceedings. All of the standard forms of contract used in the construction industry include an arbitration provision. It is, therefore, the procedure that is most commonly used for dealing with disputes that arise between the various parties concerned.

The arbitration agreement in the JCT Standard Form of Building Contract 1980 is covered in article 5 of the Articles of Agreement. The parties, under article 5.2, agree that proceedings will not take place until after practical completion has been achieved, or unless the contractor's termination of the contract has been made or if the project is abandoned. There are exceptions, however, to these rules where matters can be taken to arbitration during the progress of the works. Of course, where the two parties otherwise agree the guidelines can be amended as required. The following matters can therefore be dealt with prior to the issue of the certificate of practical completion:

Article 3	Contractor's objection to the appointment following the death of the architect
Article 4	Contractor's objection to the appointment following the death of the quantity surveyor
Clause 4	Dispute over the power to issue an instruction
Clause 3C	A certificate being improperly withheld or not being in accordance with the conditions
Clause 25	Dispute over the difference of an extension of time
Clauses 32/33	Disputes concerning outbreak of hostilities or war damage

An arbitrator's powers are very wide. They may review and revise certificates and valuations. They may also disregard opinions, decisions or notices that have already been given.

The essential features of a valid arbitration agreement are as follows:

1. The parties must be capable of entering into a legally binding contract.
2. The agreement should whenever possible be in writing.
3. It must be signed by the parties concerned.
4. It must state clearly those matters which will be submitted to arbitration, and when the proceedings will be initiated.
5. It must not contain anything that is illegal.

Arbitration Act 1979

This Act came into force on 4 April 1979, and extended the previous Act of 1950. The Act introduced a revised procedure of appeals, and reinforced the power of the arbitrator to proceed *ex parte* in some cases by adding the authority of the High Court. The Act consists of a number of provisions, some of which will apply to all arbitrations, and others to arbitrations provided by the parties in their agreement. The majority of arbitration agreements adopted by the construction industry accept the Act in its entirety.

Advantages of arbitration

- Arbitration is generally less expensive than court proceedings.
- Arbitration is a more speedy process than an action at law. A year awaiting a case to come before the courts is not uncommon.
- Arbitration hearings are usually held in private. This, therefore, avoids any bad publicity that might be associated with a case in the courts.
- The time and place of the hearing can be arranged to suit the parties concerned. Court proceedings take their place in turn amongst the other cases and at law courts concerned.
- Arbitrators are selected for their expert technical knowledge in the matter of dispute. Judges do not generally have such knowledge.
- In cases of dispute which involve a building site or property, it can be insisted that the arbitrator visit the site concerned. Although a judge may decide upon a visit, this cannot be enforced by the parties concerned.

Disadvantages of arbitration

- The courts will generally always be able to offer a sound opinion on a point of law. The arbitrator may, of course, seek the opinion of the courts, but this could easily be overlooked in which case a mistake could occur.
- An arbitrator does not have the power to bring into an arbitration a third party against their wishes. The courts are always able to do this.

Terminology

The following terminology is associated with arbitrations:

Arbitrator – The person to whom the dispute is referred for settlement. Arbitrators are often appointed by, for example, the President of the RIBA, CIArb or RICS. In practice they may be selected because of their expert technical knowledge regarding the subject matter in dispute.

Umpire – It may occasionally be preferable to appoint two arbitrators. In this event a third arbitrator, known as an umpire, is appointed to settle any dispute over which the two arbitrators cannot agree.

Reference – The actual hearing of the dispute by the arbitrator.

Award – The decision on the matter concerned made by the arbitrator.

Respondent – This is the equivalent of the defendant in a law court.

Claimant – The equivalent of the plaintiff.

Expert witness – This is a special type of witness who plays an important part in arbitrations. Ordinary witnesses must confine their evidence strictly to the statement of facts. Expert witnesses may, however, forward their opinion based upon technical knowledge and practical experience. Prior to presenting evidence, they must show by experience and academic and professional qualifications that they can be recognized as an expert in the subject matter.

Appointment of the arbitrator

An arbitrator or umpire should be a disinterested person, who is quite independent from the parties that will be involved in the proceedings. The person appointed should, however, be someone who is sufficiently qualified and experienced in the matter of the dispute. However, it is for the parties concerned to choose the arbitrator, and the courts will not generally interfere even where the person appointed is not really the most appropriate person to settle the dispute.

Arbitrators may, however, be disqualified if it can be shown that:

- They have a direct interest in the subject matter of the dispute (for example, where the decision may have direct repercussions on their own professional work).
- They may fail to do justice to the arbitration by showing a bias towards one of the parties concerned (for example, it could be argued that architects might show favour to an employer since they are normally employed on this 'side' of the industry).

Each of the parties to the arbitration agreement must be satisfied that the arbitrator who is appointed will give an impartial judgment on the matter of the dispute. The remarks expressed by the arbitrator during the conduct of the case will probably reveal any favouring of one of the parties in preference to the other. This may lead to removal by the courts of the arbitrator on the grounds of misconduct.

Once the arbitrator has been appointed he will need to establish the general matters relating to the dispute will need to be established. It will also be necessary to determine:

- the facilities available for inspecting the works;
- whether the parties will be represented by counsel;
- the matters the parties already agree upon;
- the time and place of the proposed hearing.

Outline of the procedure

The pleadings

These are the formal documents which may be prepared by counsel or solicitor. The arbitrator will first require the claimant to set out the basis of the case. These will be included in the document, termed the 'point of claim', which will then be served upon the respondent. The respondent then submits a reply in answer to the points of claim, termed the 'points of defence'. The respondent may also submit points of counterclaim, which will be served on the claimant at the same time. This may raise relevant matters that were not referred to in the points of claim. The claimant, in reply to the matters raised in the counterclaim, will submit points of reply and defence to counterclaim.

The purpose of the above documents is very important, since they will make clear to the arbitrator the matters which are in dispute. Furthermore, the parties involved cannot stray beyond the scope of the pleadings without leave from the arbitrator.

Discovery

Once the pleadings have been completed, the precise issues which the arbitrator is to decide will be very clear. Every fact to be relied upon must be pleaded, but the manner in which it is to be proved need not be disclosed until the reference. 'Discovery' means the disclosure of all documents which are in the control of each party and which are in any way relevant to the issues of arbitration. Each party must allow the other to inspect and to take copies of all or any of the documents in his list, unless they can argue on the grounds that it is privileged. The most important of these types of documents are the communications between a party and their solicitors for the purpose of obtaining legal advice. A party who refuses to allow inspection may be ordered to do so by the arbitrator.

In fixing the date and place of the hearing arbitrators have the sole discretion, subject to anything laid down in the arbitration agreement. They must, however, be seen to act in a reasonable manner. A refusal to attend the hearing by either party, after reasonable notice has been given, may empower the arbitrator to proceed without that party, i.e. *ex parte*.

The hearing

The procedure of the hearing follows the rules of evidence used in a normal court of law. The parties may or may not be represented by counsel or other representatives.

The claimant sets out the case, and calls each of the witnesses in turn. Once they have given their evidence they are cross-examined by the respondent (or counsel/representative where appropriate). The claimant is then allowed to ask these witnesses further questions on matters which have been raised by the cross-examination.

A similar procedure is then adopted by the respondent who sets out the details of the counterclaim if this is necessary. Witnesses are examined and these in turn are cross-examined by the claimant. The claimant then replies to the respondent's defence and counterclaim, and presents a defence to the counterclaim. When this has been completed the respondent sums up the case in an address to the arbitrator known as the respondent's closing speech. The claimant then has the right of reply or the last word in the case.

The trial is now ended and both parties await the publication of the award.

The arbitrator may now decide to inspect the works, if this has not already been done, or re-examine certain parts of the project in more detail. The arbitrator will usually make the decision in private, and will set the decision out in the award. This is served on the parties after the appropriate charges have been met. It is enforceable in much the same way as a judgment debt, where the successful party can reclaim such costs as the arbitrator has awarded.

Evidence

To enable the arbitrator to carry out justice between the parties, the evidence must be carefully considered. This is submitted in turn by the claimant and the respondent. Evidence is the means by which the facts are proved. There are rules of evidence which the arbitrator must ensure are observed. These have been designed to determine four main problems.

- Who is to assume the burden of proving facts? Generally speaking the person who sets forth a statement has the burden of determining its proof. The maxim, 'innocent until proved guilty' is appropriate in this context.
- What facts must be proved? A party must give proof of all material facts upon which were relied upon to establish the case, although there can be exceptions to this rule. For example, the parties may agree on formal 'admissions' in order to dispense with the necessity of proving facts which are not in dispute.
- What facts will be excluded from the cognizance of the court? In order to prevent a waste of time or to prevent certain facts from being put before juries, which might tend to lead them to unwarranted conclusions, English law permits proof of facts which are in issue and of facts which are relevant to the issue.
- How proof is to be effected? The law recognizes three kinds of proof:
  1. oral proof, which are statements made verbally by a witness in the witness box;
  2. documentary proof, which is contained in the documents that are available;
  3. real proof, which could include models or a visit to the site in order to view the subject matter.

It is usual in arbitration for the evidence to be given on oath. The giving of false evidence is perjury and is punishable accordingly by fine or imprisonment. The arbitrator has no right to call a witness, except with the consent of both parties. Witnesses will, however, usually answer favourably to the party by whom they are called, in order to further that party's case. They must not in general be asked leading questions which attempt to put the answer in the mouth of the witness. For example, 'Did you notice that the scaffold was inadequately fixed?' is a leading question. It must be rephrased: 'Did you notice anything about the scaffolding?' Leading questions can, however, be used to the opposing party's witnesses. The arbitrator must also never receive evidence from one party without the knowledge of the other. Where, for example, communications are received from one party the other party must immediately be informed.

An arbitrator must always refuse to admit evidence on the grounds that:

- The witness is incompetent, e.g. refuses to take the oath, too young, a lunatic.
- The evidence is irrelevant, e.g. evidence which has not real bearing upon the facts in the opinion of the arbitrator.
- The evidence is inadmissible, e.g. hearsay evidence since it is not made under oath and is not capable of cross-examination. (There are, however, exceptions to this rule such as statements made on behalf of one party against their own interests.)

Where documents are used as evidence it is the arbitrator's responsibility to ensure their authenticity. Where one party produces a document, this must be proved unless the other side accepts it as valid. Documents under seal must be stamped, and generally the original document must be produced wherever possible.

Stating a case

A question of law may arise during the proceedings, and the arbitrator may deal with this in one of three ways:

- decide the matter personally
- consult counsel or a solicitor
- state a case to the courts

Where the decision is to take the latter course of action, a statement is prepared outlining clearly all the facts in order that the courts may decide a point of law. Once the court has given its decision, the arbitration proceedings can continue. The arbitrator must then proceed in accordance with the court's decision. Failure to do so results in misconduct on the part of the arbitrator. The arbitrator may voluntarily take this course of action or be required to do so by one of the parties.

The arbitrator may also state a case to the courts upon the completion of the arbitration. In this case the award will be based upon the alternative findings to be resolved by the courts. The decision that the courts reach will depend upon which alternative is to be followed. For example, the arbitrator may state that a particular sum should be paid by one of the parties to the other if the courts approve the arbitrator's view of the law. Where the courts do not confirm this opinion, the arbitrator will have also indicated the course of action to be taken.

The award

The arbitrator's award is the equivalent of the judgment of the courts. The award must be made within the terms of reference, otherwise it will be invalid and therefore unenforceable. The essentials of a valid award can be summarized

as follows:
- It must be made within the prescribed time limit that has been set by the parties.
- It should comply with any special agreements regarding its form or method of publication that has been laid down in the arbitration agreement.
- It must be legal and capable of enforcement at law.
- It must cover all the matters which were referred to the proceedings.
- It must be final in that it settles all the disputes which were referred under the arbitration.
- It must be consistent and not contradictory or ambiguous. Its meaning must be clear.
- It must be confined solely to the matters in question, and not matters which are outside the scope of dispute.
- The award should generally be in writing, in order to overcome any problems of enforcing it in practice.

Publication of the award

The usual practice is for the arbitrator to notify both the parties that the award is ready for collection upon the payment of the appropriate fees to the arbitrator. If the successful party pays the fees then they are able to sue the other party for that amount, assuming that the costs follow the event. If the award is defective or bad, or it can be shown that there have been irregularities in the proceedings, application may be made to the courts to have it referred back for reconsideration or set aside altogether.

Referring back the award

The grounds on which the court are likely to refer back an award are:
- where the arbitrator makes a mistake so that it does not express the true intentions;
- where it can be shown that the arbitrator has misconducted the proceedings, for example, in hearing the evidence of one of the parties in the absence of the other;
- where new evidence, which was not known at the time of the hearing, comes to light and as such will affect the arbitrator's award.

The application to refer back an award should be made within 6 weeks after the award has been published. The courts have the full discretion regarding the costs of an abortive arbitration. There is, of course, the right of appeal against the court's decision. The arbitrator's duty in dealing with the referral will depend largely upon the order of the court. As a rule, fresh evidence will not be heard unless new evidence has come to light. The amended award should normally be made within 3 months of the date of the court's order.

Setting aside the award

When the courts set aside an award it becomes null and void. The situations where the courts will do this – similar to those for referring back an award, but much more serious – are:

- where the award is void, for example, if the arbitrator directs an illegal action;
- the discovery of evidence that was not available at the time the arbitration proceedings were held;
- where the arbitrator has made an error on some point of law;
- misconduct on the part of the arbitrator by permitting irregularities in the proceedings;
- where the award has been obtained improperly, for example, through fraud or bribery;
- where the essentials of a valid award are lacking, for example, the award is inconsistent or impossible of performance.

Misconduct by the arbitrator

Arbitrators in carrying out their duties, must do so in a professional manner. Where they are guilty of misconduct, the award can be referred back by the courts, and in a serious case the effects of setting aside an award are to make it null and void. Misconduct may be classified as 'actual' or 'technical'.

Actual misconduct would occur where arbitrators have been inspired in their decisions by some corrupt or improper motive or have shown bias to one of the parties involved.

Technical misconduct is when some irregularities in the proceedings occur, and may include:

- the hearing of evidence of one party in the absence of the other;
- the examination of witnesses in the absence of both parties;
- the refusal to state a case when requested to do so by one of the parties;
- exceeding jurisdiction beyond the terms of the reference;
- failing to give adequate notice of the time of the proceedings;
- delegating authority;
- an error of law.

Although an arbitrator may be removed because of misconduct, this will not terminate the arbitration proceedings in favour of, say, litigation. The courts, on the application of any party to the arbitration agreement, may appoint another person to act as arbitrator. The courts may also remove an arbitrator who has failed to commence the proceedings within a reasonable time or has delayed the publishing of the award.

If the arbitrator dies during the proceedings, the arbitration will not be revoked. The parties must agree upon a successor.

The parties may at any time, by mutual agreement, decide to terminate the arbitrator's appointment. Where duties have been commenced, there will be entitlement to some remuneration.

Costs

An important part of the arbitrator's award will be the directions regarding the payment of costs. These costs, which include the arbitrator's fees, can sometimes exceed the sum which is involved in the dispute. The arbitrator must exercise discretion regarding costs, but should follow the principles adopted by the courts.

The agreement generally provides for the 'costs to follow the event', which means that the loser will pay. Where an arbitration involves several issues, and the claimant succeeds on some but fails on others, the costs of the arbitration will be apportioned accordingly. If the award fails to deal with the matter of costs, then any party to the reference may apply to the arbitrator for an order directing by whom or to whom the costs shall be paid. This must be done within 14 days of the publication of the award. A provision in an arbitration agreement that a party shall bear their own costs or any part of them is void.

The entire costs of the reference, which will include not only the costs of the hearing but also the costs incurred in respect of preliminary meetings and matters of preparation, are subject to taxation by the courts. This involves the investigation of bills of costs with the objective of reducing excessive amounts and removing improper items. For example, if a party instructs an expensive counsel which the issues involved did not justify, then the fees paid will be substantially reduced. If witnesses have been placed in expensive hotels, then this may be struck from the claim as an unnecessary expense. Such items are known as 'solicitor and client charges' and have usually to be borne by the successful party.

JCT arbitration rules

In July 1988 the Joint Contracts Tribunal published a set of arbitration rules for use with all of its various forms of building contracts. The rules contain stricter time limits than those prescribed by some arbitration rules or those frequently used in practice, largely in an attempt to avoid unnecessary costs.

The rules follow much of what has previously been described but also seek to capitalize on what might be termed good practice. There are twelve rules and these are as follows:

Rule 1   Arbitration agreements in each of the JCT Forms of Contract.
Rule 2   Interpretation and provisions as to time.
Rule 3   Service of statements, documents and notices – content of statements.
Rule 4   Conduct of the arbitration – application of Rule 5, Rule 6 or Rule 7.
Rule 5   Procedure without hearing.
Rule 6   Full procedure with hearing.

Rule 7   Short procedure with hearing.
Rule 8   Inspection by arbitrator.
Rule 9   Arbitrator's fees and expenses – costs.
Rule 10 Payment to trustee–stakeholder.
Rule 11 The award.
Rule 12 Powers of arbitrator.

Alternative dispute resolution (ADR)

Alternative dispute resolution is a non-adversarial technique which is aimed at resolving disputes without resorting to the traditional forms of either litigation or arbitration. The process was developed in the USA but has also been widely used elsewhere in the world. It is claimed to be less expensive, fast and effective. It is also less threatening and stressful. ADR offers the parties who are in dispute the opportunity to participate in a process that encourages them to solve their differences in the most amicable way that is possible. Figure 5.1 illustrates a comparison between litigation, arbitration and ADR.

Before the commencement of an ADR negotiation the parties who are in dispute should have genuine desire to settle their differences without recourse to either litigation or arbitration. They must therefore be prepared to compromise some of their rights in order to achieve a settlement. Proceedings are

Characteristics	Litigation	Arbitration	Alternative dispute resolution
Place/conduct of hearing	Public court: unilateral initiation; compulsory	Private (with few exceptions); bilateral initiation; voluntary (subject to statutory provisions)	Private: bilateral initiation; voluntary
Hearing	Formal: before a judge	Formal: conforming to rules of arbitration; before an arbitrator	Informal: before a third party (a neutral)
Representation	Legal: lawyers influence settlement	Legal: lawyers influence settlement	Legal only if necessary; disputants negotiate settlement
Resolution/ disposal	Imposed by a judge after adjudication; limited right of appeal	Award imposed by an arbitrator; limited right of appeal	Mutually accepted agreements; option of arbitration if dissatisfied
Outcome	Unsatisfactory: legal win or lose	Unsatisfactory: legal or lose	Satisfactory: business relationship maintained
Time	Time-consuming	Can be time-consuming	Fast
Cost	Expensive; uneconomic	Uneconomic	Economic

Fig. 5.1   Characteristics of dispute resolution (source: Based upon *Alternative Dispute Resolution (ADR) in Construction* by A.A. Kwayke, CIOB Construction Papers No. 21, 1993)

non-binding until a mutually agreed settlement is achieved. Either party can therefore resort to arbitration or litigation if the ADR procedure fails.

Common forms of ADR

Conciliation

This is a process where a neutral adviser listens to the disputed points of each party and then explains the views of one party to the other. An agreed solution may be found by encouraging each party to see the other's point of view. With this approach, the neutral adviser plays the passive role of a facilitator. Recommendations are not made by the adviser, any agreement is reached by the parties agreeing to settle their differences. Where an agreement is achieved, then the neutral adviser will put this in writing for each of the parties to sign.

Mediation

In this scenario the neutral adviser listens to the representations from both parties and then helps them to agree upon an overall solution. An active role is played by the adviser by putting forward suggestions, encouraging discussions and persuading the parties to focus upon the key issues. Private discussions may be held with each party in order to explain the points concerned and to attempt to formulate a mutually acceptable solution to the problem. Where this is successful then the agreement is put in writing and signed by the parties concerned.

Executive Tribunal

This is a more formal arrangement undertaken by a group comprising a neutral adviser together with representatives of the parties involved in the dispute. This group has the authority to settle the matters of dispute that created the conditions of ADR in the first place. At the hearing each party makes representations to the chairman and are also able to raise questions and seek points of clarification. Witnesses may be called upon to give evidence, although this is unusual. Each of the parties in dispute then attempts to settle the matter in private in order to achieve a negotiated settlement. Again the agreement is put in writing for endorsement by the parties concerned.

Whilst the above arrangements may appear to be separate approaches to ADR, in practice a combination of the different aspects may be used in order to solve the dispute.

ADR advisers

The neutral advisers are typically from a construction professional or a lawyer background. The latter are likely have some knowledge of the construction industry and will probably have been involved in settling such disputes in the traditional way. Persons appointed as ADR advisers will need to be trusted by the different parties and acceptable to both with known impartiality and fairness. They will seek to develop a process that suits the particular circumstances involved, seek out the truth of the dispute through questioning and debate and be the sorts of individuals who are able to solve problems. They will have good communication skills and be able to put each of the parties and the witnesses at ease in order to build their trust and confidence. They will in addition be able to appreciate all of the relevant issues involved and direct the parties towards the matters that are of crucial importance to the case.

Role of advisers in ADR

The role of advisers in ADR proceedings include:

* educating the parties involved of the procedures to be employed and the outcomes expected;
* arranging the meetings, setting agendas and outlining the protocol to be used;
* managing the process;
* clarifying the issues involved and seeking conciliation rather than encouraging confrontation;
* allowing each party to state and explain their case;
* encouraging each party to see the other party's point of view;
* preparing a report and assisting the parties to accept the agreement as binding.

Institute of Commercial Litigators (ICL)

Five firms of quantity surveyors (James R. Knowles, Beard Dove, Bucknall Austin, Cyril Sweet and Tweeds) have banded together to form the Institute of Commercial Litigators. They have made an application for rights to conduct litigation to the Lord Chancellor. The Lord Chancellor's office is presently deliberating and is expected to pronounce a decision some time in 1996. The expectation from both solicitors and quantity surveyors is that the decision will favour ICL's application.

The structure of the quantity surveyors' argument fundamentally rests in two areas, legal expertise and construction costs. They argue that they have the necessary construction knowledge which solicitors do not have. They are also able to carry out such services more economically. They thus claim that clients and contractors in the construction industry will get a better deal than they are obtaining at the present time.

In the mean time, ICL has been gathering support from other interested quantity surveyors and this has already exceeded over 1,000 affiliate members. This overwhelming support indicates that this has already become a serious organization in the construction industry.

Procurement

(OBTAINING.)

Take care of – manage

Chapter 6

Forms of contract

Introduction

The United Kingdom is fortunate to have the benefit of a wide variety of published institutional standard forms of contract available for use in the building and civil engineering industries. However, a number of government-sponsored reports have also highlighted that this has major disadvantages, identifying duplication of effort and a wasteful use of resources at almost every level of their activity. It has been suggested that many of these forms also probably help to fuel the adversarial nature of the construction industry in which they are applied. It can also be argued that to write and interpret the clauses of the various forms alone, represents an industry in itself.

The widespread use of standard forms within the construction industry is also partly accounted for by the practical impossibility of writing a set of new contract conditions for every project, even if this was in any way desirable.

The construction of building and civil engineering projects represents a major investment for any client. In some cases this will represent the single highest purchase ever made in an organization. For clients who undertake construction projects as a regular part of their activities, the correct choice of a form of contract is more important, since the application of the principles involved may be seen as precedents in the administration of their contracts. Since large sums of money are likely to be involved in these activities, it is important that the contractual arrangements should always be formal and legal from the outset of the project. Where a client allows consultants or contractors to begin their work on an informal basis, then the client's bargaining position is thereafter weakened or even eliminated. Under these circumstances, a worst case scenario for clients is that they may expect to spend years, often at substantial legal expense, in arguing over the precise nature of the contractual arrangements which should have been clarified from the start of the project.

Types of contract envisaged

The building or civil engineering contract typically refers to the contractual arrangement between the client (employer in building forms of contract and promoter in civil engineering) and contractor. The large part of this book has been written with this in mind. However, it should be remembered that with the construction of most building and civil engineering projects, contracts also need to be formed between other individuals or firms. These, therefore, include, in addition to the main contract:

- engagement of the different consultants
- nominated subcontractors and suppliers
- trade or domestic subcontractors

In addition, the different contractual arrangements also require collateral warranties and performance bonds and in some cases personal and parent company guarantees.

Employer and contractor

As long ago as 1964, the Banwell Report recommended the use of a single form of contract for the whole of the construction industry, this being both desirable and practicable. More recently the Latham Report (1994) has reiterated these comments. Chapter 11 considers some of the issues raised from these reports in more detail. Unfortunately since 1964, this apparently good suggestion has been thwarted with just the opposite taking place. Since that time there has been a plethora of different forms of contract designed to suit the individual interests of particular clients and changes in the way that construction work is now often procured. The different forms of contract also have the vested interest of different parties and institutions, who for a variety of reasons whilst incorporating good practices will at the same time wish to retain their separate identity. The better (fairer) forms of contract have incorporated the views of the different interested groups within the construction industry, such as employers and contractors. Such forms have then been prepared as a joint effort between the various different parties involved. The JCT forms, for example (see below), include wide representation from different organizations in the construction industry.

The widespread use of different forms of contract is of course exacerbated where international projects are concerned. Not only are further additional forms required, but the procurement methods used can also be considerably different from those used in the United Kingdom and, of course different laws may exist. It should be understood at this point that aspects of the laws of England and Scotland themselves continue to remain at variance!

There are, as one would expect, common threads that run throughout all of the forms of contract regarding payments, variations, quality, time, etc. However, whilst the general layout and content of the various forms may appear somewhat similar, the details may in themselves vary considerably. It should also be noted that the interpretation of the individual clauses will also differ. In some cases these have been clarified through the application of case law resulting from differences of opinion being settled in a court of law. The principles of the case law may also only apply to the form of contract in question and thus may not be applied universally across all of the different forms.

The selection of a particular form of contract is dependent upon a number of different circumstances, such as the following:

Type of work to be performed: building, civil engineering, process plant engineering.

Size of project: forms are available for major and minor works and those of an in-between nature.

Status of designer: architects are more likely to prefer JCT or ACA, whereas civil engineers will opt for an ICE or NEC form.

Public or private sector: different forms are available for use by private clients and local and central government. Large industrial corporations may in addition have their own forms of contract.

Procurement method to be used.

A major advantage of using a standard document is that those who use it regularly, become familiar with its contents and able to apply it more easily and more consistently in practice. Individuals become aware of the strengths and weaknesses of a form and are able to identify the potential areas where disputes may arise, and take corrective action where possible. They are also able to identify the forms suitability for projects with which they are concerned. The range of forms adopted by consultants is often more restricted than those faced by contractors.

Main contract forms

According to *Contracts in Use* surveys (see Chapter 7), the Joint Contracts Tribunal form of contract, referred to as JCT 80, remains the most popular form of contract for building contracts in the United Kingdom. This has commonly been referred to as the Standard Form of Building Contract (SFBC). The Institution of Civil Engineers (ICE) form remains the most popular form for civil engineering contracts. Whilst JCT 80 is in common use, its original introduction in the industry faced considerable opposition. For example, it resulted in the reprinting of the older 1963 form of contract due to its more popular demand. This form still continues to be preferred by some practitioners, although its general use has now almost disappeared. It could also be argued that the introduction of JCT 80 also encouraged the Association of Consultant Architects (ACA) to prepare their own form of contract. This had similarities to the former 1963 RIBA (Royal Institute of British Architects) form. Due to the overt complexity of administering aspects of JCT 80, particularly in respect of nominated subcontractors, the Joint Contracts Tribunal introduced a new Intermediate Form of Contract (IFC 84) in 1984. The reason for introducing this form was to provide contract conditions that were more appropriate for use on 'medium' sized building projects. In practice, this form has received a more widespread use, often on the sort and size of projects that should have adopted JCT 80 as the preferred form of contract.

Joint Contracts Tribunal (JCT) forms

The JCT is widely represented from within the construction industry. Its constituent bodies are:

Royal Institute of British Architects
Building Employers' Confederation
Royal Institution of Chartered Surveyors
Association of County Councils
Association of Metropolitan Authorities
Association of District Councils
Confederation of Associations of Specialist Engineering Contractors
Federation of Associations of Specialists and Subcontractors
Association of Consulting Engineers
British Property Federation
Scottish Building Contract Committee

The following are the different forms of contract available from JCT. The date when the form was first introduced is shown alongside its abbreviated letters, e.g. JCT 80. The second date provided, lists the latest edition of the form. In some cases additional amendments may have been issued, that have yet to be fully incorporated.

1. Joint Contracts Tribunal Standard Form of Building Contract (JCT 80) (1995)

This is known colloquially as JCT 80. There are separate editions for use with either local authorities or the private sector (see Fig. 6.1). There are also different versions available for each to allow for; with quantities, without quantities or with approximate quantities. The six different versions are, however, very similar in their content throughout. Since its introduction in 1980, there have been thirteen amendments. These are as follows:

1. January 1984. Clause 19.4 Subletting; Determination of employment of domestic subcontractor.
2. November 1986. Insurance and related liability provisions.
3. March 1987. Incorporation of 'Schedules of Work', 'Contract Sum Analysis', 'Formulae for Fluctuations' and other amendments.
4. July 1987. Miscellaneous amendments.
5. January 1988. Part 1, new clauses 1.4 and 8.2.2.
Part 2, revised clause 8.4.
6. July 1988. 1. Part 4: amendments to clause 41 'Settlement of disputes – Arbitration'.

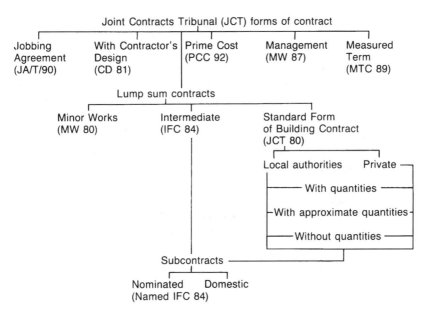

Fig. 6.1 JCT forms of contract (source: adapted from *The Standard Form of Building Contract*, Blackwell Scientific Publications)

2. Local authorities version only: omission of clause 19A 'Fair Wages'.

7. July 1988. Standard Method of Measurement 7th edition: Bills of Quantities prepared in accordance with SMM7.

8. April 1989. Amendments to VAT provisions.

9. July 1990. Miscellaneous amendments.

10. March 1991. Revised procedure for nominating a subcontractor.

11. July 1992. Determination plus other miscellaneous amendments.

12. July 1993. Additional relevant event clause.

13. January 1994. Variations.

14. March 1995. Construction (Design and Management) Regulations 1994.

15. * Conclusiveness of final certificate.

*At the time of going to publication, this amendment had yet to be issued. It results from a judgment of the Court of Appeal, *Crown Estate Commissioners* v. *John Mowlem & Co Ltd*, July 1994.

An amendment TC/94 was also introduced in April 1994 for terrorism cover. In addition there are also a number of additional supplements to cover fluctuations (three alternatives), sectional completion and contractor's designed portion. The latter should not be confused with design and build, which is an entirely different concept, with its own particular JCT form (CD 81).

JCT 80 Standard Form of Building Contract: Practice Notes

The following Practice Notes have been issued by the Joint Contracts Tribunal for the Standard Form of Building Contract. These have been issued over a period of time since JCT 80 came into use. It is likely that additional Practice Notes will continue to be issued as the need arises in order to clarify matters arising from the use of the contract in practice. Some of the Practice Notes originated with the 1963 form and have thus been adapted to suit this particular form. It should be clearly understood that the Practice Notes are not finally authoritative. They often deal with a practical application of the form, and contain material which will be included in future revisions to the form. Such notes, although they express only an opinion in legal terms, are nevertheless considered to be based upon expert legal advice. They will not, however, have the same binding effect as the decisions from courts of law.

JCT have also provided a series of Practice Notes JCT forms as follows. These are constantly being added to and updated.

1. Sectional completion supplement.
2. Clauses 21, 22, and 30.3: Insurance provisions.
3. Clause 21.2: Insurance – liability, etc., of employer – provisional sum.
4. Clauses 5.2.2 and 5.4: Drawings – additional copies.
5. Clause 30.3 and 16.2: Payment for off-site materials and goods.
6. Value added tax.
7. Standard Form of Building Contract for use with bills of approximate quantities.
8. Finance (No. 2) Act 1981 – Statutory Tax Deduction Scheme (clause 31).
9. Domestic subcontractors.
10. Nomination of subcontractors.
11. Employer/nominated subcontractor agreements (NSC/2 or NSC/2a).
12. Direct payment and final payment to nominated subcontractors.
13. Proposed nomination of a subcontractor not effected and renomination.
14. Variations and provisional sum work.
15. Nominated suppliers.
16. Extensions and liquidated damages.
17. Fluctuations.
18. Payment and retention.
19. Application and Practice Notes 9–18 to contracts in Scotland and subject to Scottish law.
20. Deciding on the appropriate form of JCT main contract.
21. The employer's position under the 1980 edition of the Standard Form of Building Contract compared to the 1963 edition.
22. The amendments to the insurance and related liability provision 1986, and guide thereto.
23. Contract sum analysis.
24. Insolvency of contractor.

25. Performance specified work.
26. Valuations and certification for interim payments including variations.
27. Application of CDM Regulations.
28. Mediation on building contracts or NSC disputes.

There are also a series of Guidance Notes that have been prepared for use with JCT contracts:

1. Joint Venture Tendering for Contracts in the UK (1985)
2. Performance Bonds (1986)
4. Pretender Meetings (1988)
5. Reproduction of Drawings for Tender Purposes (1990)
6. Collateral Warranties (1992)
7. Alternative Dispute Resolution (1993)
8. Construction Management: Selection and Appointment of Construction Manager and Trade Contractors (1994)
9. Approved and Select Lists

2. JCT Intermediate Form of Contract (IFC 84) (1992)

This form was introduced in the mid-1980s in response to the over-complexity of some of the provisions and procedures of JCT 80. This form has received similar revisions to JCT 80 and there are separate supplements covering fluctuations and sectional completion (see Chapter 27) There has been one Practice Note issued with this form, which provides a Comprehensive introduction and explanation of the form.

3. JCT Agreement for Minor Building Works (MW 80) (1994)

This was introduced at the same time as JCT 80. It contains similar provisions to JCT 80, but in a much more simplified format. It is intended for use on minor building works schemes and small projects to be carried out on a lump sum and where an architect or supervising officer has been appointed on behalf of the employer (see Chapter 26). The form cannot be used where bills of quantities have been prepared or where the employer wishes to nominate subcontractors or suppliers separately. The latest version of the form includes amendments MW1 – MW8, Practice Note M2 and Supplementary Memorandum.

4. JCT Standard Form of Building Contract with Contractor's Design (CD 81) (1991)

This is used on projects of a design and build nature. It includes many of the clauses found in the 'parent' JCT 80. It also includes clauses especially designed to deal with this type of contractual procurement arrangement. Two Practice Notes have been issued as an introduction and commentary to the form (see Chapter 30).

5. JCT Management Works Contract (MW 87) (1987)

This is used on management contracts. It includes the following:

Works Contract/1: Section 1, Management Contractor's Invitation to Tender

Works Contract/1: Section 2, Works Contract Tender

Works Contract/1: Section 3, Articles of Agreement – Attestation

Works Contract/2: Works Contract Conditions

Works Contract/3: Employer/ Works Contractor Agreement

In addition, two Practice Notes have been issued in connection with Management contracting. These provide a general introduction to management contracting under the JCT documentation and a detailed commentary on the text of the main documents to be used.

6. JCT Prime Cost Contract (PCC 92) (1992)

This form replaces the old Fixed Fee Contract. The main contract form consists of Recitals, Articles of Agreement, Attestation Clause, Conditions of Contract and eight schedules. There is in addition a fully comprehensive Practice Note and Guide which outlines the procedures for tendering and the powers of the architect.

7. JCT Standard Form of Measured Term Contract (MTC 89) (1992)

This form is designed for use by employers in both the public and private sectors who need to undertake regular maintenance, building improvements and minor works programmes. The buildings concerned are likely to be within a defined geographical area. The appointment of a contractor to carry out these works is likely to be for a specified period of time. The contract is widely used with the National Schedule of Rates.

8. JCT Standard Form of Building Works of a Jobbing Character (JA 90) (1990)

This contract is designed for use by local authorities and other employers who place a number of small jobbing contracts (up to £10,000 at 1990 prices) with various contractors and who are experienced in ordering jobbing work and dealing with contractors' accounts.

9. JCT Agreement for Renovation Grant Works (RG/A 70) (1994)

There are two versions of this form for use where a grant is receivable under the Housing Act 1974. One is used where an architect is appointed and the other where no architect is engaged.

Other main forms of contract

British Property Federation (BPF)

This is more of a procurement arrangement than a form of contract. It is described in Chapter 8.

General Conditions of Government Contracts for Building and Civil Engineering Works (GC/Works/1 and GC/Works/2)

These are published by HMSO. They are used almost exclusively by central government departments. GC/Works/1 is used on major projects and GC/Works/2 on minor building projects. There are in addition other related forms for both mechanical and electrical services in buildings. The body responsible for its contents and style and for its updating is the Department of the Environment.

General Conditions of Contract for Building and Civil Engineering Works (PSA/1)

This is a standard form of contract, for use in both the public and private sectors throughout the United Kingdom. It was developed from GC/Works/1. It is intended for use with bills of quantities, where all or most of the quantities are firm and not subject to remeasurement, giving a lump sum contract subject to adjustment for variations ordered.

Association of Consultant Architects Form of Building Agreement (ACA)

This form has been designed as an alternative to JCT 80. Its compilers were unhappy with the complexities of the JCT forms and claim that it is short, clear, legally precise and has been prepared with the advice of legal experts and in consultation with clients, contractors and the professions. However, the introduction of the IFC form, with ostensibly the same objectives, is considered by some to have eliminated the need for this form.

ICE Conditions of Contract and Form of Tender, Agreement and Bond for Use in Connection with Works of Civil Engineering Construction (ICE form)

This is published by the Institution of Civil Engineers (ICE), the Association of Consulting Engineers (ACE) and the Federation of Civil Engineering Contractors (FCEC). The sixth edition was published in 1991. In addition to the form, appendices cover an arbitration procedure, a conciliation procedure and contract price fluctuations.

ICE Conditions of Contract for Design and Construct

This new contract was launched in 1992 and has been developed from the ICE Conditions of Contract, sixth edition. The form has been designed to meet a widely felt need in the construction industry for a form of contract for use over the whole range of design and construct situations.

Conditions of Contract (International) for Works of Civil Engineering Construction (FIDIC)

This form is prepared by the International Federation of Consulting Engineers. The fourth edition was published in 1987. It is approved by several other organizations representing the construction interests of various other countries.

The New Engineering Contract (NEC)

The NEC provides a totally new approach in how engineering and construction contracts are structured and managed. Its aim is to provide a variety of contract strategies which can be adopted as necessary to suit different project, client and contractor requirements. At the same time the NEC aims to provide a stimulus whereby all parties strive towards completion of a project without the disputes and adversarial approach inherent in some other contract strategies. The contract is likely to be renamed the New Construction Contract (NCC) in the future, in a bid to gain wider application and acceptance on building as well as civil engineering works. The majority of its usage, at the present time, has, however, been abroad, particularly in South Africa (85 per cent). Its use in the UK has been less than 5 per cent of its world-wide usage (based on about 700 contracts). Those who have used the NEC have also generated widely differing responses.

The NEC is published in ten documents (see below) available either separately or combined in a slipcase. A professional service contract and an adjudicator's contract together with Guidance Notes is also available as a set.

1. New Engineering Contract
2. New Engineering Subcontract
3. Flow Charts
4. Option A: Priced Contract with Activity Schedule
5. Option B: Priced Contract with Bill of Quantities
6. Option C: Target Contract with Activity Schedule
7. Option D: Target Contract with Bill of Quantities
8. Option E: Cost Reimbursable Contract
9. Option F: Management Contract
10. Guidance Notes

Subcontract forms

Nominated subcontracts for JCT 80 (1992)

There are extensive arrangements and references in JCT 80 to the nomination procedures to be followed. These contemplate the use of the following documents and forms:

NSC/T	Part 1 Invitation to Tender
	Part 2 Tender by a Subcontractor
	Part 3 Particular Conditions
NSC/A	Agreement between Contractor and NSC
NSC/N	Nomination Instruction
NSC/W	Agreement between Employer and NSC
NSC/C	Nominated Subcontract Conditions

The above were introduced in 1991 and replaced the existing forms NSC1–4. The revised procedure for nomination of a subcontractor can be purchased as a composite document covering all of the above documents.

Nominated Suppliers Form of Tender under JCT 80

This form complies with JCT 80 clause 36, and although its use is not mandatory it is nevertheless advisable to adopt its use. The forms include:

TNS/1	Standard Form of Tender by Nominated Supplier Tender and Schedules 1 and 2
TNS/2	Form of Tender by Nominated Supplier Schedule 3

Domestic form of subcontract

These forms of subcontract have been prepared by the Building Employers' Confederation (BEC) for use with non-nominated subcontractors, i.e. those appointed directly by the contractor, commonly referred to as trade subcontractors. The documents include:

DOM/1a	Subcontract Articles of Agreement
DOM/1c	Subcontract Conditions for use with the Domestic Subcontract
DOM/2	Domestic Subcontract Article of Agreement: for use with Contractor's Design 1981
IN/SC	Domestic Subcontract Articles of Agreement: for use in connection with IFC 84

Named subcontractors for use with IFC 84

These include the following forms:

NAM/T	Form of Tender and Agreement: for a person named by the employer as a subcontractor under IFC 84
NAM/SC	Subcontract Conditions: for subcontractors named under IFC 84

ESA/1   Employer/Specialist Agreement: for use between employer and a specialist to be named under IFC 84

Standard Form of Subcontract for Nominated Subcontractors

This is referred to as the 'green form'. It is suitable for use where the subcontractor has been nominated under clause 27 of the Standard Form of Building Contract. It is prepared by BEC, FASS and CASEC.

Standard Form of Subcontract for Non-nominated Subcontractors

This is referred to as the 'blue form'. It is suitable for use where the subcontractor is not nominated and is suitable for most trades. It is prepared by BEC, FASS and CASEC.

Labour-only Subcontract Form

This form is used for work which is sublet by the main contractor under clause 19 of JCT 80. It is published (1987) by the Building Employers' Confederation (BEC). BEC also provide a shorter form for use where the labour-only subcontractor does not intend to use operatives for the execution of the subcontract works.

FCEC (Federation of Civil Engineering Contractors) Form of Subcontract

The sixth edition of this form was prepared in conjunction with the ICE form.

Form of Subcontract (International)

This form has been prepared for use with the FIDIC form of contract.

New Engineering Subcontract

This is part of the New Engineering Contract, described above.

Other forms of contract

Other forms of contract are also available, most notably those prepared by the large industrial corporations who undertake a substantial amount of construction work. Even in cases where such forms are not used and one of the more conventional forms of contract are applied, it is not uncommon to find a few pages being added as supplementary conditions. These conditions generally place the standard forms in a more favourable position with the building owner or employer. A much greater risk is therefore placed with the contractor than is usually the case. Whether this offers any real advantages to the employer is open to speculation. Under 'normal' tendering circumstances, the contractors' prices will reflect the more onerous conditions.

It is much more unusual to tamper with the contract conditions themselves, since there is always the danger of making the contract null and void, or failing to alter the conditions consistently throughout the particular form being adapted.

National Joint Consultative Committee (NJCC)

This is an advisory body concerned with practice and procedures in building contracts. It has a good practice panel and a wide range of publications concerned with contracts. It provides a range of Codes of Procedure, the most common of which is 'The Code of Procedure for Single Stage Selective Tendering' (see Chapter 8). In addition it provides codes on; tendering procedure for industrialized building projects, two-stage selective tendering, selective tendering for design and build, management contracting and the letting and management of domestic subcontract works. The NJCC also offers good practice on preparing lists of approved contractors. It provides Guidance Notes on issues such as performance bonds, collateral warranties and alternative dispute resolution. It also produces a set of Procedure Notes covering a wide range of topics such as financial controls and cash flow, placing contracts with substantial building services engineering content and the use and completion of nominated subcontracts.

Other contractual documentation

Letters and notices for contractors and subcontractors using JCT 80 forms

This has been prepared by BEC and BAS (Building Advisory Service). The letters and notices cover a variety of JCT main contract and subcontract forms. The documentation used is specially designed to observe the proper formalities under contracts.

Model Conditions of Estimate for Small Works

This has been prepared by BEC for contractors quoting for small works.

Definition of Prime Cost for Daywork Carried out under a Building Contract

This is prepared jointly by the RICS and BEC. It applies to work described as daywork carried out under and incidental to a building contract. A separate document 'Definition of Prime Cost of Building Works of a Jobbing and Maintenance Character' covers jobbing and maintenance work carried out as a main or separate contract.

Formula Rules 1987

The consolidated set of Formula Rules covers all the main contract forms, such as JCT 80, CD 81 and IFC 84.

Standard Forms of Agreement for a Collateral Warranty by a Main Contractor

The JCT has published warranties by a contractor to a purchaser or tenant of building works and to a company providing finance for building works defined as a 'funder'. These warranties have been drafted to be compatible with warranties already issued by the BPF, RIBA, RICS and ACE which are given by a consultant to a purchaser or tenant or to a funder.

Guide to Terrorism Cover 1994

Provisions in JCT forms on insurance of the works of the existing structures and contents for physical loss or damage due to fire or explosion due to terrorism.

Arbitration Rules 1988

The JCT has prepared rules for the conduct of arbitration which will be contractually binding on the parties. The rules apply to the settlement of all disputes coming within the terms of the arbitration agreements in all forms of JCT contract and subcontract and other tribunal agreements.

Guidance on the Unfair Contract Terms Act 1977

This is published by BEC.

Appointment of consultants

Whilst 'the construction contract' is between the client (employer or promoter) and the contractor, the various consultants engaged on a project will also have a contract with the appointing client. Different forms of contract are used for the appointment of:

- Architects – Royal Institute of British Architects
- Quantity surveyors – Royal Institution of Chartered Surveyors
- Structural engineers – Association of Consulting Engineers
- Building services engineers – Association of Consulting Engineers
- Project managers – Royal Institution of Chartered Surveyors
- Civil engineers – Association of Consulting Engineers

The contracts in these circumstances are for the professional services relating to the provision of the construction project. The different forms cover duty of care, fees, copyright, collateral warranties and agreements, professional indemnity insurance, etc. The forms identify materials or substances that should not be used in the construction process. These are: high alumina cement in structural elements, wood wool slabs in permanent formwork to concrete, calcium chloride in admixtures for use in reinforced concrete, asbestos products and naturally occurring aggregates for use in reinforced concrete which do not comply with British Standards 882 or 8110.

The fees charged by these consultants will be guided by the fee scales that are published by the different professional bodies. However, in common with the principles of competitive tendering, it is now usual to invite consultants to compete for work with one of the criteria being the fees charged for the consultancy work.

Chapter 7

Contract strategy

Appetite for change

In the early 1960s the clients of the construction industry had only a limited choice of procurement methods which they might wish to use for the construction of a new building. The RIBA form of contract, although even then not used universally, had yet to experience extensive rivalry from elsewhere, or even from within its own organization for a serious alternative. Bills of quantities were becoming the preferred document in place of the specification, and the mistrusted cost-plus type contracts which had been a necessity a few years earlier for the rapid repair of war-damaged property were already in decline.

We now live in a world of endless change. In recent years there have been many developments in the technologies that are used, in the types of societies in which we live, and amongst professional attitudes. The causes of these changes which have been experienced are not difficult to find. Society generally is on the look-out for something new, and the construction industry in a way mirrors that change to avoid being thought of as outdated or old-fashioned. The search is also for improvement, knowing that we have not as yet found the perfect system; even if one at all exists. In this context, largely due to improved geographical communications of the twentieth century, the construction industry has looked with interest to both east and west, to the way that others around the world arrange the procurement of capital works projects. Not surprisingly, it is the countries which appear to have been the most successful which have received most of the attention. The methods adopted in the USA or Japan for their construction industries have been in the forefront of our ideas for change.

The apparent failure of the construction industry to satisfy the perceived needs of its customers, particularly in the way it organizes and executes its projects, has been another catalyst for change. Various pressure groups too have evolved to champion the causes of the different organizations who perhaps have particular axes to grind. The 1970s oil-price crisis, which had a massive influence on inflation and hence industries' borrowing requirements, also motivated the construction industry to improve its own efficiency through the way it managed and organized its work. The depression of the 1970s, like other slumps previously, encouraged firms of all kinds to attempt to persuade employers to build, by using what were then innovative approaches to contract procurement.

Contracts in use

The construction industry can be measured in several different ways, e.g. turnover, profitability, number of firms, number of employees (see *The Construction Industry of Great Britain* by R.C. Harvey and A. Ashworth, Butterworth-Heinemann, 1993). Typically it is worth about £40–45 bn. Whatever measure is adopted this indicates a decline in activity from the boom years of the late 1980s. The industry is also diverse. About 60 per cent is repairs and maintenance, now less than 25 per cent is represented by public sector projects and civil engineering accounts for approximately 20 per cent of the total output.

During the period 1970–95 changes in the methods of construction procurement have perhaps been one of the most fundamental changes that have taken place in the construction industry. Greater comparisons have been made with procurement methods used by other industries and in other countries around the world. There has also been research undertaken in order to better inform clients, consultants and contractors. The different methods available all have their advantages and disadvantages and there is no uniform solution that emerges across the industry. The choice of method depends upon a combination and importance of the following characteristics:

- type of client
- size of project
- type of project
- risk allocation
- form of contract to be used
- major objectives of the client
- status of the designer
- relationships with contractors/consultants, such as partnering (see Chapter 11)
- sort of contract documentation required

A number of different organizations attempt to monitor procurement systems in the construction industry. The following analysis (Figs 7.1 and 7.2) has been derived from *Contracts in Use, A Survey of Building Contracts in Use during 1993*. This was prepared by the quantity surveyors Davies, Langdon & Everest and published by the RICS in 1994. The survey is done on a biennial basis.

It was noted in the second edition of *Contractual Procedures in the Construction Industry* (1991), that even by 1987 over 10 per cent of the value of new orders carried out by consultants and local authorities continued to use a variant of the 1963 form of contract. Since that time the percentage has declined to now less than 1 per cent. This is somewhat surprising since it is now (1995) over 30 years since that form was introduced and almost 15 years since JCT 80 was intended to replace it.

	Percentage by number	Percentage by value
JCT 80	19.36	33.55
JCT 63	0.31	0.81
Minor Works	26.49	1.75
With Contractor's Design	13.21	28.91
IFC 84	21.98	10.4
Other JCT	0.96	4.96
Other standard forms	5.28	8.63
Employer/quantity surveyor/contractor written	12.41	11.01
Totals	100	100

Fig. 7.1 The distribution of contracts in use (source: Davies, Langdon & Everest)

About 80 per cent of the value of the work analysed in the survey used one of the JCT family of forms. The scope of the survey excluded overseas work, civil and heavy engineering, term contracts, maintenance and repairs and subcontracts that formed a part of main contracts. Work done directly by contractors was excluded from the survey to avoid any possible double counting. This suggests that design and build represents a much larger proportion than indicated by this survey alone. This viewpoint is reinforced by the section provided later in this chapter on design and build.

The use of JCT 80 has declined since the last survey was carried out. This is largely due to the increase in the use of the Standard Form with Contractor's Design (CD 81). The survey suggests that 32 per cent of 'traditional' contracts now include at least some element of contractor design. There has also been a trend towards forms specially designed by the employer, quantity surveying practices or contractors themselves.

The JCT Intermediate Form (IFC 84) which was introduced for 'medium' size projects, but was often used on major schemes, continues to represent about 10 per cent of the total value of the projects in the survey. The minor works form was used on over a quarter of the projects in the sample, although these represented only 2 per cent of the total value of the work analysed.

It is of course difficult to derive a clear picture since the survey represents only a proportion of the total work done by consultant quantity surveyors. The effects of the continuing recession may distort the picture, since both consultants and contractors may be prepared to undertake work on less than favourable or ideal conditions. The survey represented a 15 per cent response rate, which is typical for anyone seeking information by way of questionnaires. This did, however, cover 3,827 projects worth almost £2.5bn.

Procurement methods

The survey provided some interesting data on the use of bills of quantities. As long ago as 1968, a surveyor (employed by a contractor) suggested to me that bills of quantities and quantity surveyors would cease to exist within a few

	1984	1985	1987	1989	1991	1993
Lump sum -- firm bill of quantities	58.73	59.26	52.07	52.29	48.26	41.63
Lump sum -- specification	13.13	10.2	17.76	10.26	8.35	9.98
Lump sum -- D&B	5.06	8.05	12.16	10.87	14.78	35.7
Remeasurement -- approximate bill of quantities	6.62	5.44	3.43	3.58	1.26	2.43
Prime cost -- fixed fee	4.45	2.65	5.17	1.12	0.12	0.15
Management contract	12.01	14.4	9.41	14.99	7.87	6.17
Construction management	0	0	0	6.89	19.36	3.94

Fig. 7.2   Procurement methods (source: Davies, Langdon & Everest)

years, then by the early 1970s. I chose to disagree, and when people suggest this today, I am still of the same mind. At least on the latter!

From this survey, it is quite clear that bills of quantities continue to remain in use. The survey points towards their decline; at least under the traditional arrangement of a lump sum contract with a firm bill of quantities. The survey indicates a decline from 58 per cent in 1984 to 42 per cent in 1993. It should also be remembered that some other form of quantification for costing purposes, such as work packages, will be required with the alternative procurement methods. The survey indicates that for the large projects bills of quantities are still required.

Management contracts and construction management account for only 10 per cent of the total value of the projects captured in the survey. The 1991 survey revealed a dramatic fall in the use of management contracts from 14.99 to 7.87 percent. The latest survey shows no sign in the recovery of popularity of this form of procurement. The use of construction management has experienced an even more dramatic decline. It hardly existed at all in 1987, but by 1991 represented almost 20 percent of the value of projects. By 1993 this percentage had sunk to 3.94 percent. The considerable increase in the use of design and build methods explains some of the reasons for this fall. It might also emphasize the fact that during the recession many of the large speculative developers have ceased to be involved in new construction projects. The trends suggested by this survey indicate that whilst management contracting and construction management clearly have some role to play in the future it will be design and build that is seen as the alternative and competitor to the traditional form of procurement.

Drawings and specifications continue to be used on small works projects and these remain popular up to £100,000. There are also examples where they are used on projects with a value in excess of £1 m. The construction industry in some cases has already gone full circle. Contractors being requested to prepare tenders on drawings and specifications alone then employ their own quantity surveyor to prepare quantities which they are then able to price. There are also examples recorded in these circumstances where the contractor does not price the work in detail, but prepares a tender using one of the simplified methods of estimating. The work is only priced using more detailed quantities once the contractor has succeeded in winning the contract. Also in the early days of the industrial revolution, architects used to ask trade contractors to submit individual prices for their work; this is now referred to as management contracting.

Design and build (D&B)

This method of procurement continues to increase in popularity as clients seek ever more value for money and single point responsibility for their construction projects. It is difficult to offer precise figures for comparison since these depend upon the overall amount of work available and the general economic state of the industry. Also, in the past, when the public sector contributed more to the industry's overall output, there was a bigger resistance to D&B as an option, and this therefore distorts the information.

New Builder (June 1995) reported that in 1992, D&B turnover for the top 25 D&B contractors fell by 2.19 percent. This compares with increases of 14 percent in 1993 and 18 percent in 1994. These 25 contractors include the major contractors in the industry. D&B represented, on average, 29 percent of overall turnover in 1994, compared with 24 percent in 1993. The top five D&B contractors have more than 45 percent of their turnover accounted for by D&B work. On average about 10 percent of the larger consultants' work is now described as D&B.

In the 1960s and 1970s, many people felt that D&B was only suitable for cheap and cheerful buildings. This image has now changed to provide clients with as high quality projects as any other methods of procurement. In some cases the designer is appointed by the client to prepare outline schemes before involving the D&B contractor. This has been termed as novated design and build. Many involved feel that this puts the contractor in a disadvantaged position, providing few opportunities for innovation and improvement and hence the project's overall value for money aspects. Typically buildings requiring little design aesthetics, such as industrial premises and warehouses, were selected for D&B operations. Today it would appear that D&B is used across the wide spectrum of project types.

General matters

The following are the major issues to be resolved. These are shown in Fig. 7.3.

Consultants v. contractors

The contracts survey referred to above underestimates the total amount of D&B type projects because it is almost entirely a survey of consultant organizations. The arguments for engaging a consultant rather than a contractor as the main employer's adviser are inconclusive. The respective advantages and

Consultant or contractor
↓
Price competition or negotiation
↓
Measurement or negotiation
↓
Traditional or alternative procurement

Fig. 7.3 Developing a contract procurement strategy

disadvantages may be summarized as follows. Advantages of a contractor-centred approach are said to be:

- better time management
- single point responsibility
- inherent buildability
- certainty of price
- teamwork
- inclusive design fees

Disadvantages may be:

- problems of contractor proposals matching with employer requirements
- payment clauses
- emphasis may be away from design towards other factors
- employers may still need to retain consultants for payments, inspections, etc.

Competition v. negotiation

There are a variety of ways in which a builder may seek to secure business. These include speculation, invitation, reputation, rotation arrangement, recommendation and selection. Irrespective, however, of the final contractual arrangements which are made by the employer, the method of choosing the contractor must first be established. The alternatives which are available for this purpose are either competition or negotiation.

Some form of competition on price, time or quality is desirable. All of the evidence which is available suggests that the employer under the normal circumstances of contract procurement is likely to strike a better bargain if an element of competition exists. There are, however, a number of circumstances which can arise in which a negotiated approach may be more beneficial to the employer. Some of these include:

- business relationship
- early start on site
- continuation contract
- state of the market
- contractor specialization

- financial arrangements
- geographical area

The above list is not exhaustive nor should it be assumed that negotiation would be preferable in all of these examples. Each individual project should be examined on its own merits, and a decision made bearing in mind the particular circumstances concerned and specific advantages to the employer.

Certain essential features are necessary if the negotiations are to proceed satisfactorily. These include equality of the negotiators in either party, parity of information, agreement as to the basis of negotiation and a decision on how the main items of work will be priced.

Measurement v. reimbursement

There are essentially only two ways of calculating the costs of construction work. Either the contractor adopts some form of measurement and is paid for the work on the basis of quantity multiplied by a rate, or the contractor is reimbursed the actual costs. A drawing and specification contract, for example, relies upon the contractor measuring and pricing the work, even though only a single sum is disclosed to the employer. The measurement contract allows for the payment for risk to the contractor, the cost reimbursement approach does not. Many of the measurement contracts may include for a small proportion of the work to be paid for under dayworks (a form of cost reimbursement) but it is more unusual to find cost reimbursement contracts with any measurement aspects. The points to be borne in mind when choosing between measurement or cost reimbursement contracts include the following:

- *Contract sum.* This is not available with any form of cost reimbursement contract.
- *Final price forecast.* This is not possible with any of the cost reimbursement methods or with measurement contracts which rely extensively on approximate quantities.
- *Incentive for contractor efficiency.* Cost reimbursement contracts can encourage wastage which must then be passed on to the employer.
- *Price risk.* Measurement contracts allow for this, employers may therefore pay for such non-events.
- *Cost control.* The employer has little control over costs where any form of cost reimbursement contract is used.
- *Administration.* Cost reimbursement contracts require a large amount of clerical work.

Traditional v. alternatives

Until recent times the majority of the major building projects were constructed using single-stage selective tendering. This method of procurement has many flaws, and as such, alternative procedures have been devised in an attempt to address the issues which it raised. The newer methods, or alternative procurement paths, whilst overcoming the failures of the traditional approach created their own particular problems. In fact if a single method was able to be devised which addressed all of the problems then the remaining methods would quickly fall into disuse. In choosing a method of procurement, therefore, the following issues are of importance. They are more fully described in Chapter 9.

- project size
- costs, inclusive of the design
- time, from brief to handover
- accountability
- design, function and aesthetics
- quality assurance
- organization and responsibility
- project complexity
- risk placing
- market considerations
- financial provisions

The framework of society

The correct application of contractual procurement systems is influenced by a number of factors which are present within any society. Such factors, although external to the construction industry, do have implications for the successful completion of each individual project. The appropriate recommendations today may also have different implications in the future, because the framework of society is a constantly evolving one. In selecting the right method, therefore, the following factors should be considered and evaluated:

- *Economic* – interest rates, inflation, land costs, investment policies, market levels, taxation opportunities, opportunity costs.
- *Legal* – contract law, case law, arbitration, discharge of contracts, remedies for breach of contract.
- *Technological* – new techniques, off-site manufacture, production processes, use of computers.
- *Political* – government systems, public expenditure, export regulations and guarantees, planning laws, trade-union practice, policies.
- *Social* – demography, ageing population, availability of potential employees, retraining, the environment.

Many of these factors are unstable even in a well-run economy or for the duration of the contract period, due to the influences from other world markets. An employer's satisfaction with the project relies upon the procurement adviser's skill and to some extent the intuition which can be provided, in being able to reflect on how the above are likely to influence the method recommended for contract procurement.

Employer's essential requirements

Employers when buying a particular service seek to ensure that it fully meets their needs. The consultant or contractor employed needs to identify with the employer's objectives within the context in which the employer has to operate and particularly any constraints which may be present. *A Study of Quantity Surveying Practice and Client Demand* (RICS 1984), identified some of the following criteria as important requirements for the majority of employers:

- impartial and independent advice;
- trust and fairness in all dealings;
- timely information ahead of possible events;
- implications on the interreactions of time, cost and quality;
- options from which the employer can select the best possible route;
- recommendations for action;
- good value for any fees charged;
- advice based upon a skilled consideration of the project as a whole;
- sound ability and general competence;
- reliability of advice;
- enterprise and innovation.

Procurement management

It is of considerable importance to employers who wish to have buildings erected that the appropriate advice is provided on the method of procurement to be used. The advice offered must be relevant and reliable and based upon skill and expertise. There is, however, a dearth of objective and unbiased advice available. It is often difficult to elicit the relevant facts appropriate to a proposed building project. Construction employers will tend to rely on the advice from their chosen consultant or contractor. The advice provided is usually sound, and frequently successful according to the criteria set by the employer. It may, however, tend to be biased and even in some cases tainted with self-interest. It is perhaps sometimes given on the basis of 'who gets to the client first'. Methods and procedures have now become so complex, with a wide variety of options available, that an improvement in the management approach to the procurement process is now necessary to meet the employer's needs. The need to match, for instance, the employer's requirements with the industry's response is very important if customer care and satisfaction are to be achieved. The employer's procurement manager must consider the characteristics of the various methods that are available and recommend a solution which best suits the employer's needs and aspirations. The manager will need to discuss the level of risk involved for the procurement path recommended for the project under review.

The process of procurement management may be broadly defined to include the following:

- determining the employer's requirements in terms of time, cost and quality;
- assessing the viability of the project and providing advice in terms of funding and taxation;
- advising on an organizational structure for the project as a whole;
- advising on the appointment of consultants and contractors bearing in mind the criteria set by the employer;
- managing the information and co-ordinating the activities of the consultants and contractor, through the design and construction phases.

The simplistic view is that architects design and contractors build. Those are their strengths. It is important, however, that someone is especially responsible for the contractual matters surrounding the contract.

The NEDO publication *Thinking about Building* suggests the following regarding procurement:

- DO make one of your in-house executives responsible for the project.
- DO bring in an outside adviser if the in-house resources and skills are inappropriate.
- DO take special care to define the needs for the project.
- DO choose a procurement path to fit the defined priorities.
- DO go to some trouble to select the organizations and individuals concerned.
- DO ensure that a professional appraisal is done before the scheme becomes too advanced.

The effectiveness of a procurement path is a combination of the following:

- the correct advice and decision on which procurement path to use;
- the correct implementation of the chosen path;
- the evaluation during and after its execution.

CCPI

Research at the Building Research Establishment on 50 representative building sites has shown that the biggest single cause of events which stop site managers, architects or tradesmen from working together is unclear or missing project information. Another significant cause is uncoordinated design, and at times the entire effort of site management can be directed to searching for missing information or reconciling inconsistencies in that which is available. To overcome these weaknesses, the Co-ordinating Committee for Project Information (CCPI) was formed with the task of developing a common arrangement for work sections for building works that could be used throughout the various forms of documentation.

CCPI has consulted widely to ensure that the proposals are practicable and helpful, and its work has been performed by practising professionals who are themselves fully aware of the pressures involved. Is it really more economical to produce incomplete and inconsistent, if not contradictory, project information during the design process, and then to spend time wrestling with and trying to rectify the problems on site, with the attendant waste of time in dealing with claims? Is it not better to produce complete and co-ordinated information once and thus avoid such problems? If properly co-ordinated project documentation is produced much abortive work will be avoided and costs will be so much less.

Regardless of the procurement method selected it is important that the principles of CCPI are adopted and put into practice. Procurement methods which are unable to incorporate such principles may be severely flawed in practice.

Value for money

Employers are rightly concerned with obtaining value for money. Cheapness is in itself no virtue. It is well worth while to pay a little more if as a result the gain in value exceeds the extra costs. Value for money, in any context, is a combination of subjective and objective viewpoints. There are some items which can be measured but there are other items which can only be left to opinion or at best expert judgement. The former of these can largely be proven, or at least it could if our knowledge was fully comprehensive. The professional's skill is, however, largely in the judgement area. The procurement method recommended to the employer needs to be that which offers the best value for money. The need for careful assessment is required to obtain the desired results.

Figure 7.4 illustrates the contractual terminology in both the expected and likely positions.

Fig. 7.4 Contractual terminology: (a) expected contractual position; (b) likely contractual position

Conclusions

Procurement procedures today are a dynamic activity. They are evolutionary, to suit the changing needs of society and the considerations in which the industry finds itself operating. There are no standard solutions, but each individual project, which invariably represents a one-off project, needs to be considered independently and analysed accordingly. A wide variety of factors have to be taken into account before any practical decisions can be made. The various influences concerned need to be weighed carefully, and always with the best interests of the employer in mind.

Chapter 8

Contract procurement

Introduction

The execution of a construction project requires both design work and the carrying out of construction operations on site. If these are to be done successfully, resulting in a satisfactorily completed project, then some form of recognized procedure must be employed at the outset to deal with their organization, co-ordination and procedures.

Traditionally a client who wished to have a building constructed would invariably commission an architect to prepare drawings of the proposed scheme and if the scheme was sufficiently large employ a quantity surveyor to prepare appropriate documentation on which the builder could prepare a price. These would all be based upon the client's brief, and the information used as a basis for competitive tendering. This was the common system in use at the turn of the century and still continues to be widely used in practice.

Particularly since the mid-1960s a small revolution has occurred in the way designers and builders are employed for the construction of buildings. To some extent these are the results of initiatives taken by the then Ministry of Works in the early 1960s and the Banwell committee which recommended several changes in the way that projects and contracts were organized, one of which was an attempt to try to bring the designers and the constructors closer together. The construction industry continues to examine and evaluate the methods available, and to devise new procedures which address the shortfalls and weaknesses of the current procedures.

There is, however, no panacea for the present difficulties. In fact it may be argued that change is occurring so fast that a present-day solution may be quite inappropriate for tomorrow. Each of the methods described have their own characteristics, advantages and disadvantages. All have been used in practice at some time; some more than others largely due to the familiarity and the consequent advantage of ease of application. New methods will evolve to meet the ever rapidly changing circumstances of the construction industry. These will occur in response to current deficiencies and to changes in the culture of the construction industry.

Methods of price determination

Building and civil engineering contractors are paid for the work which they carry out, on the basis of one of two methods, either measurement or cost reimbursement.

Measurement

The work is measured in place on the basis of its finished quantities. The contractor is paid for this work on the basis of quantity multiplied by a rate. Measurement may be undertaken by the employer's quantity surveyor, or by the contractor's surveyor or estimator. In the first example an accurate and detailed contract document can be prepared. In the latter the document prepared will be sufficient only to satisfy the particular builder concerned. The work may be measured as accurately as the drawings allow prior to the contract being awarded, in which case it is known as a lump-sum contract. Alternatively, the work may be measured or remeasured after it has been carried out. In the latter case it is referred to as a remeasurement contract. All contracts envisage some form of remeasurement to take into account variations. In such cases both the employer's and the contractor's surveyors measure the work together. Measurement contracts, unless they are entirely of a remeasurement type, allow for some sort of final cost to be recalculated. This offers advantages to the client for budgeting and cost-control purposes. Building contracts are more often lump-sum contracts, whereas civil engineering projects are typically of the remeasurement type.

Cost reimbursement

With these types of contractual arrangements the contractor is able to recoup the actual costs of the materials which have been purchased and the time spent on the work by his operatives, plus an amount to cover the contractor's profit. Dayworks accounts are valued on much the same basis.

Measurement contracts

The following are the main types of measurement contracts used in the construction industry.

Drawings and specification

This is the simplest type of measurement contract and is really only suitable for small works or simple projects. In recent years there has been a trend towards using this approach on schemes much larger than was originally intended. Each contractor has to measure the quantities from the drawings and interpret the specification during pricing in order to calculate the tender sum. The method is wasteful of the contractor's estimating resources, and does not easily allow for a fair comparison of the tender sums received by the employer. Interpreting the specification can be a hazardous job even for the more experienced estimator. The contractor has also to accept a greater proportion of the risk, being responsible for the prices as well as for the measurements based upon interpretation of the contract information. In order to compensate for possible errors or omissions, evidence might suggest that contractors tend to overprice this type of work.

Performance specification

This method is a much more vague approach to tendering and the evaluation of the contractor's bids. In this situation the contractor is required to prepare a price based upon the employer's brief and user requirements alone. The contractor is left to determine the method of construction and choose the materials that suit these broad conditions. The contractor in practice is likely to select materials and methods of construction which satisfy the prescribed performance standards in the least expensive way. Great precision is required in formulating a performance specification if the desired results are to be achieved.

Schedule of rates

With some projects it is not possible to predetermine the nature and full extent of the proposed building works. In these circumstances, where it is desirable to form some direct link between quantity and price, a schedule of rates may be used. This schedule is similar to a bill of quantities, but without any actual quantities being included. It should be prepared using the rules of a method of measurement. Contractors are invited to insert their rates against these items, and they are then used in comparison against other contractors' schedules in selecting a tender. Upon completion of the work it is remeasured and the rates are used to calculate the final cost. This method has the disadvantages of being unable to predict a contract sum, or an indication of the probable final cost of the project. Contractors also find it difficult realistically to price the schedule in the absence of any quantities.

Schedule of prices

An alternative to the schedule of rates is to provide the contractors with a ready-priced schedule, similar to the Property Services Agency's (PSA) Schedule of Rates. The contractors in this case adjust each rate by the addition or deduction of a percentage. In practice a single percentage adjustment is normally made to all of the rates. This standard adjustment is unsatisfactory since the contractor will view some of the prices in the schedule as high prices, and others as being inadequate in terms of covering costs. It does, however, have the supposed advantage of producing fewer errors in the pricing in the tender documents compared with the contractor's own price analysis of the work.

Bill of quantities

Even with all the new forms of contract arrangement the bill of quantities continues to remain the most common form of measurement contract, and the most common contractual arrangement for major construction projects in the United Kingdom. The contractors' tenders are able to be judged on the prices alone since they are all using the same qualitative and quantitative data. This type of documentation is recommended for all but the smallest projects.

Bill of approximate quantities

In some circumstances it is not possible to measure the work accurately. In this case a bill of approximate quantities might be prepared and the entire project remeasured upon completion. The JCT Standard Form of Building Contract with Approximate Quantities could then be used. Whilst an approximate cost of the project can be obtained, the uncertainty in the design data makes any reliable forecast impossible.

Cost reimbursement contracts

These types of contract are not favoured by many of the industry's employers, since there is an absence of a tender sum and a forecasted final account cost. Some of these types of contract also provide little incentive for the contractor to control costs, although different varieties of cost reimbursement build in incentives for the contractor to keep costs as low as possible. They are therefore often used only in special circumstances as follows:

- emergency work projects, where time is not available to allow the traditional process to be used;
- when the character and scope of the works cannot be readily determined;
- where new technology is being used;
- where a special relationship exists between the employer and the building contractor.

Cost reimbursement contracts can take many different forms but the following are three of the more popular types in use. Each of the methods repay the contractor's costs with an addition to cover profits. Prior to embarking on this type of contract it is especially important that all the parties involved are clearly aware of the definition of contractor's costs as used in this context.

Cost plus percentage

The contractor receives the costs of labour, materials, plant, subcontractors and overheads and to this sum is added a percentage to cover profits. This percentage is agreed at the outset of the project. A major disadvantage of this type of cost reimbursement is that the contractor's profits are directly geared to the contractor's expenditure. Therefore, the more the contractor spends on the building works the greater will be the profitability. Because it is an easy method to operate, this tends to be the selected method when using cost reimbursement.

Cost plus fixed fee

With this method the contractor's profit is predetermined by the agreement of a fee for the work before the commencement of the project. There is therefore some incentive for the contractor to attempt to control the costs. However, because it is difficult to predict the cost with sufficient accuracy beforehand, it can cause disagreement between the contractors and the employer's own professional advisers. The result is that the *fixed fee* may thus need to be revised on completion of the project.

Cost plus variable fee

The use of this method requires a target fee to be set for the project prior to the signing of the contract. The contractor's fee is then composed of two parts, a fixed amount and a variable amount. The total fee charged then depends upon the relationship between the target cost and the actual cost. This method provides a supposedly even greater incentive to the contractor to control the construction costs. It has the disadvantage of requiring the target cost to be fixed on the basis of a very 'rough' estimate of the proposed project.

Examples

Cost plus percentage

Estimated cost	£100,000	Final cost	£111,964
Agreed percentage profit 10%	£10,000	10% profit	£11,964
Tender	£110,000	Final account	£123,928

Cost plus fixed fee

Estimated cost	£100,000	Final cost	£111,964
Fixed fee	£12,500	Fixed fee	£12,500
Tender sum	£112,500	Final account	£124,464

Cost plus variable fee

Estimated cost	£100,000	Final cost	£111,964
Fixed fee	£10,000	Fixed fee	£10,000
Variable fee 10%		Variable fee	
+100,000		10% 11,964	−1,196
Tender sum	£110,000	Final account	£120,768

The above are examples only. It cannot be assumed that the final accounts would follow these patterns. These are the simple theories of the calculations. In practice the financial adjustments are often very complex.

Contractor selection

There are essentially two ways of choosing a contractor, either by competition or negotiation. Competition may be restricted to a few selected firms or open to almost any firm who wishes to submit a tender. The options described later are used in conjunction with one of these methods of contractor selection.

Selective competition

This is the traditional and most popular method of awarding construction contracts. In essence a number of firms of known reputation are selected by the design team to submit a price. The firm who submits the lowest tender is then awarded the contract. The NJCC (revised 1994) have developed a *Code of Procedure for Single-stage Selective Tendering*, which although not mandatory does provide guidance on the awarding of construction contracts. The Code takes into account the changes in buildings procurement and the general principles of current recommendations. The following are some of the more important points from this Code:

1. The Code assumes the use of a standard form of building contract with which the parties in the construction industry are familiar. If other forms of contract are used, some modification of detail may be necessary. There are clear advantages to all parties in the knowledge that a standard procedure will be followed in inviting and accepting tenders. Figure 8.1 illustrates the traditional contractual relationships.
2. The Code recommends that the number of tenderers should be limited to six. The number of tenderers is restricted because the cost of preparing abortive tenders will be reflected in prices generally throughout the building industry.
3. In preparing a short list of tenderers, the following must be borne in mind:
   - the firm's financial standing and record;
   - recent experience of building over similar contract periods;
   - the general experience and reputation of the firm for similar building types;

Fig. 8.1 Traditional relationships

- adequacy of management;
- adequacy of capacity.

4. Each firm on the short list should be sent a preliminary enquiry to determine its willingness to tender. The enquiry should contain:
    - job title
    - names of employer and consultants
    - location of site and general description of the works
    - approximate cost range
    - principal nominated subcontractors
    - form of contract and any amendments
    - procedure for correction of priced bills
    - contract under seal or under hand
    - anticipated date for possession
    - contract period
    - anticipated date for despatch of tender documents
    - length of tender period
    - length of time tender must remain open for acceptance
    - amount of liquidated damages
    - bond
    - special conditions

5. Once a contractor has confirmed an intention to tender, that tender should be made. If circumstances arise which make it necessary to withdraw, the architect should be notified before the tender documents are issued or, at the latest, within 2 days thereafter.

6. A contractor who has expressed a willingness to tender should be informed if not chosen for the final short list.

7. All tenderers must submit their tenders on the same basis.
    - Tender documents should be despatched on the stated day.
    - Alternative offers based on alternative contract periods may be admitted if requested on the date of despatch of the documents.
    - Standard forms of contract should not be amended.
    - A time of day should be stated for receipt of tenders and tenders received late should be returned unopened.

8. The tender period will depend on the size and complexity of the job, but

be not less than 4 working weeks, i.e. 20 days.

9. If a tenderer requires any clarification the architect must be notified who in turn should inform all tenderers of this decision.

10. If a tenderer submits a qualified tender, opportunity should be given to withdraw the qualification without amending the tender figure, otherwise the tender should normally be rejected.

11. Under English law, a tender may be withdrawn at any time before acceptance. Under Scottish law, it cannot be withdrawn unless the words 'unless previously withdrawn' are inserted in the tender after the stated period of time the tender is to remain open for acceptance.

12. After tenders are opened all but the lowest three tenderers should be informed immediately. The lowest tenderer should be asked to submit a priced bill within 4 days. The other two contractors are informed that they might be approached again.

13. After the contract has been signed, each tenderer should be supplied with a list of tender prices.

14. The quantity surveyor must keep the priced bills strictly confidential.

15. If there are any errors in pricing the Code sets out alternative ways of dealing with the situation.

   • The tenderer should be notified and given the opportunity to confirm or withdraw the offer. If it is withdrawn, the next lowest tenderer is considered. Where the offer is confirmed an endorsement should be added to the priced bills that all rates, except preliminary items, contingencies, prime cost and provisional sums are to be deemed reduced or increased, as appropriate, by the same proportion as the corrected total exceeds or falls short of the original price.

   • The tenderer should be given the opportunity of confirming the offer or correcting the errors. Where it is corrected and is no longer the lowest tender, then the next tender should be examined. If it is not corrected then an endorsement is added to the tender.

16. Corrections must be initialled or confirmed in writing and the letter of acceptance must include a reference to this. The lowest tender should be accepted, after correction or confirmation, in accordance with the alternative chosen. Problems sometimes occur because the employer will see that a tender will still be the lowest even after correction. If the first alternative has been agreed upon and notified to all tenderers at the time of invitation to tender, the choice facing the tenderer should clearly be to confirm or withdraw. The employer may require a great deal of persuading to stand by the initial agreement in such circumstances. The answer to the problem is to discuss the use of the alternatives thoroughly with the employer before the tendering process begins. The employer must be made aware that the agreement to use the Code and one of the alternatives is binding on all parties. It is possible that an employer who stipulated the first alternative and subsequently allowed price correction

could be sued by, at least, the next lowest tenderer for the abortive costs of tendering.

17.   The employer is not bound to accept the lowest or any tender and is not responsible for the costs of their preparation. There may be reasons why a decision is taken not to accept the lowest tender. Although the employer is entitled to do so, it will not please the other tenderers. The Code is devised to remove such practices.

18.   If the tender under consideration exceeds the estimated cost, negotiations should take place with the tenderer to reduce the price. The quantity surveyor then normally produces what is called 'reduction or addendum bills'. They are priced and signed by both parties as part of the contract bills.

19.   The provisions of the Code should be qualified by the supplementary procedures specified in EU Directives which provide for a 'restrictive tendering procedure' in respect of public sector construction contracts above a specified value. Guidance on the operation of this procedure is given in *DOE Circular 59/73 (England and Wales)* and *SDD Circular 47/73 (Scotland)*, both of which are obtainable from HMSO.

This method of contractor selection is appropriate for almost any type of construction project, where a suitable supply of contractors are available.

Open competition

With this method of contract procurement the details of the proposed project are often advertised in the local and trade publications, or through the local branch of the Building Employers' Confederation. The contractors who then feel that they are capable and willing to undertake such a project are requested to write in for the contract documentation. This method has the advantage of allowing new contractors or contractors who are unknown to the design team the possibility of submitting a tender for consideration. In theory any number of firms are able to submit a price. In practice a limit on the number of firms who will be supplied with the tender documents usually occurs. Unsuitable firms are removed from the list where the number of firms becomes too large. The preparation of tenders is both expensive and time consuming. The use of open tendering may relieve the employer of a moral obligation of accepting the lowest price, because firms are not generally vetted before tenders are submitted. Factors other than price must also be considered when assessing these tender bids, such as the capability of the firm who has submitted the lowest tender. There is no obligation on the part of the employer to accept any tender should the employer consider that none of the contractors' offers is suitable. Prior to the Second World War, many major building contracts, particularly those in the public sector, were awarded using this method. Although it is still commonly used on minor works its use on larger projects has been curtailed.

Negotiated contract

This method of contractor selection involves the agreement of a tender sum with a single contracting organization. Once the documents have been prepared the contractor prices them in the usual way. The priced documents are then passed to the quantity surveyor, who checks the reasonableness of the contractor's rates and prices. The two parties then meet to discuss the queries raised by the quantity surveyor and the negotiation process begins. Eventually a tender price is agreed which is acceptable to both parties. There is an absence of any competition or other restriction, other than the social acceptability of the price. It normally results in a tender sum that is higher than might have been obtained by using one of the previous procurement methods. Negotiation does, however, have particular applications as follows:

- where a business relationship exists between the client and the building contractor;
- where only one firm is capable of undertaking the work satisfactorily;
- on a continuation contract where the building contractor is already established on site;
- where an early start on site is required by the client;
- where it is beneficial to bring the contractor in during the design stage, to advise on constructional difficulties and how they might best be avoided;
- to make use of the contractor's buildability expertise.

Competitive tendering can create financial problems for both the industry and its clients due to too keen pricing which in the end benefits no one. Negotiated contracts do result in fewer errors in pricing since all of the rates are carefully examined by both parties. Fewer exaggerated claims to attempt to recoup losses on cut-throat pricing are also less likely on negotiated contracts for similar reasons. This type of procurement can also involve the contractor in some participation during the design stage, which can result in on-site time and cost savings. It should also be possible to achieve greater co-operation during the construction process between the design team and the contractor. The public sector, however, does not generally favour negotiated contracts because of:

- higher tender sums incurred
- public accountability
- suggestion of possible favouritism

Contractual options

The following contractual options are an attempt to address the employer's objectives associated with time, cost and quality of construction. They are not mutually exclusive. For example, it is possible to award a serial contract using in the first instance a design and build (D&B) arrangement. Fast tracking may be used in association with a form of management contracting. All of these options will also need to include either a selective or negotiated approach in respect of choosing a contractor.

Early selection

This method is sometimes known as two-stage tendering. Its main aim is to involve the chosen contractor for the project as soon as possible. It therefore seeks to succeed in getting the firm who knows what to build (the designer) in touch with the firm who knows how to build it (the constructor), before the design is finalized. The contractor's expertise in construction method can thus be harnessed with that of the designer to improve buildability criteria into the project. A further advantage is that the contractor may be able to start work on site sooner than where the more traditional methods of contract procurement are used. In the first instance, an appropriate contractor must be selected for the project. This is often done through some form of competition and can be achieved by selecting suitable firms to price the major items of work connected with the project. A simplified bill of quantities can be prepared which might include the following items:

- site on-costs on a time-related basis;
- major items of measured works;
- specialist items, allowing the main contractor the opportunity of pricing the profit and attendance sums.

The contractors should also be required to state their overhead and profit percentages. The prices of these items will then form the basis for the subsequent and more detailed price agreement as the project gets under way.

The NJCC have also prepared a *Code of Procedure for Two-stage Selective Tendering*. This Code is not concerned with any responsibility for design which may involve the main contractor. It assumes the use of a standard form of building contract after the second stage. During the first stage it is important to.

- provide a competitive basis for selection
- establish the layout and design
- provide clear pricing documents
- state the respective obligations and rights of the parties
- determine a programme for the second stage

Many of the conditions already outlined for single-stage selective tendering apply equally to two-stage tendering. Acceptance of the first-stage tender is a particularly delicate operation. The employer does not wish to be in the position of having accepted a contract sum at this stage. The terms of the letter of acceptance must be carefully worded to avoid such an eventuality. Depending upon the circumstances, it may be that a contract has been entered into. The question may be: What are the terms of the contract? There are two pitfalls:

- No contract exists. This is likely in many cases.
- A contract does exist, binding the employer to pay and the contractor to build. This could be the far worse situation to arise if insufficient care is

given to the drafting of the invitation to tender, the tender and the acceptance.

After a contractor has been appointed, all unsuccessful tenderers should be notified and, if feasible, a list of first-stage tender offers should be provided. If cost was not the sole reason for acceptance, this fact should be stated.

Design and build

Design and build projects aim to overcome the problem of the separation of the designing and constructing processes by providing for these two separate functions within a single organization. This single firm is generally the building contractor, who may employ the designers in-house or be responsible for employing consultants directly under their control. The major difference is, that instead of approaching the designer for a building, the employer briefs the contractor direct as shown in Fig. 8.2. The employer may choose to retain the services of an architect or quantity surveyor to assess the contractor's design or to monitor the work on site. The prudent employer will want some form of independent advice. The design evolved by the contractor is more likely to be suited to the needs of the latter's organization and construction methodology and this should result in savings in both time and costs of construction. Some argue that the design will be more attuned to the contractor's construction capabilities, rather than the design requirements of the employer. The final building should result in lower production costs on site and an overall shorter design and construction period, both of which should provide price savings to the employer. There should also be some supposed savings on the design fees even after taking into account the necessary costs of any independent advice. A further advantage to the employer is in the implied warranty of suitability because the contractor has provided the design as a part of the all-in service. Where JCT 81 is used the contractor has only a duty to use proper skills and care. A major disadvantage to the employer is the financial discouragement of possible changes to the design by the employer whilst the project is under construction. Where an employer considers these to be important to keep abreast of changing technologies or needs, excessive costs may be required to

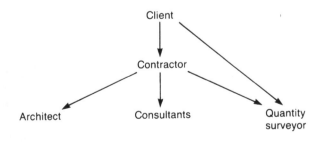

Fig. 8.2   Design and build relationships

either discourage them in the first place, or to allow for their incorporation within the partially completed building. Design and build projects usually result in the employer obtaining a single tender from a selected contractor. Where some form of competition in price is desirable then both the type and quality of the design will need to be taken into account. This can present difficulties in practice of evaluation and comparison of the different schemes. Many of these comments relate generally to D&B projects, and not specifically to those which may use the JCTCD 81 form of contract with contractor's design.

The advantages claimed therefore for a D&B approach include the following.

- The contractor is involved with the project from inception and is thus aware of all of the employer's requirements.
- The contractor is able to use his specialized knowledge and methods of construction in evolving the design.
- The time from inception to completion should be able to be reduced due to the telescoping of the various parts of the design and construction processes.
- There can be no claims for delays due to a lack of design information, since the contractor is in total control of it.
- There is direct contact between the employer and the contractor.

Package deal

In practice the terms 'package deal' and 'design and build' are interchangeable. The latter normally refers to a bespoke arrangement for a one-off project. The package deal is, however, strictly a special type of D&B project where the employer chooses a suitable building from a catalogue. The employer may also probably be able to view completed buildings of a similar design and type that have been completed elsewhere. This type of contract procurement has been used extensively for the closed systems of industrialized system buildings of timber or concrete. Multi-storey office blocks and flats, low-rise housing, workshop premises, farm buildings, etc., have been constructed on this basis. The building owner typically provides the package-deal contractor with a site and supplies the user requirements or brief. An architect may be independently employed to advise on the building type selected, to inspect the works during construction or to deal with the contract administration. This architect's role is useful to the employer for those items which are outside the scope of the system superstructure. The type of building selected is an off-the-peg type structure that often can be erected very quickly. There is even less scope, however, for variations than with the more usual D&B approach, should the employer want to change aspects of the constructional detailing. It cannot be automatically assumed that this type of procurement will be a more economic solution to the employer's needs, either initially or even in the long term. Some system buildings constructed in the 1960s are now very costly to maintain. Standard system buildings are normally constructed more quickly than the traditional solutions owing to the relative completeness of the design, the availability of standard components and the speed of construction on site.

Design and manage

This method of procurement is really the consultant's counterpart to contractor's D&B. In this case the design manager who may be an architect, engineer or surveyor has full control, not just of the design phase but also of the construction phase. The design and manage firm effectively replaces the main contractor in this role, which in the present day is one largely of management and organization and the administration and co-ordination of subcontractors. The design manager is responsible for all of the aspects of construction including the programming and progressing and the rectification of any defects which may arise. The building contract is between the design and manage firms and the employer, thus providing for the employer a single point of contractual responsibility. The work is generally let through competition in work packages to individual subcontracting firms. This method of procurement therefore offers many of the advantages of traditional tendering coupled with design and build. The design and manage firm will of course need to engage its own construction managers or develop those existing staff who have the potential in this direction. It will also need to consider continuity with this type of work.

It is suitable for all types and sizes of project, but employers undertaking large projects may, due to past experience, prefer to use a more traditional form of procurement using one of the larger contractors. A major disadvantage is with regards to the site facilities which will need to be provided by the design and manage consultant which may need to be hired in a similar way to the subcontractors.

This type of procurement method should be able to offer comparative completion times when compared with the other methods that are available. Since there is the traditional independent control of the subcontractor firms this should ensure a standard of quality at least as good as that provided by the other contracting methods. In terms of cost, since the work packages will be sought through competition, this will be no more expensive.

Turnkey method

This form of contracting is still somewhat unusual in the United Kingdom and has thus not been used to any large extent. It has, however, certain notable successes in the Middle and Far East. The true turnkey contract includes everything. This normally means everything from inception up to occupation of the finished building. The method receives its title from the 'turning-the-key' concept whereby the employer, when the project is completed can immediately start using the project since it will have been fully equipped including furnishings by the turnkey contractor. Some turnkey contracts also require the contractor to find a suitable site for development for this purpose. An all-embracing agreement is therefore formed with the one single administrative company for the entire project procurement process. It is therefore an extension of the traditional D&B arrangements, and in some cases it may even include a long-term repair and maintenance agreement. On industrial projects the appointed contractor is also likely to be responsible for the design and installation of the equipment required for the employer's manufacturing process. This type of procurement method can therefore be appropriate for use on highly specialized types of industrial and commercial construction projects.

The entire project procurement and maintenance needs can therefore be handled by a single firm accepting sole responsibility for all events. It has been argued, however, that the employer's ability to control costs, quality, performance, aesthetics and constructional details will be very variable and severely restricted by using this procurement method. A contractor who undertakes such an all-embracing project will have a variety of strengths and weaknesses and may well have fixed ideas about the importance of the different aspects of the scheme.

Management contract

Management contracting evolved at the beginning of the 1970s in the United Kingdom with an aim of building more complex projects in a shorter period of time and for a lower cost. It may be argued, therefore, that the more complex the project the more suitable management contracting may be. This method is also appropriate to a wide range of medium-sized projects.

The term 'management contract' is used to describe a method of organizing the building team and operating the building process. The main contractor provides the management expertise required on a construction project in return for a fee to cover the overheads and profit. The intention is to place the main contractor in a professional capacity to be able to provide the management skills and practical building ability for a fee. The contractor does not therefore participate in the profitability of the construction work. The construction work itself is not undertaken by the contractor, nor does the contractor employ any of the labour or plant directly, except with the possibility of setting up the site and those items normally associated with the preliminary works. Because the management contractor is employed on a fee basis, the appointment can be made early on in the design process. The contractor is therefore able to provide a substantial input into the design particularly those associated with the practical aspects of constructing the building. Each trade section required for the project is normally tendered for separately by subcontractors, either on the basis of measurement or a lump sum. This should result in the least expensive cost for each of the trades and thus for the construction works as a whole. The work on site needs a considerable amount of planning and co-ordination, more so than a traditional procurement arrangement. This is the responsibility of the management contractor and an inherent part of the acquired skills.

In common with all procurement methods, whilst there are undoubted advantages over its alternatives there are also disadvantages. It is somewhat open-ended, since the price can only be firmed up after the final works package quotation has been received. The later in the contract the work is let, the less time there will be for negotiating price reductions overall without seriously impairing a section of the works.

Management fee

Management fee contracting is a system whereby a contractor agrees to carry out building works at cost. In addition, a fee is paid by the employer to cover the overheads and profit. Some contractors are prepared to enter into an agreement to offer an incentive on the basis of a target cost. This type of procurement is a similar approach to management contracting and cost-plus contracts and has therefore similar advantages and disadvantages.

An alternative approach can also be used where a bill of quantities can be prepared and priced net of the contractor's overheads and profit, or just the profit. These items are then recovered by means of a fee. The system can be as flexible and adaptable as the parties wish. Invariably as with cost-plus contracting, the fees are generally percentage related unless some reasonably accurate forecast of cost can be made. Different contracting firms who use management fee contracting have different ways of determining the fee addition. In any case the total cost is largely unknown until completion is achieved and the records agreed. Overspending is therefore much more difficult to control, and any savings in cost which are needed tend to be required and made on the later sections of the project.

Construction management contracting

This offers a further alternative procedure to the management contract. The main difference is that the employer chooses to appoint a construction management contractor who then is responsible for appointing a design team (see Fig. 8.3) with the approval of the employer. The employer chooses to instruct the constructor rather than the designer. The construction management contractor is thus in overall project control of both the design and the construction phases. There are similarities with this method and design and build. A major difference is that the contractor would invariably appoint outside design consultants rather than choosing to employ an in-house service. The employer may thus form some contractual relationship with these consultants. In reality, it is a reversal of the traditional arrangements.

Fig. 8.3   Construction management relationships

Project management

Although the definitions of these procurement methods can mean different things in different parts of the world or even in different sectors of the construction industry, they are generally those which are understood in the building industry in the United Kingdom. Project management in this context is a function which is normally undertaken by the employer's consultants rather than by a contractor. Contractors do undertake project management but in a different context from that of contract procurement. The title of project co-ordinator is similar terminology and perhaps better describes the role of a project manager. The employer appoints the project manager who in turn appoints the various design consultants and selects the contractor (see Fig. 8.4). It is a more appropriate method for the medium- to large-sized project which requires an extensive amount of co-ordination. The function of the project manager is therefore one of organizing and co-ordinating the design and construction programmes. Any person who is professionally involved in the construction industry can become a project manager; it is the individual rather than the profession which is important.

In general terms the need for a project manager is to provide a balance between function, aesthetics, quality control, economics, and the time available for constructing. The project manager's aims are to achieve an efficient,

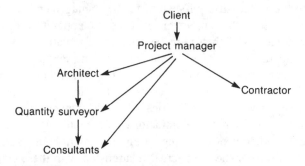

Fig. 8.4   Project management relationships

effective and economic deployment of the available resources to meet the employer's requirements. The tasks to be performed include identifying those requirements, interpreting them as necessary, and communicating them clearly to the various members of the design team and through them to the constructor. Programming and co-ordinating all of the activities and monitoring the work up to satisfactory completion are also a part of this role. A significant difference between this system and the majority of the others described, is that the employer's principal contact with his project is through the project manager rather than through the designer.

The British Property Federation system

The BPF represents substantial commercial property interests in the United Kingdom, and is thus able to exert some considerable influence on the building industry and its associated professions. The introduction of this system of building procurement to the industry created considerable interest due largely to the fact that it proposed very radical changes to the established status quo and practices and procedures. Some members of the design team felt threatened as their traditional roles and importance were questioned. The BPF system unashamedly makes the interests of the employer paramount. It attempts to devise a more efficient and co-operative method of organizing the whole building process from inception up to completion by making genuine use of all who are involved with the design and construction process. Its development was due to employer dissatisfaction with the existing arrangements where it was claimed that buildings on the whole cost too much, took too long to construct (when compared with other countries around the world) and did not always produce appropriate or credible results. The BPF manual is the only document which sets out in detail the operation of a system. Whilst the system may appear to be a rigid set of rules and procedures, its originators claim that it can be used in a flexible way and in conjunction with some of the other methods of procurement. Since the system has been devised almost entirely by only one party to the building contract, it lacks the compromises inherent in agreements devised by joint employer and contractor bodies such as JCT. The system was designed as an attempt to help to change outdated attitudes and to alter the way in which the various members of the professions and contractors dealt with one another. It seeks to create better co-operation between the various members of the building team, encourage motivation, and remove any possible overlap of effort amongst the design team. Innovations not found in the traditional methods include single-point responsibility for the employer, utilization of the contractor's buildability skills, reductions in the pre-tender period, redefinition of risks, and the preference for specifications rather than bills of quantities despite the desires of contractors for the latter.

Fast tracking

This approach to contracting results in the letting and administration of multiple construction contracts for the same project at the same time, as outlined in Fig. 8.5. It is appropriate to large construction projects where the employer's needs are to complete the project in the shortest possible time. The process results in the overlapping of the various design and construction operations of a single project. These various stages may therefore result in the creation of separate contracts or a series of phased starts and completions. When the design for a complete section of the works, such as foundations, are completed the work is then let to a contractor who will start this part of the construction work on site whilst the remainder of the project is still being designed. The contractor for this stage or section of the project will then see this work through to completion. At the same time as this is being done another work section may be let, continuing and building upon what the first contractor has already completed. This staggered letting of the work has the objective of shortening the overall design and construction period from inception through to handover. This type of procurement arrangement requires a lot of foresight since the later stages of the design must take into account what has by now already been completed. This type of arrangement will also require considerably more organization and planning, particularly from the members of the design team. In practice, where an efficient application of this procurement procedure is envisaged then a project co-ordinator will need to be engaged. Although the handover date of the project to the employer should be much earlier than any of the other methods which might be used, this might be at the expense of the

Fig. 8.5 Different contractual arrangements and their effects upon time

other facets of cost and performance. These aspects may be much inferior to those achieved by the use of the more traditional methods of procurement and arrangement.

Measured term

This type of contract is often used for major maintenance work projects. It is often awarded not just for a single building project but to cover a number of different buildings which are of a similar type. The contract will usually apply for a specified period of time, although this may be extended, depending upon the necessity of maintenance standards and requirements and the acceptability of the contractor's performance. The contractor will probably initially be offered the maintenance work for a variety of trades. The work, when completed, will then be paid for using rates from an agreed priced schedule. This schedule may have been prepared specifically for the project concerned, or it may be a standard document such as the Property Services Agency Schedule of Rates. Where the employer has provided the rates for the work, the contractor is normally given the opportunity of quoting a percentage addition or reduction to these rates. The contractor offering the most advantageous percentage will usually be awarded the contract. An indication of the amount of work involved over a defined period of time would therefore need to be provided for the contractor's better assessment of the quoted prices.

Serial tender

Serial tendering is a development of the system of negotiating further contracts, where a firm has already successfully completed a project for work of a similar type. Initially the contractors tender against each other, possibly on a selective basis, for a single project. There is, however, a contractual mechanism that several additional projects would automatically be awarded using the same contract rates. Some allowances are normally made to allow for inflation, or perhaps more commonly increased costs are added to the final accounts. The contractors would therefore know at the initial tender stage for the first project that they could expect to receive a further number of contracts which would help to provide some continuity in their workloads. Conditions would, however, be written into the documents to allow further contracts to be withheld where the contractor's performance was less than satisfactory. Serial contracting should result in lower prices to contractors since they are able to gear themselves up for such work, for example, by purchasing suitable types of plant and equipment that otherwise might be of a too speculative nature. They should therefore be able to operate to greater levels of efficiency. The employer will also achieve some financial gain since some of these lower production costs will find their way into the contractor's tenders.

A further advantage claimed for the use of serial tendering is that the same design and construction teams can remain involved for each of the projects which form part of the serial arrangement. It is claimed that this regular and close working association aids and develops an expertise which accelerates the production of the work and eases any anticipated problems. In turn the operatives on site improve their efficiency as they proceed from project to project.

Serial projects are particularly appropriate for buildings of a similar nature, such as housing and school buildings in the public sector where a large number of comparable schemes are constructed. This method may also be usefully employed in the private sector in the construction of industrial factory and warehouse units. It has also been successfully used with industrialized system building, where local authorities have worked together in a form of building consortium to gain marketing advantages from the construction industry.

Continuation contract

A continuation contract is an *ad hoc* arrangement to take advantage of an existing situation. Projects in an expanding economy are often insufficient in size to cope with current demands even before they become operational. During their construction an employer may choose to provide additional similar facilities which may be constructed upon the completion of the original scheme. Such additions, often because of their size and scope, are beyond the definition of extra work or variations. For example, a housing project may be awarded to a contractor to build 300 houses. Due to perhaps an underestimation in demand and where additional space permits, a continuation contract may be awarded to the same contractor to build an extra 100 houses on an adjacent site. Another example can occur where during the construction of a factory building it becomes apparent that it will be insufficient to meet the increased demands for the factory's product. Extensions to the factory may therefore be agreed on the basis of a continuation contract using the same designers and constructors and the same contract prices adjusted only to allow for increased costs caused by inflation.

A continuation contract can be awarded as an add-on to the majority of the contractual arrangements. Continuing with the same building team, where this has already proved to be satisfactory to the employer, is a sensible arrangement under these circumstances. Each of the parties will already be familiar with each other's working methods and will be able to offer some cost savings since they are already established on the site. Both the employer and the contractor may wish to review the contractual conditions and the new market factors which may have changed since the original contract was signed. It is also not unreasonable to expect that the contractor will want to share in the monetary savings that will be available from the already established site organization from the initial project.

Speculative work (develop and construct)

Because of the market demand, many building firms have organized a part of their function into a speculative department. Some contractors are entirely speculative builders. These firms or divisions purchase land, obtain planning approvals, design and construct buildings for sale, rent or lease. It is also described as develop and construct. Housing is the common type of speculative unit but factories, whole industrial estates, new office buildings and refurbishment projects may also fall into this category. The contractors are often in partnership agreements with financial institutions and developers who have established that the demand for a particular type of development exists in a certain geographical area. Such assumptions are based upon a detailed market research of the area which is undertaken prior to the development getting under way. The developer or speculative builder may employ their own in-house design staff or may employ consultants to do the work for them. Whilst design and build is done for a particular employer, speculative building is carried out on the basis that there is a need for certain types of buildings and that these will be purchased at some later date.

Direct labour

Some employers, notably local authorities and large industrial firms, have departments within their organizations which undertake building work. In some cases they may restrict themselves to repair and maintenance works alone or minor works schemes. Others are much larger and are capable of carrying out any size of building project. The employer, in order to execute construction projects in this way, needs to have either an extensive building programme or to be responsible for a large amount of repair and maintenance work. In-house services of this type allow the employer, at least in theory, much greater control than using some of the other methods which have been described. In practice the level of control achieved may be less than satisfactory, due to the accounting procedures which may be employed. Employers who choose to undertake their building works by this method often do so for either political or financial reasons.

Review

At the inception stage of any construction project both the designers and the contractors should ask themselves about the employer's real objectives. Almost without exception the employer's needs will be an amalgam of functional and aesthetic requirements, built to a good standard of construction and finish, completed when required, at an appropriate cost, offering value for money and easily and economically maintained. The contractual procurement arrangements used must aim to satisfy all of these requirements; some in part and others as a whole, trading between them to arrive at the best possible solution.

The traditional approach has been to appoint a team of consultants to produce a design and estimate, and to select a constructor. The latter would calculate the actual project costs, develop a programme to fit within the contract period, organize the workforce and material deliveries and build to the standards laid down in the contract documentation. In practice the quality of the workmanship was often poor, costs were higher than expected, and even where projects did not overrun the contract period they took longer to complete than in other countries around the world. Traditionally little attention or consideration has been given towards future repairs or maintenance aspects.

The obvious deficiencies in the above, largely supposedly due to the separation of the design role from that of the construction effort, have been known for some time. Employers, however, have generally wished to retain the services of an independent designer, believing that such would serve their needs better than the contractors with their own vested interests. They also wished to retain the competition element in order to keep costs down and to help to improve the efficiency of the contractor's organization. In more recent years they have seen some benefits from buildability which have been achieved through the early and integrated involvement of the contractor during the design stage. This has also had a spin-off effect in reducing costs and the time that the contractor is on site. Employers were, however, still loath to commit themselves to a single contractor at the design stage when costs might still be imprecise, and where their bargaining position might be seriously affected before the final deal could be struck.

Increasingly, however, contractors attempted to market their D&B approach as a possible solution to the employer's dissatisfaction with existing procedures. The benefits of a truly fixed price, a single point of responsibility and where the contractor assumed the full responsibility for both the design and the subsequent construction of the building were attractive propositions. Remedies open to the employer in the case of default or delay were now no longer a matter for discussion between the designer and the builder. If necessary the employer could always employ professional advisers to oversee the technical and financial aspects of the project.

The entrepreneurs of the construction industry are always seeking out new ways of satisfying the increasing demands of clients. Some are busy examining the methods that are in use in the USA, and thus seek to import systems which they believe are superior and improve the image of the construction industry. Others feel that the employers' interests would be better served by an over-arching project manager or construction manager. Contractors are themselves also going through a major evolutionary change in the way in which they employ and organize their workforce. An increase in subcontracting has occurred as fewer and fewer operatives are directly employed by main contractors. Management contracting recognizes and encourages these developments as trends which are desirable.

The construction industry will continue to evolve and adapt its systems and procedures to meet the new demands. New procurement methods will be developed which utilize new technologies and new ways of working. Construction projects are different from the majority of manufactured goods, because they are procured in advance of their manufacture. The majority of the projects are also different from the previous ones and often incorporate some new characteristics. Some projects are almost wholly original and all depend upon their peculiar site characteristics. In order to achieve value for money and client satisfaction, the appropriate procurement procedures must be selected or adapted to suit the individual needs of the employer and the project.

Chapter 9

Contract selection

Introduction

The selection of appropriate contract arrangements for any but the simplest type of project is difficult owing to the diverse range of options and professional advice which are available. Much of the advice is in conflict. For example, D&B contractors are unlikely to recommend the use of an independent designer. Such organizations are also likely to believe that the integration of design and construction is more likely to result in the provision of better buildings and to improve client satisfaction. Many of the professions hold the opposite viewpoint, and believe that their approach will produce the best solution, particularly in the long term. In the past few years there has been a significant shift in the way that construction projects are procured. This is partially in response to the changes which have occurred within the construction industry. Individual experiences, prejudices, vested interests, the desire to improve the system and the familiarity with particular methods are factors which have influenced capital project procurement recommendations. Those who have had bad experiences with a particular procurement method will be reluctant and cautious in recommending such an approach again. When this is suggested they will attempt to resist such a course of action and where the results are as expected, then this further reinforces the view that such a method of procurement has only limited use.

In reality too little is known and too little research has been undertaken properly to evaluate the various procurement options. In practice, this is difficult because there are both successful and unsuccessful projects that have used identical means and methods of contract procurement. Personal human factors and external circumstances have a major influence upon the possible outcomes. Nevertheless more reliable information, based on empirical evidence, is desirable to at least attempt to eliminate hearsay and folklore opinion.

The advice given should always be that which recommends a course of action which best serves the client's interests, and not that which is perhaps more beneficial or easy to operate for the individual who is offering the advice. This is professionalism, even though it may mean losing a commission. The employer may need to be convinced that a particular method and procedures which are recommended should be adopted as the most appropriate approach to be used. This may at times be against the employer's own better judgement or preferences, particularly where there is some familiarity with the other options that are being suggested. Some clients are resistant to change, and may require persuasion to adopt what might appear to be radical proposals. It may be necessary also to accept that because of the mechanisms employed, a better course of action cannot easily be explained until after the event, and that such a recommendation may be rejected at the outset as being speculative. Overseas clients working in a different cultural environment may find that the traditional contractual procedures used are alien to their needs and expectations. They may require even greater assurances that their project should be constructed using a particular procurement method. Individuals working within the same team will also have different expectations and views on the optimum procurement path.

Procurement advisers should offer advice in the absence of any vested interests or personal gains. Any associated interests which might influence the judgements should be declared, in order to avoid possible repercussions at a later stage. Whilst the professional institutions retain codes of conduct and disciplinary powers governing their members' activities, there has been a blurring of commercial and professional attitudes with the former vying for position with the latter. Outmoded approaches and procedures should be removed when they no longer serve any useful purpose. Sound, reliable and impartial advice is necessary from those who have the proficient skills, knowledge and expertise.

Employer's requirements

A confirmed cynic once described the construction industry as 'the design and erection of buildings that satisfy the architect and constructor alone and not the employer'. In addition, buildings often failed to function correctly, were too expensive and took too long to construct. As in most cynicism the case is vastly overstated, yet there is enough truth in the statement not to dismiss it out of hand.

One of the procurement adviser's main problems is in separating the employer's wants and needs. The employer's main trio of requirements are shown in Fig. 9.1. The numerical values result from research and attempt to weigh these broad objectives in order of their relative importance. They reflect the 'average' or typical client, and offer some guidance on the main issues associated with a construction project. The attempted optimization of these factors may not necessarily achieve the desired solution. For example, an employer may desire exceptional standards of quality and the future-use performance of the project and to achieve these may be prepared to incur extra costs or a longer contract period. Alternatively a client may require the early use of the project as the main priority and be prepared to sacrifice a bespoke

Fig. 9.1 Employer's requirements (source: after A. Walker, *Project Management in Construction*)

design or even high quality standards in order to achieve this. Clients may also choose to set contrasting objectives which are difficult to achieve using conventional procurement procedures. This may require the adviser to devise ingenious methods of procurement in order to satisfy such objectives.

In broad terms the employer's objectives are a combination of the following and the procurement path will need to identify the following priorities:

- An acceptable layout for the project in terms of function and use.
- An aesthetically pleasing design not only to the employer, but also as viewed by others.
- The final cost of the building should closely resemble the estimate.
- The quality should be in line with current expectations.
- The future performance of the building and the associated costs-in-use should fit within specified criteria.
- The project is available for handover and occupation on the date specified for completion of the works.

Factors in the decision process

The following need to be considered when choosing the most appropriate procurement path for a proposed project:

- size
- cost
- time
- accountability
- design
- quality assurance
- organization
- complexity
- risk
- market
- finance

Project size

Projects of a small size are not really suited to the more elaborate forms of contractual arrangements, since such procedures are likely to be too cumbersome and not cost effective. Smaller-sized schemes therefore rely upon the traditional and established forms of procurement, such as a form of competitive tendering or D&B. The medium- to large-scale schemes can use the whole range of options which are available. On the very large schemes a combination of different arrangements may be required to suit the project as a whole.

Cost

Open tendering will generally secure for the client the lowest possible price from a contractor. This is the evidence that competition helps to reduce costs through efficiency, and lowers the price to the customer. There are limits to how far this theory can be applied in practice. If a large number of firms, for example, have to prepare detailed tenders then this increases industry's costs, which must be either absorbed or passed on to the industry's employers through successful tenders. There is no such thing as a free estimate! Negotiated tenders, on the other hand, supposedly add around 5 per cent to the contract price. In the absence of competition, contractors will price the work 'up to what the traffic will bear'. Projects which require unusually short contract periods incur cost penalties, largely to reflect the demands placed upon the constructor for overtime working and rapid response management. The imposition of conditions of contract which favour the client or insist upon higher standards of workmanship than are usual also push up building costs. The employer under these circumstances may end up paying more for the stricter conditions which might not need to be used or for a quality of workmanship which adds little to the overall ambience of the project.

Employers in the past have been overly concerned with a lowest tender sum often at the expense of other factors, such as the principles behind the indeterminate life-cycle cost. Cash-flow projections which might have the effect of reducing the timing of expenditures are often ignored except perhaps by the most enlightened employers. A cash-flow analysis, for example, may be able to show that the lowest tender is not always the least expensive solution. The timing of cash flows on a large project may have a significant effect upon the real costs to the employer. With projects that include options on construction method then the cash-flow analysis becomes even more important. Procurement and contractual arrangements which take into account these factors should be considered more frequently.

The cost of the project is a combination of land, construction, fees and finance, and the employer will need to balance these against the various procurement systems which are available. In terms of cost savings a less expensive site elsewhere, rather than reducing the costs of quality, may be more appropriate.

Design and build projects show some form of cost savings in terms of professional fees, although the precise amount of these is difficult to calculate since they are absorbed within other charges submitted by the contractor in the bid price. Where the building is of a relatively straightforward design such as a standard warehouse unit or farm building, then it can be more cost effective to use a builder who has already completed similar projects rather than to opt for a separate design service. Cost reimbursement appears to be a fair and reasonable way of dealing with construction costs in a fair world. Society is not, and such an arrangement is often too open-ended for many of the industry's employers. Some clients may choose to use it out of necessity, setting objectives other than cost more highly. The majority of employers, however, will need to know as a minimum the approximate cost of the scheme before they begin to build, and there is nothing new in this (Luke 14: 28).

Where a firm price is required before the contract is signed then one of several procurement arrangements can be used. A firm price arrangement relies to a large extent on a relatively complete design being available. Where more price flexibility is possible then one of the more advanced forms of procurement might be used whilst at the same time achieving a measure of cost control.

Provisions exist under most forms of contractual arrangement for a fixed or fluctuating price agreement. The choice is influenced by the length of the contract period and the current and forecasted rates of inflation. Where the inflation rate is in small percentage terms and falling, then a fixed-price arrangement is preferable. When the rate of inflation is small and stable then it is common to find projects of up to 36 months' duration on this basis. When the rate of inflation is high, and particularly when it is rising then contractors will be reluctant to submit fixed-price tenders for more than about one year's duration. Although a fixed price is attractive to the employer, it cannot be assumed that this will necessarily be less expensive than a fluctuating type arrangement. Some contract conditions limit fluctuation reclaims to increases caused directly by changes in government legislation.

It is difficult to make cost-procurement comparisons, even where similar projects are being constructed under different contractual arrangements. It can be argued that competition reduces price, price certainty in the case of premeasurement or fixed price might not be the most economic, and that using serial tendering, bulk-purchase agreements and similar concepts are ways of reducing building costs. Cash flows and projected life-cycle costs on larger projects should be considered in any overall cost evaluation. The following are the cost factors to consider:

- price competition/negotiation
- fixed-price arrangements
- price certainty

- price forecasting
- contract sum
- bulk-purchase agreements
- payments and cash flows
- life-cycle costs
- cost penalties
- variations
- final cost

Time

The majority of employers, once they have made the decision to build, want the project to be completed as quickly as possible. The design and construction phases in the United Kingdom are lengthy and protracted. Some of the apparent delays are linked to the protracted planning processes rather than the design or the construction phases. It is difficult to make comparisons on a global basis since there are a wide variety of influences to be considered such as methods of construction, safety, organization of labour, quality assurance, etc. Construction techniques also vary and these in turn produce different qualities and costs. The time available will also influence the type of construction techniques which might be used. A need for rapid completion may force the employer to consider using an 'off-the-peg' type building which can be constructed quickly.

In order to secure the early completion of the project several different methods of procurement have been devised with this objective in mind. Such approaches have implications for the other factors under consideration such as design, quality or cost. There is an optimum time solution depending upon the importance which is attached to these other considerations. For example, in terms of cost, shorter or longer periods of time on site tend to increase building costs. The former is due in part to overtime costs, the latter to extended site on-costs. Some clients are prepared to pay extra costs in order to achieve earlier occupation. Different types of project also have different time concepts. A shopping centre redevelopment may require rapid completion, since earlier revenue may easily account for the extra costs. Different techniques of design and construction may also need to be used to achieve early completion. New educational building completions are linked to school term times, whereas housing starts and completions are at the rate at which they can be either let or sold.

Some research has shown that construction work should not commence on site until the project has been fully designed and ready for construction with only the minimal involvement thereafter by the designer. Variations will still be allowed, but are not encouraged. Such an approach helps to eliminate a large amount of construction uncertainty which is common on many supposedly designed projects today. This approach allows the contractor to plan the organization and management of the project better and to spend less time awaiting drawings and details. Overall the design and construction period is shortened and earlier completion is achieved. The contractor is on site for a shorter period of time which results in the saving of building costs. The difficulty of adopting this approach is that the client wants to see work beginning on site as soon as possible.

Many of the newer methods of contract procurement have been devised specifically to find a quicker route through the design and construction processes. In some ways they have been assisted by changes in the techniques used for the construction and assembly of the building products and materials. Early selection was developed to allow the construction work to start on site whilst some of the scheme was still at the design stage. It also allowed the contractor an early involvement with the project. Some form of cost forecasting and control can be used but these will be much less precise than with some of the more conventional methods of procurement. Critical path analysis can be used to find the quickest way through the construction programme, and the American fast-track system was imported for the sole purpose of securing an early completion of the project. Inaccurate design information coupled with a need for speed in completion of the works has often resulted in abortive parts of the project, poor quality control and higher costs to both the contractor and the employer. The later forms of management contracting offer some solution to the time delay problem. Project management contracts, where an independent organization controls both the design and the construction teams, has provided some good examples in terms of project co-ordination.

Faster Building for Commerce (National Economic Development Office, 1988) was a study aimed at helping the industry achieve earlier completions of its projects. The study claimed that the major influences on projects' time performance were customer participation, design quality and information, contractor's control over site operations and the integration of the subcontractors with design and construction. The study showed that fast times were 20–25 per cent shorter than the average, and the slowest times could take twice as long as the average. Overall, one-third of commercial projects finish on time, the rest overrun by a month or more, often because of extensive design alteration. These were claimed as the largest single factor affecting delays. Common ingredients in fast projects are organization to promote unity of purpose, competent management at all stages of the project and working practices which interlock smoothly and leave no gaps between activities and responsibilities. Many of the delays result from a lack of information, an underestimating of the supervision of subcontractors and late changes in requirements by employers. In some cases quality control was a problem where work needed to be redone and hence caused delays. Slow reactions by the utilities companies can cause extensive delays, especially on sites with high services contents. The following are the time factors to consider:

- completion dates
- delays and extensions of time

- phased completions
- early commencement
- optimum time
- complete information
- fast tracks
- co-ordination

Accountability

Accountability according to the dictionary definition is the responsibility for giving reasons why a particular course of action has been taken. In essence it is not simply having to do the right things, but having to explain why a particular choice was made in preference to others that were available. It is of greater significance when dealing with public employers where it is necessary to justify why a particular course of action was taken. It has also become increasingly important with all types of employers where an emphasis is placed on achieving value for money on capital works projects. The documentation used for construction works is often complex and the technical and financial implications are considerable.

Employers need the assurance that they have obtained the best possible procurement method against their list of objectives. The possible trade-offs between competing proposals will need to be evaluated. It is difficult to satisfy the accountability criteria in respect of price, where tenders are sought in the absence of any form of competition. There is also the difficulty of justifying subjective judgements where these appear to be in conflict with common practice, but the process of selection will never solely be a mechanistic process. The elimination of procedural loopholes should be such as to provide the employer with as much peace of mind as is possible.

Accountability is interlinked with finance and an emphasis on paying the smallest price for the completed project. It may be easy to demonstrate to some employers that to pay more for a perceived higher quality or earlier completion is worth while. Other employers may need more convincing and some will feel doubtful about non-monetary gains.

The procedure for the selection, award and administration of contracts must be as precise as possible. Auditing plays a useful role in the tightening up of the procedures used, with *ad hoc* arrangements that breach these procedures being discouraged. Systems that require huge amounts of documentation and the subsequent checking and cross-checking of invoices, time sheets, etc., are not favoured because of loopholes that can occur. Open-ended arrangements which are unable to provide a realistic estimate of cost are fraught with difficulties in terms of accountability. They provide difficulties in demonstrating value for money at the tender stage, since any forecast of cost will be too imprecise for reliability purposes. The following are the accountability factors to consider:

- contractor selection

- *ad hoc* arrangements
- contractual procedures
- loopholes
- simplicity
- value for money

Design

There is a good argument that the best design will be obtained from someone who is a professional designer. The design will then not be limited by the capabilities of the constructor or restrained to those designs which might be the most profitable to such a firm. However, the D&B contractor is more likely to be able to achieve a solution which takes into account buildability, and produces a design which is sound in terms of its construction. There are examples where the employer, having been provided with an unsatisfactory building, has to wait impatiently whilst the consultant and constructor argue about the liability. There are also examples where design and build projects, some using industrialized components, have had to be demolished after only a few years of life, because of their poor design concept, impossible and costly maintenance problems and unacceptable user environment which they have helped to create.

Contractors have on the whole been better at marketing their services and these have reaped benefits in the growing increase in design and build schemes. Designers have to some extent been thwarted in their response to this upsurge in activity due to the restrictions imposed on advertising by their profession and to a failure to react to the changes that have taken place. Only in recent years has the design and manage approach been introduced.

The traditional methods of contract procurement fail in many aspects of building design, not least because of the absence of any constructor input. They still, however, represent the most common method of procurement and more publicized failures might thus have been expected. Some of the forms of management contracting, which still largely retain the independence of the designer, have gained in their popularity amongst employers. Where the employer has been encouraged to form a contractual relationship with a single organization, then this has on the whole been beneficial.

Designs which evolve and develop only marginally ahead of the construction works on site must be of questionable worth in design solution terms, unless they are working within the constraints of either previously completed schemes or the confines of an existing structure. The following are the design factors to consider:

- aesthetics
- function
- maintenance
- buildability

- contractor involvement
- standard design
- design before build
- design prototypes

Quality assurance

Open tendering can result in a lower standard of workmanship than might have been achieved by using a builder who submitted a higher price. The statement 'you only get what you pay for' is true in terms of construction quality. Where a builder has had to submit an uneconomical price at cost, then quality may suffer unless improved supervision is provided. Consistent and good quality-control procedures are lacking in the construction industry and are often relegated in favour of other criteria in the list of objectives.

The quality of buildings depends upon a whole range of inputs from the soundness of the design, a correct choice of specification, efficient working details, adequate supervision and the ability of the builder. The skills of the operatives are also important, perhaps even more so today than a decade ago, now that the designs are tending to become more complex in their detailing and a higher level of craftsmanship is expected. The choice of a contractor who has a good reputation for the type and quality of work envisaged is important in achieving this objective. The use of labour-only operatives and the general subcontracting phenomena have sometimes resulted in a deterioration in quality performance, due to poor site co-ordination and supervision by site management.

The quality of D&B schemes depends largely upon the reputation of the builder selected, particularly where the employer chooses not to involve any professional advisers. The quality of the materials and workmanship will be regulated entirely by the builder alone. Speculative building schemes where the quality assurance is determined solely by the builder are not renowned for their high-quality work. Fast-track procurement methods which can involve a number of contractors on the same project can, without adequate supervision, result in widely varying standards of workmanship. There is also the difficulty of co-ordinating different contractors on the site, such as occurs with work packages on management contracts. The use of selective tendering, properly managed, continues to offer a good solution in terms of quality control.

Quality standards cannot be judged at the building's completion alone, but need to be considered in the long term. A virtually complete design prior to the commencement of work on site is likely to be beneficial in improving the qualitative aspects of the project rather than the more *ad hoc* design approach to problems as they occur on site.

The turnkey method where the designer–contractor has a contractual responsibility for the long-term repair and maintenance of the project offers advantages, particularly in terms of quality assurance. Under this method of procurement there is the incentive that the designer–contractor will wish to reduce the likelihood of future defects arising by a more careful design and effective site management during construction. This may result in less innovation but this is preferable to inconvenience and costly failures in the future. Progress in construction is necessary, but not at the expense of prototype designs which result in poor quality assurance.

Although serial and continuation contracts using the same design and detailing should improve the quality aspects, in practice this has not been achieved and poor design, detailing and construction methods have unfortunately been repeated. The following are quality-assurance factors to consider:

- quality control
- independent inspection
- team working
- co-ordination
- subcontracting
- buildability
- future maintenance
- design and detailing
- reputation of craftsmen

Organization

Allowing the contractor total control of the building project, as in D&B or management contracting, removes a layer of organization and eliminates dual responsibility. This should result in fewer things being overlooked or forgotten, work left undone or subcontractors being unable to complete their work on time owing to a lack of information. The additional tier of organization has the disadvantage of the parties blaming each other when disputes arise. However, the traditional methods of contract procurement have to a large extent set the lines of demarcation between designer and constructor quite clearly. In practice the designer probably relies too heavily on the constructor. Elaborate conditions of contract, to cope with the organization of construction work, have had to be drawn up to anticipate most of the eventualities that might arise.

The employment of a single firm, such as a D&B contractor, allows for quick response management, the ability to deal with problems as they occur, and more freedom in the execution of the works. The extent of such freedom will vary with the conditions of contract being used. Where a separate designer is used the response time is often much longer and this can result in delays to the contract. Where complex or difficult contract arrangements are employed these can have the effect of removing the initiative from the contractor.

The more parties involved with a building project the more complex will be the organization and the contractual arrangements. The employment of a group design practice should therefore result in fewer organizational difficulties than where individual firms are used. Management contracting is based upon awarding individual work packages to a range of specialist and general subcontractors. This can create problems of organization and co-ordination. There is much less control over such firms than when directly employed operatives of the main contractor are used. General contracting is, however, now unusual since about 90 per cent of construction work is subcontracted regardless of the method of procurement being used. These individual firms need to be programmed for precise periods of time, and a delay in allowing them to proceed with their work or a failure by them to complete on time can have a knock-on effect for the whole project. This presents even greater difficulties with tightly scheduled construction programmes. The following are the organizational factors to consider:

- complexity of arrangements
- single responsibility
- levels of responsibility
- number of individual firms involved
- lines of management

Complexity

Projects which are complex in design or construction require more precise and comprehensive contractual arrangements. Complexity may be the result of an innovative design, the utilization of new constructional methods, the phasing of the site operations or the necessity for highly specialized work. It can also be the result of employing several contractors on the same site at one time in order to achieve rapid progress or the complicated refurbishment of an existing building whilst still in use by its occupants. It is often necessary in circumstances of these types to devise new contractual arrangements and to apply different types of procedures to the varying parts of the construction work. Where work can be reasonably well defined and forecasted, then traditional estimating processes can be used and the work paid for on the usual basis. Where the work is indeterminate, of an experimental type or requiring a solution from the contractor, then a lump-sum or cost-reimbursement approach with contractor design may need to be employed. In the latter case the contractor is given the opportunity to offer an acceptable solution to the problem as a part of the contract.

Where the project is very complex then the employer is likely to choose a separate designer with the skills which are required to produce the right solution. It is, however, important to involve the constructor as soon as possible with the project, particularly where this might influence the sequencing of site operations. A form of two-stage tendering might therefore be appropriate against this eventuality. The following are the organizational points to consider:

- nature of complexity
- capabilities of parties
- main objectives of employer

Risk

Risk is inherent in the design and construction of a building. The employer's intentions will be to transfer as much of this as possible to either the consultants or the contractor. Risk may be defined as possible loss resulting from the difference between what was anticipated and that which actually occurred. Risk is not entirely monetary. An unsatisfactory design although completed successfully can result in a weakening of the designer's reputation with a consequent loss of future commissions. Risk can be reduced but it is difficult to eliminate it entirely. For example, the risk associated with a very specialized form of construction can be reduced by selecting a contractor with the appropriate experience.

The transfer of risk from the employer to others involved with the project may appear to satisfy the accountability criteria. It may be argued as an appropriate course to follow for the employer, but it may not be a fair and reasonable approach. It may also not be the best route for the employer to follow, since the risk needs to be evaluated. All contractors' tenders contain a premium to cover contractual risk. Where the risk does not materialize then this becomes a part of the contractor's profit. The employer may thus be better advised to assess and accept some of the risk involved and thereby reduce the contractor's tender sum and also costs accordingly. This is a more common way of dealing with risk on construction projects.

The lump-sum contract with a single price, which is not subject to any variation is at one extreme, and at the other is cost reimbursement, where risk and financial predictability are uncertain. In the former the employer is paying for eventualities which might not occur. In the latter the client is accepting the risk but only pays for events that happen. A balance has to be drawn. Risk should always be placed with the party to the contract who is in the best position to control it. Where this is not possible then it should at least be shared, although it may be difficult to convince the employer that this course of action is the most financially appropriate. Some projects involve a large amount of risk in their execution. In some cases the risk may be so high that it is impossible to get a contractor even to consider tendering under conventional arrangements. Some form of risk sharing may then become essential in order for the project to proceed. The following are risk factors to consider:

- risk evaluation
- risk sharing
- risk transfer
- risk control

Market

The selection of a method of procurement will be influenced by the state of a country's economy and the industry's workloads. An appropriate recommendation for today may have different implications for some time in the future. When there is an ample amount of work available, contractors are able to choose those schemes which are the most financially lucrative. Under these circumstances employers will be unable to insist upon onerous contractual arrangements and conditions. Where the risk involved is high it will be even more difficult to persuade contractors to tender for the work. Employers may need to be advised to delay their building projects at such times, and to wait until the economy is more favourable. Many employers will, however, be unable or unwilling to follow this advice.

When construction prices are low, then a form of cost reimbursement or management fee approach can be expensive. During times like this, contractors are sometimes prepared to do work at cost, and take a gamble with the risk factors that nothing of financial significance will go wrong. Conversely in times of full order books the opposite is true, and paying contractors their actual costs plus an agreed amount for profit can be a better proposition. When work is plentiful, contractors often have difficulty in recruiting a competent workforce of skilled operatives and this, coupled with similar restrictions in the availability of good supervision, can result in a deterioration in quality standards. When the amount of construction work available is restricted, then the standards of workmanship coupled with more intensive inspection, is likely to enhance the overall quality of the project. The following are the market factors to consider:

- availability of work
- availability of contractors
- economy affects procurement advice

Finance

The usual way of paying the contractor for the building work is through monthly or stage payments. These payments help the contractor to offset the financial borrowing that is required to pay for wages and salaries and goods and materials. Two alternatives to this can be used. The first is a delayed payment system similar to that used on speculative developments. The employer effectively pays for the work by way of a single payment upon completion of the project. The employer has to accept the design as it is built, but acquires immediate occupation of the project. The financial borrowing requirements of the contractor are higher, but the employer makes savings by paying for the work at the end of the project. The other alternative is for the employer to fund the work in advance and thereby reduce the contractor's interest charges that are otherwise included in the tender. In these situations there are cautions of which the client needs to be aware. The industry is notorious for the number of insolvencies, and the employer would thus want to ensure the financial soundness of the appointed contractor. Contractors also tend to be less interested in a project once they have received payment for work. The employer can devise remedies to deal with these factors. With the former, a performance bond can be adopted and with the latter, liquidated damages can be applied. The following are financial factors to consider:

- payment systems
- financial soundness of parties
- financial remedies
- contract funding

Conclusions

The choice of a particular method of contract procurement for a construction project involves identifying the employer's objectives, balancing these with the procurement methods which are available and taking into account the considerations outlined above. Figure 9.2 provides a comparison of some of the payment methods. It compares factors such as the information requirements with the control and risk considerations. If an employer's main priority, for example, is for a lump sum price from a contractor, then the full information at the tender stage must be provided for an accurate price to be prepared. Risk and control effort throughout the duration of the contract, will then be minimal to the employer. On large and complex projects the ability to provide this detailed information is difficult. The quality and reliability of the design information

Fig. 9.2 Range of contract types (source: adapted from R.A. Burgess (ed.), *Construction Projects, their Financial Policy and Control*, Longman, 1980, p. 149)

		Traditional selective tendering	Early selection	Design and build	Construction management	Management fee	Design and manage
TIMING – Is early completion important to the success of the project?	Yes:		*	*	*	*	*
	Average:		*	*	*	*	*
	No:	*					
VARIATIONS – Are variations to the contract important?	Yes:	*	*		*	*	*
	No:			*			
COMPLEXITY – Is the building technically complex or highly serviced?	Yes:	*	*		*	*	*
	Average:		*	*	*	*	*
QUALITY – What level of quality is required?	High:	*	*		*	*	*
	Average:		*	*	*	*	
	Basic:			*			
PRICE CERTAINTY – Is a firm price necessary before the contracts are signed?	Yes:	*	*	*			*
	No:				*	*	
RESPONSIBILITY – Do you wish to deal only with one firm?	Yes:		*	*			*
	No:	*			*	*	
PROFESSIONAL – Do you require direct professional consultant involvement?	Yes:	*	*		*	*	*
	No:			*			
RISK AVOIDANCE – Do you want someone to take the risk from you?	Yes:	*	*	*			
	Shared:				*		
	No:					*	*

Fig. 9.3 Identifying the client's priorities (source: adapted from *Thinking about Building*, EDC Report)

will determine how precise the building's costs can be forecasted and controlled. The poorer and more imprecise it is, the greater will be the risks to the employer. The risk, of course, may never materialize and hence there will be no loss to the employer.

The three broad areas of concern to the employer, and the expectations that are required from any building project have already been identified in Fig. 9.1. The balance of these will vary but their analysis will help to influence and select the most appropriate procurement method.

Figure 9.3 offers a checklist of questions to help to determine an appropriate contract strategy. It is based upon an EDC report entitled *Thinking about Building*, but has been adapted accordingly. It provides examples of some of the more usual contractual arrangements which are available. It does, however, need to be emphasized that the solutions recommended are based largely upon judgement rather than objective analysis. In answering the questions users can be provided with appropriate solutions. Under differing circumstances or where other factors need to be taken into account then the solutions must be adjusted accordingly. The questions themselves are not weighted and users will need to do this in order of importance. Some employers may wish to emphasize only a single aspect such as quality, and choose a method and contractor which are capable of securing this. The majority of employers are, however, interested in an amalgam view, trading off the various factors against each other. It is inappropriate to use the chart in an incremental fashion by adding the various answers together.

The correct choice of a procurement method is a difficult task owing to the wide variety of options which are available. Some of the changes in methods of procurement are the result of a move away from the craft base to the introduction of off-site manufacture, the use of industrialized components and the wider application of mechanical plant and equipment. The improved knowledge of production techniques coupled with the way in which the workforce is organized have enabled the contractor to be able to analyse the resources involved and move towards their greater optimization. Contractors have also a much greater influence upon the design of the project and the recognition of buildability has had an influence both upon the design and the way the work is carried out on site and hence the quality of the finished work. The time available for construction and the subsequent costs involved have also been affected by these changes.

Chapter 10

Contract documents

The contract documents under any building project should include, as a minimum, the following information:

1. *The work to be performed.* This generally requires some form of drawn information. It assists the client by way of schematic layouts and elevations. Even the non-technical employer is usually able to grasp a basic idea of the architect's intentions. Drawings will also be necessary for planning permission and building regulations approval. Finally, they will be needed by the prospective builder in order that the architect's intentions can be carried out during estimating, planning and construction. On all but the simplest types of project, therefore, some drawings will be necessary.

2. *The quality of work required.* It is not easy on drawings alone to describe fully the quality and performance of the materials and workmanship expected. It is usual, therefore, for this to be detailed either in a specification or in a bill of quantities.

3. *The contractual conditions.* In order to avoid any future mis-understandings it is preferable to have a written agreement between the employer and the builder. For simple projects the conditions appropriate to minor works may be sufficient. On more complex projects one of the more comprehensive forms of contract should be used (see Chapter 6).

4. *The cost of the finished work.* This should be predetermined, wherever possible, by an estimate of costs from the builder. On some projects it may only be feasible to assess the cost once the work has been carried out. In these circumstances the method of calculating this cost should be clearly agreed.

5. *The construction programme.* The length of time available for the construction work on site will be important to both the client and the contractor. The client will need to have some idea of how long the project will take to complete in order to plan arrangements for the handover of the project. The contractor's costs will, to some extent, be affected by the time available for construction.

The contract documents on a building contract therefore normally comprise the following:

1. Form of contract (including the Articles of Agreement and Appendix).
2. Contract drawings.
3. Bill of quantities or specification.

On a civil engineering project it is more usual to include both a bill of quantities and a specification. The JCT forms used on building contracts allow only one of these documents, depending on with or without quantities.

Form of contract

This is the principal contract document and will generally comprise one of the preprinted forms described in Chapter 6. It takes precedence over the other contract documents (JCT clause 2.2). The conditions of contract seek to establish the legal framework under which the work is to be undertaken. Although the clauses aim to be precise and explicit, and to cover any eventuality, disagreement in their interpretation does occur. In the first instance, an attempt would be made to resolve the matter by the parties concerned. Where this was not possible, it may be necessary to refer the disagreement to ADR or arbitration. The parties to a contract agree to take any dispute initially to arbitration rather than to the courts. This can save time, costs and adverse publicity that may be damaging to both parties. If the matter still cannot be resolved, it is now taken to court to establish a legal opinion. Such opinions, if held, eventually become case law and can be cited should similar disputes arise in the future.

It is always preferable to use one of the standard forms available, rather than to devise one's own personal form. There are, in practice, several private forms that have been established by the large industrial corporations for their own use. The imposition of conditions of contract which are biased in favour of the employer are not to be recommended. Contractors will tend to overprice the work, even in times of shortage of work, to cover the additional risks involved. Unless there are very good reasons to the contrary, the architect should attempt to persuade the building owner to use one of the standard forms available. The modification of some of the standard clauses, or the addition of special clauses, should only be made in exceptional cases.

The majority of the standard forms of contract comprise, in one way or another, the following three sections.

Articles of Agreement

This is that part of the contract which the parties sign. It should be noted that the contract is between the employer (building owner) and the contractor (building contractor). The blank spaces in the articles are filled in with:

(a)   the names of the employer, contractor, architect and quantity surveyor;
(b)   the date of the signing of the contract;
(c)   the location and nature of the work;
(d)   the list of the contract drawings;
(e)   the amount of the contract sum.

If the parties make any amendments to these Articles of Agreement or to any other part of the contract, then the alterations should be initialled by both parties.

In some circumstances it may be necessary or desirable to execute the contract under seal. This is often the case with local authorities and other public bodies. The spaces for the signatures are then left blank and the seals are affixed in the appropriate spaces indicated. After sealing, the contract must be taken to the Department of Customs and Excise, where upon payment of stamp duty, a stamp will be impressed on the document. Without this the contract will be unenforceable.

Conditions of Contract

The Conditions of Contract in any of the forms in general have a large degree of comparability, but are different in their details. They include, for example, the contractor's obligations in carrying out and completing the work shown on the drawings and described in the bills to the satisfaction of the architect (or supervising officer). They cover matters dealing with the quality of the work, cost, time, nominated suppliers' and subcontractors' insurances, fluctuations and VAT. Their purpose is to attempt to clarify the rights and responsibilities of the various parties in the event of a dispute arising. The JCT Standard Form of Building Contract contains 45 clauses, the last 3 of which deal with fluctuations and are published separately from the other clauses. The clauses from the JCT80 Standard Form of Building Contract are discussed in detail in Chapters 14–22.

Appendix

The Appendix to the conditions of contract needs to be completed at the time of the signing of the contract. The completed Appendix includes that part of the contract which is peculiar to the particular project in question. It includes information on the start and completion dates, the periods of interim payment and the length of the defects liability period for which the contractor is responsible. The Appendix includes recommendations for some of the information.

Contract drawings

The contract drawings should ideally be complete and finalized at tender stage. Unfortunately this is seldom the case, and both clients and architects rely too heavily upon the clause in the conditions allowing for variations. Occasionally it is due to insufficient time being made available for the pre-contract design work or, frequently, because of indecision on the part of the client and his design team. One of the intentions of SMM7 was only to allow bills of quantities to be prepared on complete drawings. Tenderers should, however, be given sufficient information to enable them to understand what is required in order that they may submit an accurate and realistic price. The contract drawings will include the general arrangement drawings showing the site location, the position of the building on the site, means of access to the site, floor plans, elevations and sections. Where these drawings are not supplied to the contractors with the other tendering information, they should be informed where and when they can be inspected. The inspection of these and other drawings is highly recommended since it may provide the opportunity for an informal discussion on the project with the designer.

The preparation of the architect's drawings should comply with the appropriate British Standard, BS 1192. Each drawing should include:
(a)   the name and address of the consultant (architect, engineer or surveyor);
(b)   the drawing number, for reference and recording purposes;
(c)   the scale, and if more than one scale is used they should be of such dissimilar proportions that they are readily distinguishable by sight;
(d)   the title, which will indicate the scope of the work covered on the drawing.

The contractor upon signing the contract will be provided with two further copies of the contract drawings. The contract drawings may include copies of the drawings sent to the contractor with the invitation to tender, together with those drawings that have been used in the preparation of either the bill of quantities or specification. In JCT 80 the contract drawings are defined in the first recital of the Articles of Agreement as those which have been signed by both parties to the contract. It will probably be necessary during the construction phase for the architect to supply the contractor with additional drawings and details. These may either explain and amplify the contract drawings, or because of variations identify and explain the changes from the original design.

The contractor must have an adequate filing system for the drawings. Superseded copies should be clearly marked. They should not, however, be discarded or destroyed until the final account has been agreed, since they may contain relevant information used for contractual claims. The drawings should be clear and accurate, but because paper expands and contracts, only figured dimensions should be used. Scaling dimensions is therefore very much a last resort. Depending upon the size and type of the project, the architect may supply the building contractor with some or all of the following drawings:

Drawing title	*Suggested scale*
Survey plan	1 : 1,250
Site plan and draining	1 : 500
Floor plans	1 : 200
Roof plan	1 : 200
Foundation plan	1 : 200
Elevations	1 : 200
Sections	1 : 100
Construction details	1 : 10, 1 : 5
Engineering services	1 : 200

Return of drawings

Once the contractor has received the final payment under the terms of the contract the drawings may be requested to be returned to the architect along with details, schedules and other documents which bear the name of the architect (clause 5.6). The copyright of the design is vested in the architect. If either the building owner or building contractor wishes to repeat the work, then a further fee must be paid to the architect. None of the documents prepared especially for the project can be used for any other purpose than the contract (clause 5.7). Also, the contractor's rates must not be divulged to others or used for any purpose other than the contract.

Schedules

The preparation and use of schedules is particularly appropriate for items of work such as:

(a) windows;
(b) doors;
(c) manholes;
(d) internal finishings.

Schedules provide an improved means of communicating information between the architect and the builder. They are also invaluable to the quantity surveyor during the preparation of the bills of quantities. They have several advantages over attempting to provide the same information by way of either correspondence or further drawings. The checking for possible errors is simplified, and the schedules can also be used for the placing of orders for materials or components.

During the preparation of schedules two questions must be borne in mind.

1. Who will use the schedule?
2. What information is required to be conveyed?

The architect must supply the building contractor with two copies of these schedules that have been prepared for use in carrying out the works (clause 5.3.1). This should be done soon after the signing of the contract, or as soon as possible thereafter should they not be available at this time.

Contract bills

Some form of bill of quantities or measured schedules should be prepared for all types of building projects, other than those of a minor nature. The bill comprises a list of items of work to be carried out, providing a brief description and the quantities of the finished work in the building. A bill of quantities allows each contractor tendering for a project to price on the same information using a minimum of effort. The bill may include firm or approximate quantities depending upon the completeness of the drawings and other information from which it was prepared.

Uses

Although the main use of a bill of quantities is to properly assist the contractor during the process of tendering, it can be used for many other purposes, such as:

(a) preparation of interim valuations in order that the architect may issue the certificate;

(b) valuation of variations that have either been authorized or sanctioned by the architect;

(c) ordering of materials if care is properly exercised in the checking of quantities and future variations;

(d) preparation of the final account; the bill is used as a basis for agreement;

(e) production of a cost analysis for the building project;

(f) determination of the quality of materials and workmanship by reference to preamble clauses;

(g) useful in obtaining domestic subcontract quotations for sections of the measured work.

(h) use as a form of cost data (noting the provision of clause 5.7)

Preparation

The preparation of bills of quantities should be undertaken by the quantity surveyor. The items of work should have been measured in accordance with a recognized method of measurement. Building projects are generally measured in accordance with the Standard Method of Measurement of Building Works (SMM7). There are several other methods of measurement available to the construction industry. On mass housing projects it may be preferable to use a simplified version such as the Code of Measurement of Building Works in Small Dwellings. Methods also exist for work of a civil engineering nature, and many countries abroad have developed their own rules for measurement. The descriptions and quantities are derived from the contract drawings and SMM7, on the basis generally of the quantities of finished work in the completed building.

Contents

The contents of a bill of quantities are briefly as follows:

1. Preliminaries

This covers the employer's requirements and the contractor's obligations in carrying out the work. SMM7 provides a framework for this section of the bill. It includes, for example,

(a) names of parties;

(b) description of the works;

(c)   form and type of contract;
(d)   general facilities to be provided by the contractor.

In practice, although the preliminaries may comprise over 20 pages of the bill, only a small number of items are priced. The remainder are included for information and contractual purposes. The value of these items may account for up to 15 per cent of the contract sum.

2. Preambles

The preamble clauses contain descriptions relating to:
(a)   the quality and performance of materials;
(b)   the standard of workmanship;
(c)   the testing of materials and workmanship;
(d)   samples of materials and workmanship.

Some government departments have now replaced this section of the bill with a set of standard and comprehensive preamble clauses. The contents of the usual preambles bill are generally extracted from sets of standard clauses. Contractors rarely price this section of the bill.

3. Measured works

This section of the bill includes the items of work to be undertaken by the main contractor or to be sublet to domestic subcontractors. There are several different forms of presentation available for this work, for example:

Trade format.   The items in the bill are grouped under their respective trades. The advantages of this format are that similar items are grouped together, there is a minimum of repetition, and it is useful to the contractor when subletting.

Elemental format.   This groups the items according to their position in the building, on the basis of a recognized elemental subdivision of the project, e.g. external walls, roofs, wall finishes, sanitary appliances. This type of bill should, in theory, help in tendering by locating the work more precisely. In practice contractors tend to dislike it since it involves a considerable amount of repetition. It is, however, useful to the quantity surveyor for cost analysis purposes and during future cost planning.

A recognized order for the inclusion of the various items is important, in order to provide quick and easy reference.

4. Prime cost and provisional sums

Some parts of the building project are not measured in detail but are included in the bill as a lump sum item. These sums of money are intended to cover work not normally carried out by the general contractor (prime cost sum) or for work which cannot be entirely foreseen, defined or detailed at the time that the tendering documents are issued (provisional sum). They are separately described as for defined or undefined work. Prime cost sums cover work undertaken by nominated subcontractors, nominated suppliers and statutory undertakings.

5. Appendices

The final section of the bill includes the tender summary, a list of the main contractors and subcontractors, a basic price list of materials and nominated subcontractor's work for which the main contractor desires to tender.

   The form of tender is the contractor's written offer to 'undertake and execute the works in accordance with the contract documents for a contract sum of money', and will also state the contract period and whether the contract is on the basis of a fixed price. The tenders are submitted to the architect who will then make a recommendation regarding the acceptance of a tender to the client. If the client decides to go ahead with the project, the successful tenderer is invited to submit a bill of quantities for checking. The form of tender may also state that the employer

(a)   may not accept any tender;
(b)   may not accept the lowest tender;
(c)   has no responsibility for the costs incurred in their preparation.

Contract specification

In certain circumstances it may be more appropriate to provide documentation by way of a specification rather than a bill of quantities. The types of project where this may be appropriate include:

(a)   minor building projects;
(b)   small-scale alteration projects.

   The specification is similar to a bill of quantities. The difference is that it does not include a measured works section, but this is replaced by detailed descriptions of the work to be carried out. A specification is used during:

(a)   tendering, to help the estimator to price the work that is required to be carried out; and
(b)   construction by the designer in order to determine the requirements of the contract, legally, technically and financially, and by the building contractor to determine the work to be carried out on site.

Schedule of rates

A schedule of rates is a compromise between a specification and a bill of quantities. It is essentially a bill of quantities that has omitted to include any

quantities for the work to be carried out. Its main purpose is therefore in valuing the items of work once they have been completed and measured. A schedule of rates may be used on:
(a) jobbing work;
(b) maintenance or repair contracts;
(c) projects that cannot be adequately defined at the time of tender;
(d) urgent works;
(e) redecoration projects.

Master programme

The contractor must provide the architect with a master programme showing when the works will be carried out (clause 5.3.1.2). Unless otherwise directed by the architect, the type of programme and the details to be included are to be at the discretion of the contractor. If the architect agrees to a change in the completion date because of an extension of time (clause 25.3.1) then the contractor should provide the architect with amendments and revisions to the programme within 14 days.

Contractual provisions

Copies of contract documents

Clause 5.2 requests the architect to supply the contractor with the following documents:
(a) one copy of the form of contract certified by the employer;
(b) two further copies of the contract drawings;
(c) two copies of the unpriced bill of quantities.
   Clause 5.1 states that the contract drawings and the contract bills will remain in the custody of the employer. These are to be available for inspection at all reasonable times.
   Where there are no bills of quantities, then the building contractor will be provided with copies of a specification or schedule rates as may be appropriate.

Availability of documents on site

Clause 5.5 requires the building contractor to keep one copy of the following documents on site at all times for reasonable inspection:
(a) contract drawings;
(b) bills of quantities (unpriced);
(c) descriptive schedules;
(d) master programme;
(e) additional drawings and details.

Discrepancies in documents

Clause 2.3 asks the contractor to write to the architect should any discrepancies between the documents be found. Only the form of contract takes precedence over the other documents. The contractor cannot therefore assume that the drawings are more important than the bills. However, large-scale drawings will take precedence over the smaller-scale drawings.

Clause 6.1.2 expects the contractor to adopt a similar course of action should a divergence be found between statutory requirements and the contract documents.

Chapter 11

Procurement issues

Introduction

Traditionally clients who wished to have projects constructed would invariably commission a designer, normally an architect for building projects or an engineer for civil engineering projects. These would prepare drawings for the proposed scheme and, where the project was of a sufficient size, a quantity surveyor would prepare estimates and documentation on which contractors could prepare their prices. This was the procedure used during the early part of the century. Even up to 1965 there was a limited choice available of methods used for contract procurement purposes. However, since the early 1960s there have been several catalysts for changes in the way that projects are procured. These are:

- Government intervention through committees, such as the Banwell Reports of the 1960s and more recently through the Department of the Environment and the Latham Report
- Pressure groups formed to encourage change for their members, most notably the British Property Federation
- International comparisons, particularly with the USA and Japan, and influence of the Single European Market in 1992
- The apparent failure of the construction industry to satisfy the perceived needs of its customers, particularly in the way in which the industry organizes and executes its projects
- Influence of educational developments and research
- Trends towards greater efficiency
- Rapid changes in information technology both in respect of office practice and manufacturing processes
- Attitudes amongst the professions
- Clients' desire for single point responsibility

There is no panacea and procedures will continue to evolve in order to meet new circumstances and situations. Procurement methods of a hybrid nature are taking place in an attempt to utilize the best practice from the various competing alternatives. Each of the different methods have all been used at some time in the industry; some more than others, due largely to user familiarity, ease of application, recognition and reliability. New procurement systems will continue to be developed to meet new requirements and demands from clients, contractors and the professions.

Published reports

Several different reports, many of which have been government sponsored, have been issued over the past 50 years. Their overall themes have been aimed at improving the way that the industry is organized and the way that construction work is procured. These various reports are listed below:

The Placing and Management of Building Contracts. 1944 (The Simon Report)

A Code of Procedure for Selective Tendering. 1959

Survey of Problems before the Construction Industry. 1962 (The Emmerson Report)

The Placing and Management of Contracts for Building and Civil Engineering Works. 1967 (The Banwell Report)

Action on the Banwell Report. 1967

Faster Building for Industry. 1983

The Manual of the British Property Federation System. 1983

Construction Contract Arrangements in European Union (EU) Countries. 1983

Thinking about Building. 1985

Faster Building for Commerce. 1988

Building towards 2001. 1991

Trust and Money. 1993

Constructing the Team. 1994 (The Latham Report)

Constructing the Team (Latham)

A large number of the issues raised in this chapter result from the Latham Report (HMSO Publications, 1994). This report provides a review of the construction industry. It was jointly commissioned by the government and the industry. It also included contributions from various client bodies on their expectations when undertaking major capital works programmes.

The Joint Review of Procurement and Contractual Arrangements in the United Kingdom Construction Industry was announced in the House of Commons in 1993. The interim report, entitled *Trust and Money*, was published later that year. The funding parties to the review included the Department of the Environment (DOE), the Construction Industry Council (CIC), the Construction Industry Employers Council (CIEC), the National Specialist Contractors Council (NSCC) and the Specialist Engineering Contractors Group (SECG). Clients have continued to be closely involved in the review and were represented by the British Property Federation (BPF) and the Chartered Institute of Purchasing and Supply (CIPS).

The interim report sought to:

1. Describe the background to the review and its parameters.
2. Define the concerns of the differing parties to the construction process, some of which were mutually exclusive.
3. Pose questions about how performance could be improved and genuine grievances or problems assessed.
4. Reiterate and expand upon what has long been accepted as good practice in the industry, but is often honoured more in the breach than in the observance.

As suggested above, several other government-sponsored studies of the organization and management of the construction industry have also been undertaken this century. Whilst the industry has responded in some measure to change, this has been more attributed to pragmatic courses of action and commercial pressures rather than the advice offered by government or industry committees.

The construction industry comprises many different parties, organizations and professions. These represent many with vested interests and traditions that in some cases represent power and authority. Such bodies are clearly loath to relinquish these positions freely.

Some recommendations of these reports have been implemented. Other problems continue to persist, even though the structure of the industry and its clients have changed dramatically. The Latham Report initiative must be taken by government, in conjunction with major clients and other leaders of the construction process.

Clients are at the core of the process and their needs must be met by industry. Implementation, after all, begins with them. Clients are also dispersed and vary greatly. Government, in the past used to act as a monolithic client. The privatization of many government departments and activities has changed this perception, resulting in the fragmentation of this important client base. Even existing government departments now operate different procurement strategies and practices. This became more pronounced after the demise of the Property Services Agency (PSA).

Fair Construction Contracts

The Construction Sponsorship Directorate of the Department of the Environment published a consultation paper under the above title in May 1995. The review recognized that present arrangements used in the industry militated against co-operation and teamwork and therefore against the client's requirements. These also contribute towards helping to perpetuate the generally poor image of the construction industry.

This consultation paper identifies four areas which it describes as essential terms in any fair construction contract;

1. *Dispute resolution:* emphasizing the need to adopt ADR procedures (see

Chapter 5).

2. *Right to set off:* This principle is widely applied beyond the remit of the construction industry. The principle is as follows; where A claims money from B, B is entitled to deduct any money that A owes before paying the balance. The Latham Report recommends that the right to set-off should be restrained as follows:

    (a) a requirement to give advance notification (with reasons) of the intention to apply set-off;
    (b) set-off subject to adjudication;
    (c) set-off only to be allowable in respect of work covered by the contract.

3. *Prompt payment:* with added interest in the case of default.

4. *Protection against insolvency:* the use of trust funds (see below).

This report summarizes what it considers are the fundamental principles of a modern contract. These points made are as follows:

- dealing fairly with each other and an atmosphere of mutual co-operation;
- firm duties of teamwork, with shared financial motivation to pursue those objectives;
- an interrelated package of documents, clearly identifying roles and duties;
- comprehensible language with guidance notes;
- separation of the roles of contract administrator, project or lead manager and adjudicator. The project manager should be clearly defined as the client's representative;
- allocating risks to the party best able to control them;
- avoiding the need, wherever possible, of changes to pretender information;
- assessing interim payments through milestones or activity schedules rather than through monthly measurement;
- clearly setting out the periods for interim payments and automatically adding interest where this is not complied with;
- the provision of secure trust funds;
- provision of speedy dispute resolution;
- provision of incentives for exceptional performance;
- making provision for advance payment to contractors and subcontractors for prefabricated off-site materials and components.

Trust funds

It is fundamental to trust within the construction industry, that those involved should be paid the correct amounts at the right time for the work that they have carried out. It may be argued that a problem does not exist and that:

- Clients only award work to firms with integrity.
- Contractors are at liberty to decline work from dubious clients.
- Subcontractors can adopt similar business practices.

- Bonds and indemnities are already available.
- Bad debts are not singularly a problem in the construction industry.

However diligently clients, contractors and subcontractors verify each other, the realities of the construction industry and its markets continue to exist. In circumstances such as a recession, contractors and subcontractors are almost prepared to undertake work for any client. This is frequently done at a minimal profit margin. Bad debt insurance is available but adds extra costs at times when firms are seeking to reduce overheads. In times of prosperity, clients are prepared to undertake work with almost any firm that is available in order to get an important project constructed.

The construction industry is unique. Its characteristics separate it from all other industries. These include:

- The physical nature of the product.
- Manufacture normally takes place on the clients own construction site.
- Projects often represent a bespoke design.
- The arrangement of the industry with design being separate from manufacture is not mirrored in other industries.
- The organization of the construction process.
- The methods and manner of price determination.

The contractor's goods and services become part of the landownership once incorporated within the project. Any 'retention of title' clause that might be incorporated by suppliers or contractors in their trading agreements does not protect them once the materials are incorporated within the works. The building contractor is also likely to be sufficiently far down the queue, where an employer is unable to make payment within the terms of the contract. In some countries around the world, legislation has been provided to deal with the potential injustice that might be suffered. The most comprehensive is the Ontario Construction Lien Act 1993.

An effective way of dealing with this problem is to set up a trust fund for interim payments and retention monies. A client, for example, could be requested to pay into such a fund at the start of the payment period, e.g. at the beginning of the month. The correct payment, duly authorized, would then be paid to the contractor at the appropriate time. Where a form of stage payments was used, then the amount of the particular programme stage would be deposited in the trust fund at the commencement of the work in this stage. Where a bill of quantities was used then the client's quantity surveyor would request an appropriate amount of money to be placed in the trust fund to cover the next monthly certificate. The amounts authorized should correspond with the contractor's approved contract programme. The main contractor and the subcontractors would be informed of the amounts deposited. If any party considers that the sums are inadequate then they should have the option of applying to the adjudicator for its increase. There may be some argument for making payments to the subcontractors directly from this fund rather than through the main contractor's account.

Whether trust funds should be provided for all contracts is a matter of some debate. Some in the industry suggest that trust funds should only be available for projects with long contract periods or for contracts of a certain monetary size. The figure suggested for the latter is £0.25m. On very small projects the agreement is often reached about making no payment until all of the work is fully completed.

Any monetary interest accrued in the trust fund belongs to the client. Where the fund necessitates bank charges, then these costs need to be determined at the time of tender.

Such funds are not really required for public works projects, since it is not likely that such bodies will become insolvent. However, such funds will be a source of reassurance for subcontractors, if the main contractor becomes insolvent during the course of the work. If trust funds are to be used in the construction industry then they should be used in the public as well as the private sector.

Compulsory competitive tendering (CCT)

The government philosophy behind CCT is that if market forces are allowed to operate then services can be provided with greater efficiency and at a lower cost. Government accounting and purchasing policies have made it clear that value for money and not the lowest price should be the aim. This was endorsed in *Competitiveness – Helping Business to Win* (HMSO, 1994). CCT was intended to lead towards better managed, more innovative and more responsive services. However, some argue that if the Transfer of Undertakings Regulations (TUPE) apply then much of the opportunities for cost savings could be lost. The provision of publicly funded services through CCT has been growing in recent years around the world. It remains highly controversial in Australia and in the industrialized areas of Europe and the USA. It raises fundamental questions about competition and ownership in the provision of such services. Some of the more problematic issues with policy implementation are:
- fair and effective competition
- incentive compatibility
- performance monitoring
- whether CCT provides the best value for money

The preliminary assessments of contracting suggest generally successful outcomes. Empirical evidence at the present time suggests that efficiency gains have been made and, effectiveness and quality of service have been maintained, if not enhanced. Few professional consultants who come within this directive are likely to admit openly that they have reduced their services because of professional fees. However, a survey by the Association of Consulting Engineers found that less time, resources and consideration was given to projects where competition on fees was applied.

Whilst the basic legal principles of CCT are also applied throughout the EU, through Council Directive 77/187, recent studies have indicated that as many as 99 per cent of public contracts are awarded to the same member state, for some of the following reasons:

- favour own national policies
- lack of information and advertising of contracts to tender
- discriminatory technical specifications and standards
- ignorance of legal procedures
- excessive use of exclusion rules or restrictive procedures

Reverse auction tendering

Under reverse auction tendering (RAT) contractors bid against each other in a live telephone auction to offer the lowest possible price or the best value for money bid. Bidders remain anonymous, with their bids relayed through an auction assistant to the auctioneer, who acts for the client. The aim is to do away with the often unfair practice of one-off, sealed bids and to offer contractors a chance to lower their bids against their competitors. Whilst a number of different client groups are considering piloting this idea, contractors are understandably much less enthusiastic. Contractors are raising issues of confidentiality, cartels, inequitable pricing and intellectual property rights. It is important that clients obtain the best possible price. However, if such a system resulted in contractors bidding too low to obtain work, this might have repercussions in terms of disputes arising or even more liquidation amongst construction firms and their suppliers. This would benefit no one.

Project partnering

During the 1990s the United Kingdom construction industry suffered one of its most severe recessions this century. Many of the largest and best contractors and design firms made losses in successive years and many of the smaller and not the worst firms ceased to trade.

There are many in the construction industry who now recognize the need to move away from the confrontational relationships which cause the majority of disputes, problems, delays and ultimately expense.

The definition of partnering proposed by the National Economic Development Council is a long-term commitment between two or more organizations for the purpose of achieving specific business objectives by maximizing the effectiveness of each participant's resources.

The Banwell Report (1967) recognized that there was scope for the awarding of contracts without the use of competitive tendering under certain circumstances. For example, where a contractor had established a good working relationship with a client over a period of time, completing projects within the time allowed, at the quality expected and for a reasonable cost. These circumstances may have arisen through serial contracting and particularly in those situations of continuation contracts where projects had been awarded on a phase basis.

There has always been some reluctance on the part of public bodies to adopt such procedures, since they may lack elements of accountability, even though it could be shown that a good deal had been obtained for the public sector body concerned. Public sector bodies also need to follow EU procedures where appropriate. In 1995 a government white paper on purchasing will give the official seal of approval to partnering in the public sector. This will provide an environment that is similar to the private sector approach with a number of construction firms developing long-term relationships with public clients. Effectively partnering will be possible where:

- It does not create an uncompetitive environment.
- It does not create monopoly conditions.
- The partnering arrangement is tested competitively.
- It is established on clearly defined needs and objectives over a specified period of time.
- The construction firm does not become over-dependent on the partnering arrangement.

Partnering is now well established in the USA offering benefits to all those who are involved. It has also been used in the UK, successfully, by a number of different major companies such as Marks and Spencer, Rover Group, British Airports Authority and Norwich Union. The partnering arrangement may last for a specific length of time or for an indefinite period. The parties agree to work together in a relationship of trust, to achieve specific objectives by maximizing the effectiveness of each participant's resources and expertise. It is most effective on large construction projects or projects that are repeated throughout the country where the expertise developed can be retained and used again. The McDonald's chain of restaurants provides a good example of the latter. This arrangement, coupled with innovative construction techniques, has helped towards reducing the costs and time of construction by 60 per cent since the start of the 1990s. Its on-site activities have been reduced from 155 days to 15 days for a typical restaurant building.

The concept of partnering extends beyond the client, contractor and consultants and includes subcontractors, suppliers and other specialist organizations who are able to add value to the project. The establishment of good relationships in the industry, based upon mutual trust, benefits the client.

Appointment of specialist firms

The traditional arrangement of appointing specialist firms on a construction project is to use one of the nomination procedures (see Chapter 15). Whilst many specialist firms would like this procedure to be extended, it has been estimated that under JCT 80 as few as 11 per cent of specialist engineering contractors are appointed in this way (Latham). Part of its decline in use has arisen due to the long and tedious procurement route that has been advocated using this form. Other alternative methods are available, such as follows.

Joint ventures. These are a particularly helpful approach where there is a large engineering services input to the project. The joint venture arrangement is between the main contractor, who may typically carry out the role of a project manager, and the specialist contractor. The companies work together as a joint company. It is therefore suitable for D&B arrangements.

Separate contracts. The client in this case will let different contracts to different firms, i.e. the main contractor and the specialist contractor. This has in the past not been easy to administer particularly where problems have arisen (see clause 29 of JCT 80).

Management/construction management. This is believed to be the most effective way of dealing with such firms. The different trade and specialist firms are appointed and a contractual arrangement formed with each company (see Chapter 8). This arrangement allows for full participation by the firms in design and commercial decisions at an early date.

Appointing a specialist firm as the main contractor. Where the specialist work represents the largest portion of the project, then the client may choose to reverse the arrangements and appoint a specialist firm as the main contractor. The more usual construction trades would then be employed by this firm.

Construction (Design and Management) Regulations 1994 (CDM)

The construction industry is a dangerous environment. It has a poor health and safety record. Serious injury and death happen far too frequently as a result of construction activities especially on site. These affect not only the construction workers employed on site, but also members of the general public. Improving the management process is essential in helping to prevent accidents and ill health in the industry.

Different governments have initiated measures aimed at reducing accidents on construction sites. The most common of this legislation is the Health and Safety at Work Act 1974, which applies to all industries. However, it is recognized that some industries are more dangerous than others. The data shown in Fig 11.1 and 11.2 help to illustrate this point. Falling from a height was the most common cause of fatality in the industry. Being struck by a moving vehicle was the next most common. Lifting and carrying accounted for nearly a quarter of all reported injuries in 1992/93.

The CDM Regulations which became operative in 1995, place new duties on clients, planning supervisors, designers and contractors to plan, co-ordinate and manage health and safety throughout all stages of a construction project.

	Rates per 100,000 employees			
	1986/87	1988/89	1990/91	1993/94
Fatal and major				
Construction	293	296	291	233
All industries	101	94	92	79
All reported injuries				
Construction	1,995	1,928	1,907	1,416
All industries	862	842	818	710

Fig. 11.1 Injuries to employees: construction and all industries (source: Department of the Environment)

	Fatal	Major	Total
Contact with moving machinery	2	71	73
Struck by flying object	7	310	317
Struck by moving vehicle	14	90	104
Slip, trip or fall	1	366	367
Fall from height	27	808	835
Trapped by collapse	6	76	82
Exposure to harmful substance	4	41	45
Contact with electricity	8	63	71
Other	0	231	231
Totals	69	2,056	2,125

Fig. 11.2 Injuries to employees in the construction industry 1992/93 (source: Department of the Environment)

Anyone who appoints a designer or contractor has to ensure that they are competent for the work and will allocate adequate resources for health and safety. The regulations apply to construction projects and everyone associated with their design and construction. The regulations are about the management of health and safety. There are five key parties, firms or individuals, who are involved; each has specific duties to perform.

Clients. These should be satisfied that only competent people are appointed as planning supervisor and principal contractor. This also applies when making arrangements for the appointment of designers and contractors. They should ensure that sufficient resources have been allocated to ensure that the project can be carried out safely.

Designers. These should ensure that structures are designed to minimize risks to health and safety whilst they are being constructed and maintained. Where risks are unable to be avoided, adequate information must be provided. The design includes both drawn and written information, e.g. specifications.

Planning supervisors. These have the overall responsibility for co-ordinating the health and safety aspects of the design and planning phase and for the early stages of health and safety plan and the health and safety file.

Principal contractors. These should take account of health and safety issues when preparing and presenting tenders or similar documents. The principal contractors have to develop health and safety plans and co-ordinate the activities of all contractors to ensure that each complies with the appropriate health and safety legislation and regulations. The principal contractors also have the duties to check on the provision of information and training for employees and for consulting with employees and the self-employed on health and safety matters.

Contractors and the self-employed. These should co-operate with the principal contractor and provide relevant information on the heath and safety risks created by their work and how they will be controlled. Contractors also have duties for the provision of other information to the principal contractor and to employees. The self-employed have similar duties to contractors.

Employees on construction sites should be better informed and have the opportunity to become more involved in health and safety matters.

The new procedures will also cost the industry and hence its clients more money and time to implement and monitor, at least during the early stages of its use. However, these procedures may over the longer period of time help to reduce costs through developing better construction practices. They should help to save lives and reduce accidents and the disruption that these sometimes cause to work on site. They will reinforce the need for co-ordinating and managing health and safety from inception to completion and during the use of the completed project.

Quality assurance

Every client in the construction industry has the right to assume a standard of quality that has been specified for the project. The Building Research Establishment (BRE) has in conjunction with a number of sponsors recently launched the Construction Quality Forum. At the launch of this organization, BRE reported that each year defects or failures in design and construction cost the industry, and its clients, more than £1 bn. This represents 2 per cent of total turnover. This is a high percentage taking into account that contractors typically only make 6 per cent profit on turnover *(The Construction Industry of Great Britain* by R.C. Harvey and A. Ashworth, Butterworth-Heinemann, 1993).

The construction industry is an industry in which:

- There has never been a requirement for the workforce to be formally qualified and skills are generally developed through time serving.
- Much of the work is carried out by subcontractors in a climate in which

some 50 firms come into existence every day and a similar number go into liquidation or become bankrupt every day.

- There is a paucity of R&D involving new materials and designs.
- There is often poor management and supervision.

Studies have indicated that about 50 per cent of faults originate in the design office, 30 per cent on site and about 20 per cent in the manufacture of materials and components. An investment in quality assurance methods can therefore reap substantial long-term benefits by helping to reduce such faults, the inevitable delays and costs of repairs and the all too frequent legal costs that often follow.

BS 5750 certification has been increasingly taken up within the construction industry by consultants and contractors. Quality assurance is therefore seen as a good thing for the industry. Contract procurement methods that fail to address this issue adequately are not doing the industry or its clients any favours. The use of quality certified firms, who have been independently assessed and registered, therefore offers some protection within the context of getting it right first time. Work that is below acceptable quality and standards, that has to be rectified, is rarely as good as making sure that it is carried out correctly in the first place.

BS 5750 is seen by some firms as an additional expense, with the cost of accreditation as an unnecessary overhead. Also whilst it should ensure that quality standards are achieved it does not ensure that the appropriate quality has already been set in the first place. However, some clients are now not prepared to employ consultants, contractors or suppliers who do not have this kitemark in the first place. Within the total quality management scenario, quality remains an ongoing process of continued improvement. Quality must be appropriate to the work being performed. It should only be insisted upon where it adds value to the finished construction project.

Latent Defects Liability and 'Build' Insurance

The Construction Sponsorship Directorate of the Department of the Environment published this consultation paper in April 1995. The review recommended the introduction of a Construction Contracts Bill and that this bill should contain provision for compulsory latent defects insurance or BUILD (Building Users' Insurance against Latent Defects) (National Economic Development Organization) insurance.

Construction clients naturally look for some degree of protection against:

- the risk of latent defects
- the costs of remedying any defects
- the cost of any damage caused by defect, including consequential losses (e.g. loss of rents, profits, etc.)

The physical complexity of the construction process and the integration of its constituent parts, the number of (temporary) teams involved, the sums of money involved and the complex tangle of potential legal and financial responsibilities of the different parties in the construction process need greater clarity. The main issues arising from the considerations on latent defects liability pertain to:

- joint and several liability
- limitation periods and prescription of actions
- transfer of clients' rights

Difficulties exist where more than one party is involved and hence the desire by some clients for a single point responsibility for the project. The proposal in the consultative document is that the period of liability should commence from the date of practical completion of the works. This might appear unfair to those specialist firms who have completed their portion of the project, perhaps several years earlier on a large project.

The provisions of the Limitation Act 1980 and the Latent Damage Act 1986 should be brought into line with the provisions of the Consumer Protection Act 1987, which provides for a 10 year limitation period. This should apply for all future new commercial, retail and industrial building works in both the public and private sectors.

The doctrine of privity of contract means that, as a general rule, a contract cannot confer rights or impose obligations arising under it on any person except the parties to it. The tenants and the subsequent owners have no privity of contract with contractors or consultants. In July 1991 a House of Lords judgment (*Murphy* v. *Brentwood*) closed down the law of negligence as a route for recovery of economic loss, except in exceptional cases. Since then owners or tenants without privity of contract have used other contractual techniques such as collateral warranties to create contractual rights where none would otherwise have existed.

The BUILD insurance would be financed by the client at currently about 1 per cent of the contract cost. Such policies normally cover the structure foundations and the weather shield envelope. They often exclude engineering services, and this is seen as a weakness. The possibility of mechanical or electrical failure could be provided for an additional premium. Policies could also include for loss of rental or extra rental expenditure.

Cost reductions

A recommendation from the 'Latham Report' was regarding the possibility of reducing (initial) building costs by 30 per cent. The report does not suggest how this might be achieved. Such cost reductions should not generally reduce quality but should at least maintain and preferably improve the quality of buildings. When compared against the motor car, clients' views of buildings score poorly (see Fig. 11.3). The implication for the construction industry is adding value with the principle of doing more with less. It is also important that such cost reductions do not refocus the construction industry backwards 50

Wants	Modern motor car	Modern buildings		
		Domestic	Commercial	Industrial
Value for money	●●●●	●●●●●	●●●	●●●●
Pleasing to look at	●●●●	●●●●	●●●	●●●
(largely) Free from faults	●●●●●	●●●	●	●●
Timely delivery	●●●●	●●●●	●●●●	●●●●
Fit for purpose	●●●●●	●●●●	●●	●●●
Guarantee	●●●●●	●●●●	●	●
Reasonable running costs	●●●●	●●●●	●●	●●●
Durability	●●●●	●●●	●●	●●
Customer delight	●●●●●	●●●	●●	●●

Fig. 11.3 Construction industry performance compared to car industry (source: Latham Report)

years towards the emphasis on initial costs alone. The importance of ensuring that life-cycle costs are given their rightful importance in the overall building process must be maintained.

The reduction of building costs must be considered in the light of the fact that the industry is currently in one of its worst recessions this century, it is a low-wage industry, and that cost efficiencies have already been achieved over the past 50 years principally through the study of building economics. The following are some of the areas of possible investigation in attempting to meet this aim:

- reduce changes to the design
- optimize specifications
- improve design cost effectiveness
- apportion risk efficiently
- improve productivity
- reduce waste
- examine cost efficient procurement arrangements
- improve the use of high technology for both design and construction
- reduce government stop–go policies
- develop more off-site prefabrication components
- standardize components
- consider construction as a manufacturing process
- get it right first time, i.e. avoid defects
- make better use of mechanization
- improve the education and training of operatives
- reduction of 'men' noting their high costs and their reduction in manufacturing industry

Private finance initiative (PFI)

The purpose of this initiative was to encourage partnerships between the public and private sectors in the provision of public services. The scheme is outlined in *Private Finance and Public Money* (Department of the Environment, 1993). In 1992, the Chancellor of the Exchequer announced a new initiative to find ways of mobilizing the private sector to meet needs that had traditionally been met by the public sector. Achieving an increase in private sector investment will mean that more projects will be able to be undertaken. This takes into account the government's objective that public spending should decline in the medium term. The broad aims of such a partnership will be to:

- achieve objectives and deliver outputs effectively
- use public money to best effect
- respond positively to private sector ideas

In exploring the possibilities for private finance, including proposals from the private sector, the options being considered include:

- Can the project be financially free standing?
- Is it suitable for a joint venture?
- Is there potential for leasing agreements?
- Is there potential for government to buy a service from the private sector?
- Can two or more of these elements be brought together in combination in any particular instance to form innovative solutions?

Concessonary contracting falls neatly into such an arrangement, whereby the private sector is encouraged to construct public projects, such as roads, and then charge a levy on this provision, for a fixed period of time specified in the contract. The contractor throughout the entire period is responsible for the maintenance of the works. Upon eventual handover to the public sector the contract will also specify the required condition of the asset.

Part 3

Process and parties

Chapter 12

Process and parties associated with construction contracts

The following is a brief summary of processes used during the design stage and the construction stage of a building project.

Construction process

There are several different ways of describing the process which might be used for the construction of a building. Perhaps the most commonly referred to is the RIBA Plan of Work. This has been adapted and modified in all sorts of ways but essentially comprises the following range of tasks and activities. There are basically two separate groupings; pre-contract and post-contract. Some writers, however, identify four separate stages by separating the tentative (feasibility) from the definite (design) and the construction from the maintenance aspects. Certainly the latter aspect of property care has been greatly undervalued and underutilized, and in terms of its time span and the need to protect an investment it has become of much greater significance in recent years. Figure 12.1 illustrates a process which might be used.

Pre-contract process

This is the period during which the need for the project, and the idea in terms of size, function and appearance, are formulated into plans that are capable of being used for the construction of a complete building. Although variations are expected even after the work has commenced on site, this should not provide an excuse for a delay in the design requirements. Indications are currently showing that this lack of decision, prior to commencement on site, is an important factor affecting the trio of time, cost and quality of the finished project.

Client's brief

On a traditional project the client will first approach the architect regarding his requirements. In other circumstances the client may decide to go straight to the

Architect	Quantity surveyor	Engineer	Contractor

Pre-contract

Client's brief

Architect	Quantity surveyor	Engineer	Contractor
Identifying the client's needs and wants in terms of space, function and aesthetics	Guide cost information Financial factors such as taxation and funding		Only involved if negotiation, design and build or two-stage tendering

Investigation

Architect	Quantity surveyor	Engineer	Contractor
Feasibility and viability	Approximate estimate	Site survey and investigation	
Planning possibilities	Initial cost plan	Preliminary structural calculations	
Alternative sorts/ types of construction			
Outline design approval			

Sketch design

Architect	Quantity surveyor	Engineer	Contractor
Outline planning permission	Final cost plan		
Major planning problems solved	Life-cycle cost plan		

Design

Architect	Quantity surveyor	Engineer	Contractor
Development of sketch plans	Cost implications and cost checking	Constructional methods decided	
Constructional details determined		Preliminary schemes for services	
Constructional methods decided		Design schemes for structure	

Working drawings

Architect	Quantity surveyor	Engineer	Contractor
All construction drawings and details completed	Quotations from specialist firms	All construction drawings and details completed	
	Final cost checks		
	Bills of quantities		

Tender stage

Architect	Quantity surveyor	Engineer	Contractor
All members of the design team check their calculations			Contractors prepare tenders
	Receipt of tenders and tender checking		Materials and sub-contractor quotations
			Determination of market factors
			Contractor's method statements

Post-contract construction

Architect	Quantity surveyor	Engineer	Contractor
Inspections of quality	Valuations, forecasts and payments	Inspection of quality	Construction programme agreed
Subcontractor nomination			Planning and progress control
Issue of instructions			Subcontractor control
Issue of certificates			

Maintenance

Contractually up to the end of the defects liability period in-use repair and maintenance, changes in use, conservation, demolition, alteration and reconstruction, asset valuation, etc.

Fig. 12.1 The construction process

builder for a design and build scheme, or to a firm who can offer an 'off-peg' project that may meet the requirements. The purpose of this first meeting is to distinguish between the client's needs and wants in respect of the design and spatial requirements. The majority of clients today will have a precise idea on how much they intend to spend. This they will have determined on the basis of their capital resources and funding ability. The architect would be wise to obtain some cost information from the quantity surveyor, rather than to attempt to go it alone. The quantity surveyor should therefore be able to provide guide costs based upon the floor area or some other functional requirement. The quantity surveyor should also be able to suggest in very general terms the comparative costs of alternative design suggestions.

Investigation

Assuming that the initial requirements can be agreed, the project then moves towards a second stage. During this period many of the aspects are examined to ascertain the viability of the project. A site survey and investigation should be carried out to determine the nature of the ground and site conditions, and to locate the building's position on site. Bad ground conditions may have implications on the overall aspects of the design. They will also inevitably increase construction costs. Alternative methods of construction both in terms of design and costs will be considered. The quantity surveyor should by now have prepared an approximate estimate. Once the outline design is approved, the quantity surveyor's cost plan will begin to be formulated. Preliminary ideas from the structual engineer may also be necessary, where this can significantly alter the design or the building costs.

Sketch design

During this stage the architect will be able to obtain outline planning permission. There will previously have been discussions with the planners on the possibility of such a scheme being approved. This the architect will have been able to assess upon the knowledge of the structure and district plans. The major planning problems will thus be solved, and the quantity surveyor's cost plan finalized.

Design

This is the period during which the sketch plans are developed and the constructional details and methods are selected. Preliminary schemes should now be available for the engineering services and structure. The quantity surveyor will need to know the cost implications of these various solutions and whether or not the cost plan is on target.

Working drawings

All of the drawn information should be completed during this stage. The practice of leaving parts of the design until later is to be deprecated. If the scheme has been fully designed, it should now be possible to obtain quotations from nominated suppliers and tenders from nominated subcontractors. The quantity surveyor, prior to preparing the bill of quantities, should complete extensive cost checks to ensure that the design does not exceed the projected costs, when pace during the design stage will now have speeded up as the project moves towards the general tender period.

Tender stage

During this stage of the project tenders are invited from those firms who have already expressed their willingness to submit a price. Whilst tenderers are busy pricing the documents, the architect and the other consultants will be checking through their own calculations. The pressure for progress has now moved, however, entirely to the contractor. During pricing the latter will obtain domestic subcontractor quotations, and current information from various suppliers on the costs of materials. The contractor will also need to be aware of the current state of the market in order to submit a price that is the most favourable. Tenders will be returned by a stated date, and the process of their checking and reporting is largely that of the quantity surveyor. Finally, a tender will be recommended for acceptance, and once the contract has been signed the project moves into the post-contract phase.

Post-contract process

Construction

The project should have been completely designed prior to release to the contractor for tendering purposes. Although the contract allows for and expects the occurrence of variations, this should not provide an excuse for only a partly finished design. One of the architect's main duties during this stage is to ensure that the contractor has all the information required for construction purposes. In addition the architect will be responsible for the smooth running of the works. As the work is carried out, the architect's role is largely that of a supervisor ensuring that the contractor complies with all the requirements. A clerk of works may be employed, whose duties consist almost entirely of inspecting the work and materials during construction. The clerk of works may also act as a liaison officer on site, and this person's relationship with the contractor can either improve or reduce the overall success of the project.

The quantity surveyor during the construction of the works will prepare the valuations for the interim certificate. Certification is, however, entirely the responsibility of the architect. It is preferable if the varied or provisional works can be remeasured and agreed soon after they have been completed. In this case the work items will still be clear in everyone's minds, and the possibility of errors arising is therefore reduced.

The various subcontractors will come on to the site to carry out their own work. Even the major subcontractors will only be on site for a relatively short period of time, compared with the main contractor. The architect is unlikely to have completed the process of nomination for every firm, and some of these will therefore need to be done during the construction stage.

The local authority will have little to do with the building project in the majority of circumstances, but may choose to inspect the works at different stages. This will be done to make sure that each stage complies with the appropriate building regulation. The local authority will, however, take action where local regulations are infringed or where a nuisance is caused to nearby properties due to the carrying out of the construction works.

Maintenance

The project becomes officially complete when the architect issues the certificate of practical completion. The contractor is responsible for making good any of his defects from this date for about 6 months. The actual length of time will be specified in the appendix to the conditions of contract. The architect should ensure that all defects are made good prior to the issue of the final certificate. The quantity surveyor during this period will prepare and agree the final account with the contractor's surveyor. At the commencement of the defects liability period, one-half of the retention is released to the contractor, with the other half being paid with the final certificate. Although the contractor is contractually responsible for work up to the end of this period, liability under common law will extend for a much longer period.

Parties involved with the construction process

Local authorities

The construction industry is subject to a variety of controls, some of which are mandatory. Both the design and the contracting organizations must naturally comply with the general laws of the country, but in addition there are special regulations appertaining only to the construction industry. Such laws and regulations initially arise by an Act of Parliament, but their administration is generally undertaken by local government.

Local government is broadly divided into county councils and district councils, each with their own function. A major reorganization of local authorities was introduced by the Local Government Act 1972, which came into operation in 1974. Further reorganization is expected in the mid-1990s. The allocation of the various functions appropriate to construction are as follows:

Building regulations – district council.

Highways – county council, although much of the maintenance work is undertaken on their behalf, and with their agreement, by the district council.

Housing – district council.

Refuse – collection by the district council; disposal by the county council. This means that it is the county council's responsibility to find tipping sites.

Town planning – structure plans by the county council and local plans by the district council. This means that the county authority determines the outline plan for an area with the district council completing the details.

Water and sewage – dealt with by the regional water authorities.

Local government is restricted in the way it can exercise its powers as follows:

1. *Area.* It is generally confined to a defined geographical area. It works with adjoining authorities on matters of common interest through joint committees and joint boards.

2. *Central government.* The control of a local authority is exercised through the Secretary of State for the Environment. In some governments a local government Minister has been appointed to carry out this control. Central government control may be exercised by way of supervision where a statutory inspection can take place, and because a local government relies to a large extent on the finances from central government. All the local authority's accounts must be properly audited. In some cases the Minister concerned has powers to carry out a local authority's functions in cases where it defaults.

3. *Judicial control.* Because local authorities are created by statute, they derive their powers and functions in this way. They must therefore act within the laws afforded to them. Building owners and contractors are likely to encounter the local authority concerned initially for the approval of planning permission, where an appropriate fee is payable, and during construction where they must conform to the building regulations and other statutory documents.

During the 1980s there was political direction from Parliament via central government which has resulted in the privatization of certain aspects of local government services. This has in many cases required local authorities to tender against private companies for the services which they have traditionally provided.

The Crown

The Crown is used in this context to denote the governmental powers which are exercised through the civil service. This means central government offices rather than local government. Central government has many powers conferred upon it by Parliament. It does, for example, exert a certain measure of control over local government. This may be achieved by:

1.   *Supervision*. The Secretary of State has power through statutes to supervise the activities of local authorities. For example, some town planning decisions may need to be referred to the Secretary of State. Some local services such as fire, police and education are subject to statutory inspection.
2.   *Finance*. Much of a local authority's finances are obtained from central government. The Minister therefore can exercise considerable pressure on proposed expenditure, and also through the auditing of the local authority's accounts.
3.   *Supersession*. In some cases the Minister concerned has power to supersede in certain functions in case of default by a local authority.

Because government is a major spender in the construction industry they are considered to be a very important client. They can also severely restrict and regulate how the work will be carried out. Although the privatized Property Services Agency (PSA) still undertakes a large amount of central government's building work, other departments also have extensive construction programmes. Much of the central government's work is undertaken on the GC/Works/1 form of contract.

The employer

The main purpose of construction activity is to provide a completed project for the building owner. This project may include the substance of a building contract, a project constructed speculatively for a developer or infrastructure works such as roads, bridges or pipelines. The employers, clients or promoters of the construction industry are many and varied. They include the public sector bodies such as central and local government and private companies involved in building for domestic, commercial, industrial and retailing purposes. They also now include a range of the quasi-public companies that were formerly part of the nationalized industries. These include the industries of coal, electricity, gas, water supply, sewage treatment, etc. Many of these latter companies are virtual monopolies, with limited competition from other organizations.

Construction activity is typically divided on a 60–40 per cent basis in favour of new projects compared with repair and maintenance activities. This figure remained almost at a constant level throughout the 1980s and early 1990s. The division between public and private sector workloads has, however, changed markedly largely due to the privatization programme of the Conservative government during this time. Civil engineering works are worth about 20 per cent of the output of the industry. Typically the private sector used to account for about 50 per cent of the total output. By the start of the 1990s this had fallen to less than 25 per cent. Work done by British companies overseas currently accounts for 10 per cent of the total output of the construction industry. One of the largest clients of the construction industry, the British Airports Authority, spends about £1 m. per day on construction work.

Each separate organization is given a considerable amount of autonomy by the government of the day, and it is interesting to note the wide diversification in the methods used for the procurement and execution of major and minor capital works projects. Little uniformity exists either in the design procedures employed or the contract conditions that are used. The private sector includes all those organizations that are not directly funded by some form of government money supply. It must be stressed, however, that even in the private sector individuals and companies may be able to secure funds for a variety of types of building work. For example, grants may be available for housing improvement and renovation or for the attraction of industry to a particular location.

Clients in the public sector may be influenced by both social and political trends and needs, and the desire to build may be limited by these factors. They will, nevertheless, be restricted in their aspirations by the amount of capital they are allowed to borrow for these purposes. The private sector, which encompasses the individual house owner and the large multinational corporation, will probably direct its capital spending to the ventures that are considered to be monetary profitable. In both sectors, however, there has in recent years been a particular emphasis upon securing value for money. This has tended to be viewed on a building's life cycle rather than upon initial construction costs alone.

The employer is one of the parties to the contract, the other being the contractor. Each client will have different priorities but essentially there will be a combination of:

(a) *Performance* in terms of quality, function and durability;
(b) *Time* available for completion by the date agreed in the contract documents; and
(c) *Cost* as determined in the budget estimate and the contract sum.

If employers are to be satisfied with the product (i.e. their construction project), then these three conditions must be critically examined.

The important references to the employer in JCT 80 are as follows:

(a) appointment of the architect;
(b) powers regarding insurances;
(c) duty to give possession of the site to the contractor;
(d) powers in respect of damages for non-completion;
(e) powers to determine the employment of the contractor;
(f) powers to engage directly employed contractors;
(g) duties regarding certificates;
(h) procedure in respect of arbitration.

The architect

The architect has traditionally been the leader of the design team. In the building process, where design and construction are separate entities, it is the architect who receives the commission from the client. Because projects today require a large amount of specialized knowledge to complete the design, the architect may require the assistance of consultants from other professional disciplines.

The architect's function is to provide the client with an acceptable and satisfactory building upon completion. This will involve the proper arrangement of space within the building, shape, form, type of construction and materials used, environmental controls and aesthetic considerations – all within the concept of total life-cycle design.

The architect's duties and powers are described under the JCT Standard Form of Building Contract 1980. A contractor who believes that the architect is attempting to exercise powers beyond those assigned under the contract, can insist that the architect specifies in writing the conditions that allow such powers (clause 4.2). The architect will generally operate under the rules of agency on the part of the employer. This means that instructions given to the contractor will be accepted and paid for by the employer.

In some forms of contract the architect is termed the supervising officer. This is the name used, for example, in the GC/Works/1 form of contract, and is one of the alternative titles suggested in the JCT group of forms. It is used in the GC/Works/1 form since the designer may be an engineer rather than an architect, and the terminology has been extended to the JCT form for a similar assumption.

The scope of the work undertaken by the architect may be broadly divided into pre-contract and post-contract duties. Although it is more common for an architect to provide a fully comprehensive design and supervision service, a design-only service may be required by the employer. It is less common to expect the architect to supervise construction work only, although it could arise in situations where prefabricated buildings are used. However, even in these circumstances, the architect is more likely to be asked for advice on a particular system building, during the design stage.

In the normal pre-contract stage the architect's basic duty is to prepare a design for the works. This may involve three facets: architectural design, constructional detailing and administration of the scheme. This latter aspect will entail integrating the work of the various job architects and other consultants, and ensuring that the information is available for a start on site when required. The architect during the work must exhibit reasonable skill and care in the design of the works. This duty may be established in accordance with normal trade practice. The architect will also generally be held responsible for any work delegated to another. In the JCT form of contract, for example, although the quantity surveyor is responsible for most of the financial arrangements, the architect is ultimately responsible regarding the certification of monies to be paid. If part of the design is undertaken by a nominated subcontractor, then some protection may be afforded by means of a warranty from that firm.

During the post-contract stage the work undertaken by the architect is largely supervision and administration. Some drawings and details may still need to be prepared, particularly where such information is reasonably requested by the contractor. The purpose of supervision is to ensure that the works are carried out in accordance with the contract. The amount of supervision necessary will vary from project to project. A complex refurbishment project will require more frequent visits than the construction of a large warehouse shed. On very large contracts the architect may even be resident on the site. The duties of administration are used to describe the various functions, such as issuing instructions to the contractor, that must be carried out during the progress of the works. The post-contract stage involves those duties described in the JCT Standard Form of Building Contract, some of the more important of which are as follows:

1. Instructions

- Discrepancies and divergencies between documents
- Justification of instructions
- Instructions to be in writing
- Confirmation of verbal instructions
- Divergence between statutory regulations and project documents
- Opening up of work for inspection
- Removal from site of work, materials or goods which are not in accordance with the contract
- Exclusion from the works of any person
- Instructions given to person-in-charge
- Variations requirements
- Expenditure of prime cost and provisional sums
- Sanction in writing of variations created by the contractor
- Defects in the contractor's work
- Postponement of any work
- Execution of protective work after an outbreak of hostilities
- War damage
- Antiquities
- Nominated subcontractors
- Nominated suppliers

2. Certificates

- Practical completion of works
- Completion of making good defects
- Estimate of the approximate total value of partial possession
- Completion of making good defects after partial possession
- Failure to complete the works by the completion date
- Determination

- Interim certificates
- Final certificate

3. Other matters

- provision of documents, schedules and drawings
- stating levels and setting out the works
- access to site and workshops
- limitation of assignment and subletting
- granting an extension of time
- reimbursement of loss and expense to the contractor
- arbitration

The quantity surveyor

The quantity surveyor has developed from the function of a measurer to a building accountant and a cost adviser. The emphasis of the quantity surveyor's work has moved from one solely associated with accounting functions, to one involved in all matters of forecasting finance and costing.

The function of the quantity surveyor in connection with construction projects is therefore threefold: first, as a cost adviser, attempting to forecast and evaluate the design in economic terms both on an initial and life-cycle cost basis; second, preparing of much of the tendering documentation used by contractors; and third, in an accounting role during the construction period where the quantity surveyor will report on interim payments and financial progress and the preparation and control of the final expenditure for the project.

Quantity surveyors are employed on behalf of both the building owner and the building contractor, the latter tending to specialize in post-contract functions or commercial management. The duties of the quantity surveyor are listed below.

1. Pre-contract stage

- initial cost advice
- approximate estimating
- cost planning/value engineering/life-cycle costing
- bills of quantities and tender documentation
- specification writing (where the bills are not required)
- procurement
- tender evaluation

2. Post-contract stage

- valuations for interim certificates

- final accounts
- remeasurement of the whole or part of the works
- measuring and valuing variations
- daywork accounts
- adjustment to prime cost sums
- increased cost assessment
- evaluation of contractual claims
- cost analysis

In addition, the contractor's surveyor will be involved in the agreement of subcontractors' work, other duties of a commercial nature and possible bonus payments and ancillary functions.

Although the quantity surveyor has been accepted in the building industry as an essential member of the construction team, the situation is somewhat different in engineering. The acceptance of the quantity surveyor, for example, in civil engineering has not been easy, although there is considerable evidence that this has now changed. Many engineers now accept that the employment of the quantity surveyor is essential if economic and financial control is to be properly exercised. Of course, civil engineering contractors have been employing quantity surveyors since the turn of this century. A similar situation occurs in environmental services engineering and the petro-chemical industry. The quantity surveyor's work frequently extends beyond that described above. Loss adjusting, arbitration and auditing are other areas where quantity surveyors are employed.

The role of the quantity surveyor within the JCT form of contract, although vague, is more precise than in other forms of contract. In the ICE form these duties are placed with the engineer, but in practice it is the quantity surveyor who will carry them out. In JCT 80 the quantity surveyor is mentioned in the following list of operations:

(a) confidential nature of contractor's prices;
(b) valuing variations;
(c) calculation of loss and expense;
(d) preparation of interim valuations;
(e) preparation of the final account;
(f) accounts of nominated subcontractors and suppliers;
(g) fluctuations.

The clerk of works

The clerk of works is employed under the direction of the architect as an inspector of the works under construction. The clerk of works may give instructions to the contractor, but these are of no effect unless they are subsequently authorized by the architect.

The contractor must give the clerk of works every reasonable facility to carry out all duties. The clerk of works is the counterpart of the person-in-charge employed on behalf of the contractor. Duties include ensuring that the contract in terms of the specification and further instructions from the architect are fully complied with. The clerk of works will attempt to make sure that the materials used and the workmanship carried out are in accordance with the contract requirements. This will involve: inspecting the materials prior to their incorporation within the works; obtaining samples where necessary for the approval of the architect; testing materials such as concrete, bricks and timber to the specified codes of practice; and generally ensuring that the construction work complies with accepted good practice.

The engineer

There is a wide range of different types of engineers employed in the construction industry. These may range from civil and structural engineers to building services engineers. Civil engineers are responsible for the design and supervision of civil and public works engineering, and are employed in a similar way to that of architects employed on a building contract. In addition, the engineer's counterpart working for the contractor is often a civil engineer. Their work can be very diverse, and may include projects associated with transportation, energy requirements, sewage schemes or land reclamation projects. Structural engineers are usually employed by the architect on behalf of the client. They act as consultants to design the frame and the other structural members in buildings. The building services engineers are responsible for designing the environmental conditions that are required in today's modern buildings. There has in recent years been an upsurge in their membership as greater attention is paid towards this aspect of building design.

Engineers are not mentioned by name in JCT 80, although the supervising officer that is mentioned in some of the forms may equally be an engineer or a surveyor or an architect, depending upon who is largely responsible for the design and supervision of the works.

Person-in-charge

The person-in-charge is responsible for the effective control of the contractor's work and workpeople on site, also being responsible for organization and supervision on the contractor's behalf, and for receiving instructions from the architect. Depending upon the size and nature of the works and the type of firm, this may be a general foreman, or a site agent, or a project manager. The person-in-charge may have received initial training as a trade craftsman or be a chartered builder or engineer. The responsibilities will vary with the size of the project and company policy. On the larger projects considerable assistance will be received from other site staff. The person-in-charge, whatever the title, is the site manager on behalf of the main contractor and is very often a member of the Chartered Institute of Building.

Main contractor

The majority of the construction work in the United Kingdom is undertaken by a general contractor. These firms, which will be public limited companies (PLCs), will vary in size, having from just a few to many hundreds of employees. Many of the larger companies are household names and have developed only since the beginning of the twentieth century. Although there is no clear dividing line between building and civil engineering works, many firms tend to specialize in only one of these sectors. Even in the larger companies, separate divisions or companies exist, often trading and structured in entirely different ways depending upon the sector in which they are employed. Even the operatives' unions and the rules under which they are engaged are different.

The smallest building firms may specialize in one trade, and as such may act as either domestic subcontractors or jobbing builders carrying out mainly repairs and small alterations. The medium-sized firms may be a combination of trades operating as general contractors within one town or region. These firms may specialize in certain types of building projects or be speculative house builders. The largest firms may be almost autonomous units, although it is uncommon even in these companies to find them undertaking a complete range of work. On the very large projects it is generally usual to find specialist firms for piling, steelwork and high-class joinery.

It has been suggested that one-quarter to one-third of the work of the construction industry is minor in nature, being largely of repairs and maintenance. This work is often carried out by the smallest companies. A recent survey also indicated that one-third of the building firms in Britain do not employ any operatives, but the work is carried out by the partners of the firm. The larger companies may be represented by less than 100 firms throughout the country. In more recent years there has been a trend away from the multi-million pound project, resulting in a slight reduction in the number of these firms. Overseas projects of this size have helped to keep such firms viable within the UK. The reduction in the size of projects has also meant the breaking down of some of the larger firms into smaller-sized units working on a more localized basis.

The contractors under JCT 80 and the other forms of contract agree to carry out the works in accordance with the contract documents and the instructions from the architect. They agree to do this usually within a stipulated period of time and for an agreed amount of money. The main contractor must also comply with all statutory laws and regulations during the execution of the work, and ensure that all who are employed on the site abide by these conditions. The contractor will still be responsible contractually for any defects that may occur, for the period of time stipulated in the conditions of contract (normally 6 months). The responsibility, however, of the contractor for the project does not end here. In common law the rights of the employer will last for 6 years and 12 years respectively, depending upon whether the contract was under hand or seal.

The contractor is mentioned extensively in the conditions of contract, largely because, along with the employer, they are one of the parties to the contract. Some of the more important provisions are listed below.

1. Quality

- contractor's obligations
- compliance with architect's instructions
- duties in setting-out
- compliance with the standards described
- responsibility for faulty workmanship
- duty to keep on site a person-in-charge
- requirement for access for the architect to the site and workshops
- limitations on assignments and subletting
- right to object to nominated subcontractors
- duty to employer's directly employed contractors

2. Time

- procedure for partial possession
- necessity to proceed diligently with the works
- liabilities in the event of non-completion
- duty to inform the architect of any delays
- rights in cases of determination of the contract

3. Cost

- duty to ask for any loss or expense
- responsibility for payment to nominated subcontractors
- procedure for certificates and payments

4. Others

- liability for injuries to persons and property
- duties regarding insurances

Suppliers

Building materials delivered to a site may be described under one of three headings: materials, components and goods.

Materials are the raw materials to be used for building purposes and include, for example, cement, bricks, timber, plaster. The items included within this description will, in total, probably represent the largest expense on the traditional building site. As more and more of the construction processes are carried out off site, so the value of this section will diminish.

The second category of items, the components, represent those items delivered to site in almost 'kit' form. They may include joinery items such as door sets or joinery fittings to be assembled on site. The industrialized building process is based to a large extent on the assumption that many items can come to site in component form to be assembled very quickly for a very small amount of money.

The third section, described as goods, includes those items that are generally of a standard nature which can be purchased directly from a catalogue – for example, sanitary ware, ironmongery, electrical fittings.

The contractor's source of supply for these items may vary, but must in all circumstances comply with those specified in the contract documents, regarding quality and performance. The contractor will probably make extensive use of builders' merchants, because they stock a wide variety of items that can be purchased at short notice. Some of the items will need to be obtained directly from the manufacturer, and in other circumstances specialist local suppliers of timber or ready-mixed concrete will be used. Contractors are able to secure trade discounts for the items that they purchase, and such discounts will be increased either to attract trade or because of large orders. Some clients, who undertake extensive building work, are able to arrange with suppliers a bulk purchase agreement. This helps to reduce their own costs of construction because they are able to secure very reasonable rates for the items. The contractor must then obtain the appropriate items described from such suppliers.

The JCT Standard Form of Building Contract refers to two special types of suppliers, i.e. named suppliers and nominated suppliers. A named supplier is a firm specified in the contract documents from whom the contractor should obtain certain materials, components or goods. It is usual to suggest a list of alternative suppliers or sometimes to add the words 'other equal and approved'. The contractor would then need to show that the items proposed to be purchased for the work complied with those specified. In other circumstances a single supplier or manufacturer may be named, where the intention of the architect is not to diverge to any other alternative. This is often the case in respect of sanitary ware, where a particular design is selected, or for suspended ceilings and kitchen fittings.

In some situations the architect may choose to nominate a particular supplier to provide some of the various materials, components or goods. In these circumstances the architect chooses to include these items as a prime cost sum in the bills. The appropriate conditions of clause 36 then apply, and these are described in the context of that clause.

Subcontractors

It is very unusual today for a single contractor to undertake all the contract work with his own workforce. Even in the case of minor building projects the main contractor is likely to require the assistance of specialist trade firms. Work undertaken by firms other than the main contractor are often described as subcontractors, although in some situations it is not uncommon to find specialist firms working on the site beyond the normal jurisdiction and confines of the main contractor.

The employer may, for example, choose to employ such firms directly, and in this context these firms are not to be considered as subcontractors of the main contractor. Provision is made in the conditions of contract for such firms in order that they may have access to the contractor's site (clause 29). For example, a firm constructing a sculpture may come into the confines of this clause. Second, the employer may choose to nominate particular firms to undertake the specialist work that will be required. In these cases the employer may adopt this approach in order to gain a greater measure of control over those who carry out the work. These subcontractors enjoy a special relationship with the employer, as discussed in clause 35. Although after nomination they are often supposedly treated like one of the main contractor's own subcontractors, they do have some special rights, for example, in respect of their payment.

The architect may also choose to name subcontractors in the bills of quantities or specification, who will be acceptable for the execution of some of the measured work. This procedure avoids the lengthy process of nomination, but still provides a substantial measure of control on the part of the architect. Provisions are found within the conditions of contract, clause 19, and a requirement is to name at least three firms who will be acceptable to the architect. This provides for some measure of competition and allows the contractor a choice of firms. The contractor may also add to this list with the approval of the architect, and this should not unreasonably be refused.

All the remaining work is still unlikely to be carried out by the main contractor, and provision is also made for the use of the contractor's own subcontractors. These subcontractors are referred to in the conditions as the main contractor's domestic subcontractors (clause 19). Named subcontractors are employed to undertake that work (a) for which contractors makes no provision within their companies, or (b) when their own employed labour are busy elsewhere. The contractor must seek the approval of the architect in this respect, but it is unusual for this approval not to be given.

A further group of subcontractors are those described as statutory undertakers, e.g. gas, water, electricity. These are separately described for the following reasons: the employer and contractor often have no choice in employing them because of their statutory rights; they sometimes require payment in advance; and they refuse to give any cash discount for prompt payment.

The Intermediate Form of Contract identifies another type of subcontractor, known as the named subcontractor, who is akin to the nominated subcontractor. More about these is mentioned in Chapter 27 covering the IFC.

Direct labour

The public sector employer is a large client of the construction industry. They carry out work ranging from multi-million pound engineering projects to the repair and maintenance of local authority dwellings. Although there have been some discussions regarding a publicly owned national building corporation operating on a regional basis, this has not yet been developed and is not in practice. There are, however, the direct labour construction departments employed within the majority of borough and county councils. The expansion or contraction of all of these organizations is a politically sensitive issue and opinions regarding their efficiency and necessity will depend much on one's viewpoint. In some local authorities the direct labour departments may be responsible for no more than building and highway maintenance. In others they may be large enough to undertake major projects. They will generally only work within the confines of their geographical area, although they have been known to tender for other local authorities' building work. They do not work in the private sector, nor do they work for other publicly controlled organizations such as, for example, the health service. Where capital projects are envisaged they are usually required to tender for this work against private contractors. Maintenance work may be undertaken by the direct labour department as a matter of course, although even within this sphere of work some element of competition is now envisaged.

The building surveyor

Traditionally the building surveyor's role was in assisting other colleagues and clients with the maintenance and repair of buildings and preparing survey reports for the prospective purchasers and users of real estate. Building surveying is today a rapidly expanding profession. Some of this is due to the growing popularity of building conversion and renovation and the poor and deteriorating nature of our buildings stock. It is also due to some extent to the nature of our society with its make-do-and-mend approach and the desire for the conservation of older properties. As a profession it is somewhat unusual in being largely restricted to the United Kingdom and some of its ex-colonies at the present time. Building surveyors are, however, rarely concerned with projects of a large size, and are not specifically referred to in the forms of contract.

The peripheral professions

There is a wide range of other professions who are associated with the construction industry. One's viewpoint will determine whether these represent an unnecessary fragmentation of the industry or a desirable specialization. The clear demarcation of activities has now become blurred, particularly as we look forward towards the end of the century and consider the characteristics of the European community and the USA. Certainly the amount of knowledge which is now available and the skills which are required are too great for a single person to control and some specialization even within a conglomerate of the professions is essential. Figure 12.2 lists the major professional bodies which currently exist in the United Kingdom and the following list describes some of the other activities involved.

Building control officer – normally employed on behalf of the local authority to ensure that the building plans and proposals comply with the building regulations and by-laws made under the public health and building laws.

Estimator – responsible for calculating in advance of building, the cost of the project to a particular contractor based upon the total costs of all the labour, materials and plant that will be needed.

General practice surveyor – responsible for the acquisition of the building site for the owner or developer and negotiating with adjoining owners before, during and after construction and the disposal (sales or lettings) of the scheme upon completion.

Interior designer – developing the internal shell of buildings to provide good aesthetic and working conditions to create an acceptable ambience for the owner and user.

Landscape architect – helps to create the all-important context and space in which the building is set. Increasingly in modern buildings this often includes internal spaces.

Planner – involved with the legislative aspects of the building's location in interpreting the structure and district plans of local authorities. Ensures that the building fits into the environment.

The built environment professional bodies

Designing, costing, forecasting, planning, organizing, motivating, controlling and co-ordinating are some of the roles of the professions involved in managing construction, whether it be new build, refurbishment or maintenance. These activities also include research, development, innovation and improving standards and performance.

The Royal Institute of British Architects

The RIBA is the main professional body for architects in England and Wales. In Scotland, there is a similar body, the Royal Incorporation of Architects in Scotland (RIAS). Under the Architects Registration Act 1938 it continues to be illegal for anyone to carry out a business describing themselves as an architect unless they are registered with the Architects' Registration Council (ARCUK) established under an Act of 1931. Registration involves appropriate training and education as evidenced by the possession of qualifications set out in the Act or approved by the council. However, this does not prohibit anyone from carrying out architectural work such as the design of buildings.

The Royal Institution of Chartered Surveyors

The institution was formed in 1868 and incorporated by Royal Charter in 1881. It originated from the Surveyors' Institute and has grown as a result of a number of mergers with other institutes, most notably the Land Agents (1970) and the Institute of Quantity Surveyors (1982). The RICS is currently administered in seven divisions which represent the varying interests of different chartered surveyors. The General Practice (42 per cent) and Quantity Surveying (37 per cent) divisions account for over three-quarters of the membership.

The Institution of Civil Engineers

The term 'civil engineer' appeared for the first time in the minutes of the Society of Civil Engineers which was founded in 1771. It marked the recognition of a new profession in Britain as distinct from the much older profession of military engineer. The members of the Society of Civil Engineers were developing the technology of the Industrial Revolution. The Royal Charter of the institution contains the often quoted definition of civil engineering as being 'the art of directing the great sources of power in nature for use and convenience of mankind'.

The Institution of Structural Engineers

The Institution of Structural Engineers began its life as the Concrete Institute in 1908, was renamed in 1922 and was incorporated by Royal Charter in 1934. Its aims include promoting the science and art of structural engineering in all its forms and furthering the education, training and competencies of its members. The science of structural engineering is the technical justification in terms of strength, safety, durability and serviceability of buildings and other structures.

The Chartered Institution of Building Services Engineers

The grant of a Royal Charter in 1976 enabled the Institution of Heating and Ventilating Engineers which was founded in 1897 to amalgamate with the Illuminating Engineering Society of 1909 to create an institution embracing the whole sphere of building services engineering. The objectives of CIBSE are set out in their charter as the promotion of the art, science and practice of building services engineering for the benefit of all, and the advancement of education and research in this area of work.

The Chartered Institute of Building

The CIOB was formed in 1834, incorporated under the Companies Acts in 1984 and granted a Royal Charter in 1980. It originally started as the Builders' Society, which was a small exclusive club which had a wide influence and was responsible for helping to produce the early forms of contract. The objectives of the institute are the promotion, for public benefit, the science and practice of building, the advancement of education and science including research, and the establishment and maintenance of appropriate standards of competence and conduct for those engaged in building. The institute encourages the professional manager and technologist to work together with their technician counterparts in order to achieve a ladder of opportunity as a main objective of the training and examination structure of the institute.

Chartered body membership

A proportion of members in the construction professions hold membership of more than one institution. Several members of the profession are also represented in other professional bodies which are more broadly based than construction alone. For example, a large proportion of the Chartered Institute of Arbitrators (CIArb) are members of the construction professions, whereas in the British Institute of Management (BIM) membership includes only a small proportion of those connected with the construction industry. Figure 12.2 lists the main professional bodies in the construction industry and their relative sizes.

Non-chartered bodies

There are also a number of non-chartered professional bodies with memberships ranging from as few as 1,000 to nearly 10,000. These include the Institution of Surveyors, Valuers and Auctioneers (ISVA), the British Institute of Architectural Technicians (BIAT), the Association of Building Engineers (ABE), the Institution of Civil Engineering Surveyors (ICES) and Institute of Building Control Officers (IBCO). Some have been developed in association with institutions from other countries such as the Association of

	Total numbers	Per cent Chartered	Percentage share
Royal Institution of Chartered Surveyors	87,000	75	32
Institution of Civil Engineers	76,000	65	27
Chartered Institute of Building	32,000	32	11
Royal Institute of British Architects	31,000	92	11
Institution of Structural Engineers	22,000	56	8
Royal Town Planning Institute	17,000	76	6
Chartered Institute of Building Services Engineers	15,000	58	5
			100

Fig. 12.2 Chartered professional bodies in the construction industry

Cost Engineers which has strong links in the USA. Others are as a result of the changing needs and emphasis of the construction industry, with professional bodies such as the Association of Project Managers.

Europe and the USA

There are wide cultural considerations to be taken into account in any comparison between the construction industry professions in Britain with those in other parts of the world, notably, Europe, the USA and Japan. Historically, the industry and practice developed differently. In much of the rest of the world, architects and engineers dominate the construction industry. The ratio between building and civil engineering works in other countries is similar, at about 80: 20. The various professional disciplines in Britain are not mirrored elsewhere, other than in Commonwealth and ex-Commonwealth countries. The role of the professional bodies also varies. In Britain a professional qualification is one by which to practise. In Europe a professional body is more of an exclusive club, of which relatively few of those engaged in practice are members. In the USA there is the emerging discipline of construction management alongside those of architect and engineer. In Britain the architect is the only registered profession and this is also the case on mainland Europe. But its practice in Europe is more controlled. An architect, for example, must be employed to sign the plans in Europe, otherwise a building cannot be constructed.

Professional liability

The subject of professional liability is something that only a few years ago was a subject of little interest. They were the days when the relationship between client and consultant was characterized by trust and confidence. From the 1970s onwards much occurred which eroded that trust, replacing it with conflict, uncertainty, risk and the possibility of litigation arising at some point. Also several other events have taken place to accelerate these issues, such as the NEDO building users insurance against latent defects report (1988), the Department of Trade and Industry and the Department of the Environment review of professional liability (1987), the harmonization initiative launched by the Directorate General III of the European Commission, and action by the Construction Industry Council (CIC) in response to these initiatives. The liability for professional negligence has been well reported. Architects and engineers have already been required to make substantial payments for design faults or inadequate supervision and surveyors have in the past been sued for negligent building surveys.

Construction Industry Council

The Construction Industry Council represents the construction industry professions. Membership includes the seven major chartered bodies (CIOB, CIBSE, ICE, IStructE, RIBA, RICS and the RTPI), business organizations which represent some of these professions and a number of the non-chartered bodies. Their objectives cover the following areas:

- membership of CIC by all professional bodies in construction;
- generate effective relationships with employer organizations, trade associations and others;
- oversee standards development and co-ordinate NVQs relevant to members;
- promote the integration of compatible areas of professional education and training;
- broaden the income base of CIC;
- raise the profile, and increase understanding, of the construction industry;
- promote continuing professional development;
- promote more extensive research and development;
- encourage improved industry practices and procedures and reduce duplication;
- represent members' interests to government;
- co-ordinate and develop members' interests in Europe;
- collect and disseminate information.

Construction employers' associations

The construction industry has typically been seen as two sectors, building and civil engineering. This distinction is also seen at employer level with the separate Building Employers' Confederation (BEC) and the Federation of Civil Engineering Contractors (FCEC). A third group, the Export Group for the Constructional Industries, includes those contractors with extensive overseas interests. These organizations seek to represent the contractors' interests at national level and to influence government policy for the benefit of their members. Most of the largest 20 firms belong to all three organizations. The BEC has a membership of 8,000; this was over 10,000 prior to the recession of the early 1990s. The number of firms in FCEC is much smaller at 300 (700 previously), although the typical size of firm is much larger. In addition, there are other subsidiary groupings of firms such as the House Builders Federation. Many of the activities which are undertaken by the different organizations are replicated and add to the costs of administration. There has also, in recent years, been an increased level of co-operation between the different bodies on matters such as European harmonization and health and safety. These activities are seen as steps towards an eventual merger representing all firms with subsidiary committees for special interest groups. Many of the contractors believe that the construction industry's poor image, educational framework, lobbying strength and relationships with clients and the professions will be improved only through such a united single voice.

The National Contractors Group (NCG)

The NCG is one of the five sectors of the Building Employers' Confederation. This group comprises the largest companies who are in membership with BEC, and includes about 75 firms. The group has its own code of practice to ensure high standards of reliability and efficiency. Its members must amongst other things:

- develop and maintain the good name of the member firm by conducting its business affairs with integrity;
- carry out work with proper consideration for and minimum disturbance to the general public;
- observe recognized standards of good tendering practice;
- use every endeavour within the limits of the contract conditions to:
    - complete contracts on time and within cost limits,
    - fulfil all their obligations under the contract,
    - help to promote the clients understanding of the contract;
- co-operate with and form good relations with the client's consultants;
- observe the National Working Rule Agreement and support the National Joint Council for the Building Industry;
- act in accordance with good business practice when dealing with other contractors and subcontractors;
- maintain good industrial relations;
- have proper regard for recognized standards of safety and welfare and set an example in accident prevention;
- keep pace with technology and the development of modern techniques and methods;
- provide adequate training and the development of employees to ensure the provision of skills and expertise to meet the needs of a progressive construction industry;
- keep the public informed of the nature of the contracting operations.

Within all organizations there are tensions, particularly where a group do not believe that they receive adequate representation. As the major 20–25 firms have grown the issues which they feel need to be addressed are now different from the other firms. Their focus is towards the international business environment.

Construction Industry Training Board

The Construction Industry Training Board (CITB) was established by an Act of Parliament in 1964 to improve the quality of training, improve the facilities available for training and help to provide enough trained people for the construction industry. It is partially funded through government, but most of its income is derived from a levy system on contractors based upon the number of their employees. In addition to being appointed as the primary managing agent for the construction industry's Youth Training Scheme, the CITB also provides for a range of skills training at its national training centres. Whilst the emphasis of its activities are on practical craft skills training it also offers courses in supervisory management.

Construction Industry Standing Conference

The Construction Industry Standing Conference (CISC) was established in 1990 to produce a framework of qualifications for the NVQ accreditation covering technical, professional and the managerial occupations within the construction industry. CISC's membership is drawn from the chartered and non-chartered professional bodies, the awarding bodies such as the BTEC, employer, business and trade organizations. There are strong links with further and higher education. An early task of the CISC was to prepare an occupational map of the construction industry in order to identify the tasks and responsibilities performed by the different professional disciplines. This was published in 1991. The second objective was to develop standards by analysing the different job roles into elements of competence. These are grouped into units and will form the basis of the NVQs. It is intended to prepare instruments for assessing the standards for accreditation purposes and finally a strategy for implementing and maintaining the NVQ system. The merits of this approach are:

- development by the industry
- nationally agreed
- relevant
- accessible
- transferable

Chapter 13

Site communications

Introduction

The construction of buildings and engineering structures utilizes a range of different resources such as men, machines, money, materials, mechanical plant, management and methods. It seeks to combine these together in the most effective, efficient and economic manner.

The construction industry is a unique industry. It is one of the few industries that separate design from production, although this has now changed with the proliferation of design and build projects. It also undertakes the bulk of its work on the client's premises. The industry does not build replicas and whilst projects may appear to be similar they are different in certain respects. Even comparable housing units on an estate will differ in their location, levels, amount of work below ground level, plot size and hence the external works that are required.

Site managers do not move materials, operate plant or carry out the physical production function. Site management organizes, informs, co-ordinates, orders, instructs and motivates others to undertake these tasks. The effectiveness of performance will depend upon the ability to listen, read, speak and write. More importantly, effectiveness will be evident in being understood by others and to understand another person's point of view.

Site communications therefore includes gathering information to ascertain the needs of those involved with the project, as a necessary tool of management to integrate the functions of departments and as a vital link between manager and subordinate in order to get the job completed.

Communication principles

Communication is a key to success in this work and the social interactions involved. Communication skills and strategies are necessary to share ideas and experiences, to find out about things and to explain to others what you want. Developing ways of communicating including language and body signals is essential in expressing feelings and insights. Learning to communicate effectively may mean the difference between barely coping with life as you know it and actively shaping your world as you would like it to be. Some of the components of good communications are:

- Know what to say
- Gain the attention of the listener
- Establish and maintain relationships
- Know the listener's likes and interests
- Choose how to communicate from a range of options
- Skilful in communicating
- Choose when and where to communicate
- Clear, brief and coherent
- Active listening
- Understand and clarify messages they received
- Not easily distracted
- Know how to close conversation or communication

Effective communication starts with a purpose or objective to achieve in transferring the information. This should be done in the most suitable form to suit the receiver. It also needs to be the most effective way. Provision should also be allowed for feedback and the need for action on that feedback appreciated. The points that should be present in all communications are:

- Clarity, i.e. easily understood.
- Presentable, i.e. creating a favourable impression.
- New information, i.e. attracting interest.
- Drive, i.e. demanding the necessary action.
- Tone, i.e. creating a responsive attitude.
- Feedback, i.e. ensuring that the transfer of information is achieved.

Forms of communication

There are three basic methods of communication.

Written. Taking the form of letters, reports, bills of quantities, specifications, site instructions, British Standards. This method is used when the subject matter is complex, important or likely to have possible legal implications and where a permanent record is required for future reference.

Visual. This can take the form of films, slides, posters, graphs, charts. It includes the project drawings and works programmes. This sort of communication often has a greater impact upon the receiver. Where messages are less complex, this form of communication is the most effective.

Oral. This method is instant and often generates an immediate response. Attitudes and behaviour can also be observed. The face-to-face confrontation is appropriate when the subject matter may be difficult or disagreeable. It is also used in those circumstances for simple, less important and informal messages.

Barriers to communication

An organization that is suffering from poor morale or lacks confidence in its future is likely to see problems in communications increase. In these circumstances there is sometimes a lack of will to communicate effectively. However, nearly all barriers to good communication can be classified as follows:

Physical.   These might include disability on the part of the receiver such as deafness or blindness. It might include noise on site, poor telephone lines and layers of site management. These can sometimes have the effect of distortion and inaccuracy in the information that is being transmitted.

Psychological.   This is the biggest cause of communication breakdown. It affects the attitudes, feelings and emotions of the receiver. Sometimes, individuals will only hear what they expect to hear. Preconceived ideas are used to interpret the information, in ways not anticipated by the giver of the information. Feelings and emotions affect the ability to receive a true message. When worried the receiver feels threatened. When angry the information may be simply rejected.

Intellectual.   These affect concepts and perceptions that may have been built up over a lifetime of work. Difficulties may arise because the information was not transmitted properly in the first place. It may use excessive technical jargon or attempt to use words that are out of context.

Site information

In addition to the everyday running and organizing of a contract, it is also the site foreman's responsibility to maintain accurate records of the important happenings on site. This information should be properly recorded, so that whenever necessary it can be quickly retrieved for future use. The types of site records normally kept include:
- daily reports
- site diaries
- materials received sheets
- advice of variations
- daily labour allocation sheets
- drawing registers
- confirmation of verbal instructions
- weather reports
- daywork records
- subcontractor files
- site correspondence

If this information is to be valuable for future reference it must be characterized by being:

- Precise: it should be clear, straightforward, as simple as possible and well thought out.
- Accurate: true and correct in all of its details.
- Definite: future users should be left in no doubt as to what the message means.
- Relevant: to the particular situation and the people who will use it.
- Referenced: wherever possible the information should be linked to other documents being used by the contractor.

Site meetings

Site meetings are held for a variety of different purposes. They may be held with the contractor's staff only to establish how the works should be carried out or to deal with an internal matter that has arisen in connection with the project. They frequently involve other parties such as subcontractors and suppliers. The general site meeting would usually involve the client, architect, quantity surveyor, other consultants, subcontractors, clerk of works as well as the main contractor. These meetings frequently take place on a monthly basis, depending upon the size of the project and the issues that may need to be resolved. The site meeting is a vehicle to pass information from one party to another or for consultation purposes of how to tackle a problem that has arisen. The normal site meeting is also used for decision-making purposes and it may be used to try to persuade the parties involved of a different way of solving a particular problem. In essence it is, 'What do we need to know?' 'How are we getting on?' and 'What's wrong and how can this be corrected?' Information on meetings preparation is listed below:

- Determine meeting's objectives
- Attendance list
- Decide on the time and place
- Determine its style
- Circulate agenda and other information
- Identify if special facilities are required (e.g. audio/visual)
- Rank and set times for each item
- Assess possible areas of conflict
- Pre-discuss items with individuals where necessary
- Determine sorts of minutes that are required
- Adequately brief participants
- Other matters: refreshments, car parking, etc.

Frequently, the architect will chair the site meeting and prepare an agenda, often in consultation with the contractor. The agenda will follow the format of a business meeting, with apologies for absence, matters arising from the previous minutes, any other business and the date and place of the next meeting. In addition, items of a routine nature, such as the main contractor's report and special items that address current issues, will also be included.

The minutes of the meeting are the follow-up and as such are vital to the effectiveness of the meeting. The minutes ensure the collective views of the meeting. They should also identify the areas where responsibility for further action lies. They may include an action plan in order to minimize future problems or difficulties that might be encountered. Points to remember that should help meetings to flow more easily and become more productive:

- Prepare an agenda and establish rules of procedure
- Start promptly and use brevity
- Listen actively; practise this skill, it leads to good questions, improves group understanding, keeps meetings good humoured
- Give direct replies; keep the meeting to the point to avoid wasting time
- Clarify issues: 'Are you suggesting that you provide this material by the end of the month?'
- Summarize progress
- Restate important points
- Be prepared to change strategy if necessary
- Be supportive: 'That sounds like good idea'
- Confront issues: Are we really prepared to ...'
- Question critically; 'What exactly do you mean?'
- Provide accurate supporting information
- Do not allow the meeting to be interrupted by telephone calls, etc.
- Avoid interrupting
- Do not be afraid to make your feelings known
- Refrain from distracting behaviour
- Do not talk to others during presentations
- Never lose your temper, except deliberately
- Do not embarrass others

Site diaries

The site dairy if well maintained with the correct sort of information is a very useful document retained by the contractor. It will contain information that can be used where disputes occur between the different parties concerned with the project. They have been used in litigation as valuable evidence to help substantiate a case put forward by the contractors. The diary should record information that generally does not warrant separate records being kept. This will vary with the size and type of project, the nature of the client and the information records kept by the contractor. Figure 13.1 provides a typical form that can be used for this purpose.

Weather conditions.   These will have a major influence upon the progress of the works. They must therefore be recorded, especially where they cause a delay or suspension of the works.

Details:	Date:
1. Weather conditions	Temperature
2. Drawings received	Number
3. Instructions: oral/written	Given by
4. Variation orders received	Number
5. Dayworks: reasons/descriptions	Sheet numbers
6. Delays: reasons	Labour on-site required
7. Lost time: reasons	
8. Urgent requirements	Visitors to site
9. Unusual occurrences	

Fig. 13.1 Site diary (source: adapted from W.H. Davies, *Construction Site Studies 4*, Butterworth, 1982)

Drawings received. The site manager must ensure that there is an adequate system for the receipt and recording of architect's and engineer's drawings. Although there will be a drawing register, the site diary should also record when this information is received. There will also be times when information will be requested from the consultants. This should always be in writing giving sufficient notice to avoid the possibility of delays. The late receipt of information is one of the reasons available for an extension of time under JCT 80 (clause 25.4.6) where this is considered to be a relevant event. In addition if the delay in the receipt of such information causes the works to be suspended for longer than the period named in the Appendix, usually 3 months, then the contractor may determine the contract (clause 28.3.5). The contractor in each case must have requested further instructions and drawings and the date for the period of delay will commence from that date.

Architect's instructions. During the visit to the site by the architect, and more frequently through the clerk of works, instructions will be given both orally and in writing. These need to be recorded in the site diary under the heading of site instructions. It needs to be remembered that in order to be valid, all instructions must eventually be in writing (clause 4.3.1). The JCT form also lays down procedures to be followed in the case of dealing with oral instructions (clause 4.3.2) (see also p. 269). The site manager therefore needs to record precisely when the instruction was given.

Variation orders (VOs). These are a special type of architect's instruction since they may alter or modify the design, quality or quantity works shown on the drawings and in the bills (clause 13.11). A variation may also alter the conditions under which the work is to be carried out. In many other respects VOs are similar to those of other architect's instructions (see also p. 202).

Dayworks. Clause 13.5.4 defines daywork as 'work which cannot be properly valued by measurement.' The site manager should record in the site diary reasons why some of the work should be paid for on this basis. Prior to arriving at this decision the contractor's own quantity surveyor should also be consulted for an opinion. Where dayworks are envisaged then the architect should be informed in order that the clerk of works can carry out the necessary checks on the labour and materials used on such work. The inclusion of large numbers of dayworks in the site manager's diary may lead towards the conclusion that the nature of the project has changed from that which was originally tendered.

Delay. The contractor will have prepared a master programme for the project (clause 5.3) for use both by the contractor and the architect. The contractual implications of this are slightly different under the ICE Conditions of Contract, nevertheless the architect should have assessed its appropriateness. The programme will indicate how the contractor intends to carry out and complete the works. It also assists the architect on the dates when the contractor requires the various pieces of information. The programme provides the contractor with the best indication that the works are being constructed as planned, when progress is measured against it. Where the progress shown is different then the reasons for such variation will need to be established.

Lost time. A record of any delays will be made in the site diary at the time that they actually occur. This will be the most accurate record of these events. Where the delays are due to factors that the contractor should have controlled, these will need to be remedied at the contractor's own expense. This will then avoid liquidated damages being applied for late completion.

Urgent requirements. The site diary will also be used to remind the site manager of any urgent requirements. These may include a note, in advance, of items that are expected for delivery or action on a certain date. This information can be included in the following manner:
- Sanitary fittings for delivery next Tuesday; storage provision required.
- Latest date for forwarding design details of external screens, since the manufacturer requires 6 weeks prior to delivery.

- Inform refuse chute subcontractor when they will be required on site. They require 3 weeks' notice.

Unusual occurrences. Any unusual happening on the site will need to be recorded for possible future reference by the contractor. Disputes may occur between the parties concerned and it is important to establish as soon as possible the reasons why such disputes have arisen. The following are typical examples:

- Local stoppage on site for 2 hours due to a disagreement over bonus payments.
- Mr R. Taylor fractured his ankle. An accident report has been completed.
- Intruders entered the site last evening. No damage or theft occurred. Police have been informed.
- Raining-in below patent glazing. Architect and subcontractor have been informed.

Labour records. The site manager will need to keep a careful record of both labour that was required and that employed on site.

Visitors to the site. Visitors should always be recorded especially those who might have a direct impact upon the work. The diary record may show:

The architect visited the site at 10.00 am. A tour was made with the site manager and clerk of works. Satisfaction with the quality and progress of the works was noted.

The contractor cannot refuse reasonable entry to the site for the architect or representatives (clause 11). The building owner owns the site and is therefore allowed access. This must be done to cause as little inconvenience to the contractor as possible. Building control officers, health and safety inspectors and similar officials have a legal entry to the site at any reasonable time.

Recording of information

If the site diary is to be of any value then it is important that the events are entered each day in a logical, careful and legible manner. The information will thus provide an accurate assessment of the site's daily progress together with the labour and plant that have been used. Any matters that affect the following must be regularly and accurately recorded:

- completion date
- costs
- quality and standards of work
- contractor's performance

The site diary must be completed daily in order that the salient points are not forgotten for ever. The completion of the task will require some self-discipline on the part of the site manager, particularly when other aspects of work are requiring attention. The information should be accurate and represent a fair picture of the day's events. Exaggerated information or hearsay remarks should not be included. Where proper and adequate records are not maintained then the contractor may suffer because of:

- a loss of reputation of a well-run organization;
- having liquidated damages imposed through late completion of the works;
- being refused additional payments for losses incurred;
- having the contract unfairly terminated due to client dissatisfaction;
- being levied with further damages to redress the client's loss.

Planning, programming and progressing

A programme or schedule is developed by breaking down the work involved in a construction project into a series of operations which are then shown in an ordered stage by stage representation. Without a programme of work which specifies the time and resources allocation in order to undertake each stage of the project, the execution of the contract will be haphazard and disordered. There are several different methods that may be used for this purpose, such as bar charts (sometimes referred to as the Gantt chart) or network analysis (critical path analysis). A detailed description of these methods is outside of the scope of this book. The bar chart is perhaps the best known of all the planning techniques. In its simplest form the sequential relationships between activities are not completely prescribed. However, they can be linked to show the relationship between an activity and the preceding and succeeding ones. Thus, dependency between the activities highlights the effect of delays. The resources required can also be calculated.

The linkage between preceding and succeeding activities combined with a set of arrows to represent the bars of the bar chart gave rise to a simple network diagram. This forms the basis of a network analysis, which identifies the longest irreducible sequence of events. It also defines quickly those parts of the programme which could benefit from the use of increased resources and thereby benefit the project. As networks are rarely the best method for communication, the output of the analysis is often presented as a bar chart. Network analysis has been used for many large and complex projects. It is claimed that up to a 40 per cent reduction in time has been achieved by its use.

Resources

The time taken to complete an activity in the programme is dependent on the resources allocated to that activity. The approaches used in assessing the required resources can be based on completing the project in a given time or completing the project with specified limited resources. Once the level of resourcing has been finalized, the overall resource demands are smoothed if necessary by rescheduling activities to ensure an acceptable overall demand for the project.

There is a measure of uncertainty in estimating the time for each activity particularly as delays in delivery of materials and adverse weather can delay work in progress. Probabilistic distributions have been used for the generation of the most likely times for activities. An approach that was used in early projects was the project evaluation and review technique (PERT). The flexibility of the contractor's workforce has changed in recent years. Previously a contractor, using its own workforce, would operate a number of sites in an area. There were thus ample opportunities for transferring workpeople between the different sites. However, the widespread use of labour-only subcontracting has to some extent curtailed this opportunity. This has reduced the adaptability of day-to-day site management resulting in a greater measure of pre-site planning. Also the construction industry, when compared with manufacturing, remains a labour-intensive industry. The widespread use of plant and machinery on site is perhaps less developed than it ought to be.

Monitoring and control

With a programme of work and the resource requirements for each activity having been determined, it is possible to monitor the construction work as it progresses. In practice, updating will take place and control will be exercised. This will involve the rescheduling of activities and the revision of resources. The planning model is often used to explore the overall development of the project before work on site is undertaken. This assists in investigating the influence of different construction techniques and the timing of the individual activities to better optimize the use of resources.

Ensuring that the works are constructed to the specified level of quality is essential. This extends from the initial setting out of the project to the inspection, storage, handling and incorporation of the specified materials within the finished building. All site operations must be governed by appropriate safety measures which start with a safe design and erection procedures for permanent and temporary works. The construction industry remains one of the largest single contributors to fatal accidents (see p. 140).

Planning into practice

The construction industry is usually involved on one-off projects; these are invariably managed with a new team. As the location of each project varies widely, the workforce is largely new and the conditions under which the project is undertaken can differ depending on the site conditions, climate etc. Unlike manufacturing industry, the approach to a project is rarely uniform. The size of the main contractor's site organization, which is comprised of technical and non-technical staff, often depends on the size of the works. However, as the use

Cause of hold-up and delay	Case studies % projects
Subcontracting	49
Tenant/client variations	45
Ground problems – water, rock, etc.	37
Bad weather	27
Materials delivery	25
Sewer/drains obstruction or rerouteing	20
Information late	20
Poor site management and supervision	18
Steel strike	16
Statutory undertakers	14
Labour shortage	10
Design complexity	6

Fig. 13.2   Delays in industrial buildings (source: *Faster Building for Industry*, NEDO, 1983)

of subcontractors has become more widespread, the main contractor's team has reduced in size.

The work can be carried out efficiently if the site is laid out in such a way that the temporary buildings, for example offices, stores and workshops, are conveniently located with respect to the permanent works. This results in an orderly arrangement which facilitates the economy of construction and administration. The construction of a high-rise building on a confined city-centre site, for example, requires the efficient storage of materials, off-peak deliveries, high-speed vertical travel with site facilities placed to minimize operative travel.

Figure 13.2 indicates some of the reasons for the delays that occurred in the construction of industrial buildings together with the frequency of their occurrence. The influence of these delays on the total site time varies. For example, ground problems or bad weather occurred on sites which achieved both fast and slow site times, suggesting that there was less overall effect. However, poor site management and supervision, late information and deliveries, design complexities, difficulties with statutory undertakers and labour shortages were usually associated with construction overruns of 2 months or more. These factors were judged to be the most damaging to the more effective organization of the construction process.

Part 4

Standard Form of Building Contract

Chapter 14

Introduction, Articles of Agreement and the Appendix

Introduction

The Standard Form of Building Contract is known throughout the industry as JCT 80. It replaced the previous form of 1963. Since 1980 there have been fourteen amendments with a fifteenth proposed on the conclusiveness of the final certificate. These have been listed in Chapter 6. Some of these deal with a single change to a particular clause whereas others deal with a multiplicity of amendments. The content of the JCT 80 form is as follows:

    Articles of Agreement.
    Conditions – Part 1. General clauses.
                 Part 2. Nominated subcontractors and nominated suppliers.
                 Part 3. Fluctuations.
                 Part 4. Arbitration.

The principle of the form is that it is an entire contract which is modified by a number of its own provisions. Separate editions are available for private clients and local authority clients. The differences between the two are, however, minimal. Financially it is a lump-sum contract using three variants of with quantities, without quantities, or with approximate quantities. The two parties involved are the employer (client) and the contractor. The employer is responsible for making payments to the contractor, who in turn has obligations to complete the works in accordance with the contract provisions. Neither the architect nor the quantity surveyor are parties to the contract. The former acts on behalf of the employer but sometimes in an impartial way. The quantity surveyor accounts for the financial transactions.

Articles of Agreement

The Articles of Agreement precede the Conditions of Contract, and include the information that is specific to a particular contract. They define the various persons referred to in the contract, and also describe the procedure to be followed in the case of arbitration. The following information therefore needs to be written into the Articles of Agreement:

1. *The date.* This is the date when the agreement is made. It is not the date of tender, which may have some significance in respect of fluctuation contracts; nor is it the date when the project will start on site. This date is defined in the Appendix to the form of contract, as the date of possession and included in clause 1. The date in the Articles of Agreement will therefore have little significance as far as the contract is concerned.

2. *The parties.* The contract is between the employer and the contractor, and their names and addresses must be inserted in the Articles of Agreement. These names are used consistently throughout the Conditions of Contract.

3. *The works.* The employer requires the contractor to complete the works in accordance with the drawings and bills of quantities. The works are essentially the building project, but by implication in the Conditions of Contract may also mean the site. A description of the project and its location (address) should be given. The contractor is given possession of the site on the date of possession as stated in clause 23 and detailed in the Appendix.

4. *The drawings and bills of quantities.* These, together with the form of contract, constitute the contract documents. They are defined in clause 1 and discussed in clause 2 of the Conditions of Contract. The contract drawings are formally registered by their numbers and should be signed by both parties. The contract bills, which are a priced copy of the bills of quantities, are also to be signed by the parties.

5. *The architect* (article 3). The drawings and bills of quantities are prepared under the direction of the pre-contract architect. It emphasizes that the design is the responsibility of the architect and not the contractor. On some contracts the designer may not be the person who supervises the work on site. The architect referred to in the conditions comes within this latter definition. In the event of the architect's death, or when no longer fulfilling this function, the employer must nominate a replacement architect. If the contractor has a reasonable objection, then the employer must appoint an architect with whom the contractor approves. Such an appointee must not revoke decisions already acted upon by the contractors. The new architect can of course, ask the contractor to rebuild part of the completed works, but if these have previously been accepted then the contractor is entitled to an appropriate payment. In some cases the supervisor of the works may not be an architect within the definition of the Architects' Registration Act 1938. In this case the term 'supervising officer' is used to refer, perhaps, to an engineer or surveyor.

In the local authorities version the term 'architect' has been substituted by architect/contract administrator. This reflects the view held by some, that some contractual matters are probably better dealt with by someone other than the architect.

6. *The quantity surveyor* (article 4). This refers to the client's quantity surveyor. In the event of death, or when replaced by the architect, this must be done with the approval of the contractor. Any objection by the contractor must be sufficient to invoke the appointment of the arbitrator.

7. *The contract sum* (article 2). The employer's main obligation is towards the payment of the contractor for the work executed. The total amount is described as the contract sum (clause 14) and this will be paid by instalment (clause 30). Although this sum is agreed upon by the two parties, it will be subject to adjustment within the terms of the contract (clause 30) as the project progresses.

8. *The employer.* The status of the employer for the purpose of the statutory tax deduction scheme must be stated in the Appendix. This refers to clause 31 and generally to labour-only subcontractors.

9. *Contractor's obligations* (article 1). The contractor's obligations under the terms of the agreement are to carry out and complete the works in accordance with the contract documents. These obligations are further reinforced in clause 2 of the conditions.

10. *The planning supervisor.* This is the person, either the architect or other person, appointed as a result of regulation 6(5) of the CDM Regulations.

11. *The principal contractor.* This refers to the main contractor in pursuant of regulation 6(5) of the CDM Regulations.

Settlement of disputes -- arbitration (article 5)

Where disputes or differences of opinion occur between the employer (or architect) and the contractor, the parties agree to attempt to settle the matter first of all through arbitration. Arbitration is described in the Arbitration Act of 1979. Article 5 constitutes an arbitration agreement under the said Act. Disputes that may be referred to arbitration can arise both during and after construction or should the works be abandoned. Arbitration is now covered in clause 41 and the JCT Arbitration Agreement. Disputes may occur for a variety of reasons. The following instances will not generally be referred to arbitration:

(a) differences in the interpretation of the statutory tax deduction scheme – the appropriate Act may direct some alternative method of resolving such a dispute;

(b) disagreements regarding the possibility of exemption of the VAT agreement.

The reason why the above matters are not referred to arbitration is largely due to the statutory powers and responsibilities of the various government departments. The interpretation of the various Acts is therefore largely their own prerogative.

	Clauses etc.	
Statutory tax decustion scheme – Finance (No. 2) Act 1975	Fourth recital and 31	Employer at Base Date *is a 'contractor'/is not a 'contractor' for the purposes of the Act and the Regulations
Base Date	1.3	
Date for Completion	1.3	
VAT Agreement	15.2	Clasue 1A of the VAT Agreement *applies/does not apply [k.1]
Defects Liability Period (if none other stated is 6 months from the day named in the Certificate of Practical Completion of the Works)	17.2	
Assignment by Employer of benefits after Practical Completion	19.1.2	Clause 19.1.2 *applies/does not apply
Insurance cover for any one occurrence or series of occur-rences arising out of one event	21.1.1	£ _____
Insurance – liability of Employer	21.2.1	Insurance *may be required/is not required Amount of indemnity for any one occurrence or series of occurrences arising out of one event £ _____ [y.1]
Insurance of the Works – alternative clauses	22.1	*Clause 22A/Clause 22B/Clause 22C applies (See Footnote [m] to clause 22)
Percentage to cover professional fees	*22A 22B.1 22C.2	
Annual renewal date of insurance as supplied by Contractor	22A.3.1	

Footnotes

* Delete as applicable

[k.1] Clause 1A can only apply where the Contractor is satisfied at the date the Contract is entered into that his output tax on all supplies to the Employer under the Contract will be at either a positive or a zero rate of tax.

On and from 1 April 1989 the supply in respect of a building designed for a 'relevant charitable purpose' (as defined in the legislation which gives

statutory effect to the VAT changes operative from 1 April 1989) is only zero rated if the person to whom the supply is made has given to the Contractor a certificate in statutory form: see the VAT leaflet 708 revised 1989. Where a contract supply is zero rated by the certificate only the person holding the certificate (usually the Contractor) may zero rate his supply.

This footnote repeats footnote [k.1] for clause 15.2.

[y.1] If the indemnity is to be for an aggregate amount and not for any one occurrence or series of

Fig. 14.1 Appendix to the Form of Contract

Insurance for Employer's loss of liquidated damages – clause 25.4.3	22D	Insurance *may be required/is not required
	22D.2	Period of time
		_____
Date of Possession	23.1.1	_____
Deferment of the Date of Possession	23.1.2 25.4.13 26.1	Clause 23.1.2 *applies/does not apply
		Period of deferment if it is to be less than 6 weeks is
		_____
Liquidated and ascertained damages	24.2	at the rate of
		£ _____ per _____
Period of suspension (if none stated is 1 month)	28.2.2	_____
Period of delay (if none stated is, in respect of clauses 28A.1.1.1 to 28A.1.1.3, 3 months, and, in respect of clauses 28A.1.1.4 to 28A.1.1.6, 1 month)	28A.1.1.1 to 28.1.1.3 28A.1.1.4 to 28A.1.1.6	_____ _____
Period of interim Certificates (if none stated is 1 month)	30.1.3	_____
Retention Percentage (if less than 5 per cent) [aa]	30.4.1.1	_____
Work reserved for Nominated Sub-Contractors for which the Contractor desires to tender	35.2	_____
Fluctuations: (if alternative required is not shown clause 38 shall apply)	37	clause 38 [cc] clause 39 clause 40
Percentage addition	38.7 or 39.8	_____
Formula Rules	40.1.1.1	
	rule 3	Base Month
		_____ 19 _____
	rules 10 and 30(i)	Part I/Part II [dd] of Section 2 of the Formula Rules is to apply

Attestation

The attestation page is for the parties to sign the contract and for the signatures to be witnessed. The signatories must have the necessary authority to sign for this purpose to provide validity to the contract. The contract may be executed under seal or under hand, and the Limitation Act of 1963 states that actions become barred after 12 years and 6 years, respectively. The current ruling suggests that the cause of action begins to accrue when the damage is discovered, or when it should reasonably have been discovered. The actual time of discovery may therefore not be relevant. There is no contract between the parties until the Articles of Agreement have been executed, unless the facts show otherwise. The carrying out of work prior to contract may indicate an intention on both parties, and therefore, if the project does not proceed, a claim for *quantum meruit* may result.

The Appendix

The Appendix (see Fig. 14.1) provides a considerable amount of information about the contract that is of particular importance to the project. The purpose is to set out in one place a schedule of these details. The completion of the Appendix is necessary to give the conditions their full meaning. Each subject listed in the Appendix is discussed in detail under the clause concerned. There are, however, some differences in principle between the treatment of items in the Appendix. Some items will always need to be completed to make sense, whereas others can be left blank. In other circumstances the Appendix makes a recommendation, and unless anything is entered to the contrary this suggestion will apply.

Chapter 15

Quality of work during construction

The following clauses from the Conditions of Contract have a particular influence in the way that the work is carried out, and hence the resultant quality of the finished project.

Clause 6   Statutory obligations, notices, fees and charges.
Clause 6A   Provisions for use where the appendix states that all the CDM regulations apply.
Clause 7   Levels and setting out of the works.
Clause 8   Work, materials and goods.
Clause 9   Royalties and patent rights.
Clause 10   Person-in-charge.
Clause 11   Access for architect to the works.
Clause 12   Clerk of works.
Clause 42   Performance specified work.

The combination of ensuring that the contractor complies with the statutory regulations, and the specification of the works described, should result in a building that achieves the desired standards and quality. In addition, there is the provision for inspection by the clerk of works regularly, and by the architect intermittently. There is also the added precaution for the inspection of goods and materials in the workshops off site, should this be so desired. The contractor, on the other hand, must seek to ensure that competent tradesmen are employed to do the work. Someone must be constantly on the site who is able to accept instructions from the architect and who will also be responsible for the daily site management of the project. In addition, there are clauses covering levels and setting out – making sure that the project is off to a correct start. There is also provision for uncovering work for inspection if the architect feels that this is necessary.

Statutory obligations, notices, fees and charges (clause 6)

The contractor must comply with and give all notices required by any Act of Parliament, statutory instrument, regulation or by-law of any local authority or statutory undertaker which has any jurisdiction with regard to the works. The contractor, however, will not be liable for compliance with this requirement where the works themselves do not comply with these requirements. The contractor should not deliberately and knowingly execute work that will contravene these regulations, and as such will require future modification. On the other hand, the contractor is not a watchdog to ensure that architects carry out their duties properly and efficiently.

If the contractor finds any divergence between the statutory requirements and any of the contract documents or architect's instructions the architect should immediately be informed in writing, pointing out the discrepancy. The architect must then, within 7 seven days of the receipt of this notice, issue instructions in relation to the divergence. If the instruction requires the work to be varied then this should be treated in the same way as other variations, in accordance with clause 13.

In some circumstances it may be necessary for the contractor to comply urgently with a statutory regulation; for example, where an existing structure on the site is in danger of collapsing or where health is in danger. This may require the contractor to supply materials or execute work prior to receiving instructions from the architect. The contractor should do that which is reasonably necessary to secure the immediate compliance with the statutory requirement. The contractor must then inform the architect of this action. The materials and work executed in these circumstances will then be treated as a variation under clause 13.

The contractor must pay and indemnify the employer against ability in respect of any fees, charges, rates, taxes, etc. These may be required under an Act of Parliament, regulation or by-law. The amount of such fees and charges will be added to the contract sum unless:

(a)   they arise in respect of goods or work done by a local authority or statutory undertaker;

(b)   they are included in the contract sum by the contractor;

(c)   they are included as a provisional sum in the contract bills.

Provisions for use where the appendix states that all the CDM regulations apply (clause 6A)

The CDM Regulations are the Construction (Design and Management) Regulations 1994, and their subsequent amendments. The employer shall ensure:

1.   That the planning supervisor (defined as an architect or other person named in article 6.1) carries out the relevant duties under the CDM Regulations.

2.   Where the contractor is not the principal contractor, that contractor carries out the duties of the principal contractor.

The contractor must ensure that the health and safety plan has the features required by regulation 15(4) of the CDM Regulations. Any amendment to this plan by the contractor shall be notified to the employer, who in turn will notify the planning supervisor and the architect. The contractor should also ensure the compliance with this provision of the subcontractors working on the site.

Level and setting out of the works (clause 7)

The architect is responsible for providing the contractor with all the information necessary in order that the contractor can set out the works at ground level. This information should comprise properly dimensioned drawings and levels. The actual setting out of the works from this information is entirely the responsibility of the contractor. If mistakes are made during this process the contractor must correct them without cost or charge to the employer. Delays in the presentation of the information from the architect could result in an extension of time. One possible problem could arise from the inaccurate setting out of the works by trespassing on the land of an adjoining owner. In this situation the contractor would be liable to indemnify the employer under clause 20. With the consent of the employer, the architect may instruct that such errors will not be amended and an appropriate deduction for such errors will be made from the contract sum.

Work, materials and goods (clause 8)

This clause seeks to ensure that the quality of materials and workmanship will be as specified in the contract bills. It therefore reinforces the information contained in the bills of quantities. Where the quality specified becomes no longer possible to obtain then, before proceeding with some alternative, the contractor should seek instructions from the architect. The contractor must, whenever required to do so, prove that the materials being used are in accordance with the specified requirements (clause 2.1). This may be done by providing the architect with applicable quotations and invoices. The contractor shall not substitute any materials or goods contained in a performance specification without the architect's consent. All work would be carried out in a workmanlike manner.

In other circumstances this may involve the contractor in testing the materials, goods or workmanship in accordance with the tests described in the contract bills. If the architect requires tests to be performed that have not been specified, then these must be carried out by the contractor, but will form an additional charge to the contract sum. Routine tests at regular intervals are generally described adequately in the contract bills. The contractor must therefore expect that some of these tests will be required. It may be useful in other circumstances to include a provisional sum for abnormal testing in case this is required.

The architect also has the powers to request the inspection or test of any part of the works up to the issue of the final certificate. This may require the contractor to open up the works for inspection or testing. The purpose of this is to ensure that the work is in accordance with that specified in the contract. The costs of opening up the works for this purpose will be borne by the contractor if the inspection or tests show that it is not in accordance with the contract. Where it is in agreement to that specified, then the costs of opening up and making good will be added to the contract sum. This may also result in other repercussions such as an extension of time (clause 25.4.5.2) or a claim for loss and expense (clause 26.2.2).

The architect may also issue instructions in regard to the removal from site of materials that do not conform with the contract. In other circumstances, once the materials arrive on site they cannot be removed without the architect's permission (clause 16). The materials that are removed must be replaced with materials that do conform, and at no extra expense to the contract. There is no limit in time when such defective materials should be discovered. The architect will, however, seek to inspect the works reasonably as they progress. If, however, a failure in the foundations did not occur until the building was suitably loaded, and such a failure was due to the use of defective materials, the contractor would be liable fully to rectify the problem to the satisfaction of the architect. (Note: article 1 of the Articles of Agreement.) The architect should, however, express any dissatisfaction within a reasonable time from the execution of the unsatisfactory work (clause 8.2).

If any of the work, materials or goods are not in accordance with the contract the architect may.

1.   Issue instructions for their removal.
2.   Allow such work to remain and confirm this in writing to the contractor. This is not to be construed as a variation, but will probably result in an appropriate deduction from the contract sum.
3.   Issue instructions requiring a variation but allow no addition to the contract sum or an extension of time.
4.   Issue instructions for opening up inspection using the following Code of Practice.

A Code of Practice has been written to assist in the operation of clause 8.4.4. The architect and contractor should agree to the amount and method of opening up or testing in accordance with the following criteria.

1.   The event of the non-compliance is unique and is unlikely to happen again.
2.   The need to discover whether any non-compliance in a primary structural element is a failure of workmanship and/or materials such that rigorous testing of similar elements must take place. Where the non-compliance is less significant and can be simply repaired.
3.   The significance of the non-compliance having regard to the nature of the work in which it has occurred.
4.   The consequence of any similar non-compliance on the safety of buildings, its effect on users, adjoining property, the public, and compliance with any statutory requirements.
5.   The level and standard of supervision and control of the works by the contractor.
6.   The relevant records of the contractor and where relevant of any

subcontractor resulting from the supervision and control referred to above.

7. Any Codes of Practice or similar advice issued by a responsible body which are applicable to the non-complying work, materials or goods.

8. Any failure by the contractor to carry out, or to secure the carrying out of, any tests specified in the contract documents or in an instruction to the architect.

9. The reason for the non-compliance when this has been established.

10. Any technical advice that the contractor has obtained in respect of the non-complying work, materials or goods.

11. Current recognized testing procedures.

12. The practicability of progressive testing in establishing whether any similar non-compliance is reasonably likely.

13. If alternative testing methods are available, the time required for and the consequential costs of such alternative testing methods.

14. Any proposals of the contractor.

15. Any other relevant matters.

The architect may also issue instructions excluding anyone from the site. This must not be done unreasonably or to the specific annoyance of the contractor. The contractor should therefore have been previously warned of this impending situation, in order that appropriate corrective action may be taken. It is, however, an uncommon occurrence, but it may arise in circumstances where persistently bad workmanship arises or where a member of the contractor's staff has consistently failed to carry out the architect's instructions as requested.

Royalties and patent rights (clause 9)

All royalties and other similar sums included for work described in the contract's bills are deemed to be included in the contract sum by the contractor. The contractor must also indemnify the employer against any actions that might be brought in connection with royalties. The contractor may, for example, have used a patented system of scaffolding, the royalties of which are entirely the contractor's responsibility.

If, however, the contractor is requested to use a patented system under an architect's instruction, the royalties that may be payable in these circumstances will be added to the contract sum. Presumably in this case such royalties would be agreed when valuing the variation.

Person-in-charge (clause 10)

The contractor must keep a site manager constantly on site. This is the person who is responsible for the daily running of the site, and to whom the architect can give instructions, or to whom the clerk of works can give directions. In the construction industry several names are used from project manager to general foreman. A contracts manager, however, who is often responsible for several sites, will not easily fit within this description since such a person is not 'kept up on the works'. The instructions given by the architect to the person-in-charge will be deemed to have been issued to the contractor. In order to satisfy this last requirement the person-in-charge may delegate an assistant who can receive instructions in his absence. The term 'constantly on site' means at all reasonable times, to ensure that the work is correctly executed and to receive any instructions from the architect.

Access for architect to the works (clause 11)

The architect and the architect's representatives have the right of access, at all reasonable times, to the construction site and the contractor's workshops. This clause is extended to cover the workshops of domestic and nominated subcontractors. The term 'architect and the architect's representatives' can also, presumably, be extended to quantity surveyors and engineers of different kinds. In some circumstances, for example, it may be important for the structural engineer to be allowed access to the fabrication process of the steelworker. The purpose of this clause, therefore, is largely to inspect the quality control of the firm concerned. It should be noted, however, that suppliers are not listed here, since their contract is a contract of sale of completed goods, and inspection may be inappropriate, particularly in the case of mass-produced goods.

Due to the increasing amount of specialist work included in buildings, provision is now necessary and is provided to protect the proprietary interests of the contractor or subcontractor, whilst not detracting from the right of access given to the architect. This might be achieved through confidentiality agreements or limiting the inspections of specialist manufacturing processes where some form of indemnity could be provided.

Clerk of works (clause 12)

The employer has the option of appointing a clerk of works whose duty is to act 'solely as an inspector' on behalf of the employer. The clerk of works is employed for this purpose under the directions of the architect. The contractor should provide the clerk of works with all reasonable facilities in order that the designated duties can be performed. The clerk of works is not employed in the capacity of the architect's representative, since employment is solely for inspection purposes. If the clerk of works chooses to give the contractor instructions, even in writing, they will have only little contractual effect unless they are confirmed by the architect. This must be done within 2 working days of the instruction, and must be in writing, which will then constitute an architect's works instruction. If the architect chooses to confirm a clerk of work's suggestion orally, then the appropriate procedures to put this in writing must then be taken up by either the contractor or the architect (see clause 4). The clerk of works is generally resident on site and in constant touch with the works, in circumstances that often require a quick decision. In practice, therefore, the contractor must receive many statements from the clerk of works in good faith.

Performance specified work (clause 42)

The term 'performance specified work' means:
1. Identified in the Appendix.
2. Which is to be provided by the contractor.
3. For which certain requirements have been predetermined and are shown on the contract drawings.
4. In respect of which the performance which the employer requires from such work, and which is included in the bills of quantities as either:
   (a) work that the contractor has priced, or
   (b) has been included in the contract as a provisional sum.

Practice Note 25 describes the sort of work which is not to be treated as performance specified work.

Before carrying out such work the contractor will provide the architect with documents referred to as the 'contractor's statement'. The work is then carried out in accordance with the terms and conditions of this approved statement. The statement should be sufficiently detailed to adequately explain the contractor's proposals. This may include drawings and schedules. The date for the receipt of the statement may be stated in the bills or provided by means of an architect's instruction. If the contractor's statement is deficient then the architect can require this to be amended. Such a deficiency, for example, could adversely affect the performance of the work as required by the employer.

A provisional sum for this type of work can be included in the bills of quantities if the following information is provided:
1. The performance which the employer requires from such work.
2. The location of such work in the building.
3. Sufficient information has been provided to allow for:
   (a) the contractor's programme to be prepared;
   (b) the preliminary items that are relevant to this work to be adequately priced.

If in the contract bills there are errors or omissions of information in connection with this work then they are to be corrected by a variation order issued by the architect. The architect also has powers within the terms of the contract to issue instructions that may vary this work from what was originally envisaged. Where the bills of quantities do not provide for an analysis of this type of work, then the architect can request such an analysis which must then be provided within 14 days.

The contractor should exercise reasonable skill and care in the provision of this work maintaining the general obligations in respect of the supply of workmanship, materials and goods. Performance specified work should not be implied to assume a guarantee of fitness for purpose. This clause specifically excludes the provision of this work under a nominated subcontract.

Chapter 16

Costs of construction

An important factor in any construction contract is the calculation and payment of the sum of money by the employer to the building contractor. The importance of the contract sum and its relationship to the final account, together with the matters relating to the timing of payments, are discussed in this chapter.

Clause 3   Contract sum – additions or deductions – adjustment – interim certificates.

Clause 13   Variations and provisional sums.

Clause 13A Variation instruction – contractor's quotation in compliance with the instruction.

Clause 14   Contract sum.

Clause 16   Materials and goods unfixed or off site.

Clause 24   Damages for non-completion.

Clause 26   Loss and expense caused by matters materially affecting regular progress of the works.

Clause 30   Certificates and payments.

The project starts with the contract sum and the integrity of this amount is clarified within the contract conditions. It is extremely unusual for this amount to remain unchanged and be paid as the final account upon completion. Changes beyond the contractor's control will be made, and these must eventually be costed to the appropriate amount. Changes occur particularly in respect of foundation costs, the nomination of specialist firms and variations to the design instigated by the employer or architect, and occasionally by the building contractor. Rules are laid down on how these changes are to be evaluated in terms of cost. In some circumstances the contractors may feel that they have been improperly reimbursed, and there is provision in the contract to rectify this should the case be proven. In other circumstances the employer may have suffered damages due to a late completion by the contractor. There is also provision to deal with these circumstances should this situation occur. On the majority of contracts of any size, the contractor will be unable to complete the works without some form of interim payment. Clause 30 describes the procedures involved for calculating the amounts owing to the contractor both during the period of construction and also upon final completion of the contract. Matters covering valuation periods, retention and the time allowed for payment to be made are also included in this clause.

Contract sum -- additions or deductions -- adjustment -- interim certificates (clause 3)

If the conditions refer to the addition to or deduction from the contract sum, then once this adjustment has been calculated it shall be paid and included in the value of the next interim certificate. Several clauses refer back to this clause in respect of extra expense caused by changes to the contract. Some of these items are as follows:

Clause 6   Statutory obligations, notices, fees and charges.

Clause 7   Levels and setting out the works.

Clause 8   Opening up for inspection and testing of the works where found to be correct.

Clause 9   Royalties and patent rights.

Clause 17   Repair of defects, the costs of which are accepted by the architect.

Clause 21   Certain insurance matters.

Variations and provisional sums (clause 13)

Most of the forms of contract used in the United Kingdom allow for variations arising at some stages during the contract. The absence of such a clause would necessitate a new contract being arranged if variations did arise. The disadvantage of such a clause is that it allows the architect to delay making some decisions almost until the last possible moment. The building owner will be bound by any variation given by the architect as long as the architect does not exceed the powers under the terms of the contract.

The question sometimes arises as to what constitutes a variation. Clause 13 aptly describes those circumstances where a variation can arise, but it must be presumed and implied that a limit on these change orders will apply in practice. If the nature of the works described in the contract documents can be shown to be 'substantially' different from that carried out then the main contractor will be entitled to reprice the work accordingly. 'Substantially different', however, may require the courts to formulate a decision in individual cases. A variation resulting in a change in the size of a window will be admissible. The increase in the size of a proposed extension from 200 to $2,000 \, \text{m}^2$ of floor space may not. The contractor may be willing to carry out the work, but on a different contractual basis.

Clause 13.1 attempts to define a variation in normal circumstances. A variation from the contract occurs where the actual work to be carried out changes, or where the circumstances in which the work is to be carried out changes. The first category includes the alteration or modification of the design, quality or quantity of works including:

1.   The addition, omission or substitution of any work.

2.   The alteration of the kind or standard of materials or goods.

3. The removal from site of work, materials or goods that were formerly in accordance with the contract is also included under this section.

A change in the circumstances in which the work is carried out also comes within this definition and is defined to include access and use of the site, limitations of working space, limitations of working hours, and a change in the sequence of work.

However, clause 13.1.3 places some restrictions in the way that the architect can go about issuing variation instructions. Work that has been described in the contract bills as the main contractor's (or one of the domestic subcontractors should the intention have been to sublet it) cannot be omitted and then awarded to a nominated subcontractor. It can be omitted entirely and done after the contract has been completed. It can also be awarded to a firm employed directly by the building owner, assuming that the main contractor will allow access to the works, for this purpose, during the contract period. Of course, if the main contractor agrees to this nomination, then this will override the condition.

Instructions will also be required from the architect in the expenditure of provisional sums in the contract bills and in nominated subcontracts (clause 13.3).

All instructions from the architect requiring a variation from the contract must be in writing. This is in pursuance of clause 4.3. The quantity surveyor has no power to measure and value varied work without this written instruction (clause 13.4). Any variation made by either the architect or the contractor (clause 13.2.4) can be confirmed in writing at any time prior to the issue of the final certificate (clause 4.3.2.2).

The rules for the valuation of variations are detailed in clause 13.5. The two alternative ways of valuing the construction work are described in clause 13.5.1 (by measurement) and clause 13.5.4 (by cost reimbursement). The rules for measurement state that the same principles used for the preparation of the contract bills should be adopted (clause 13.5.3.1). Four situations are described and these are shown diagrammatically in Fig. 16.1.

1. Where the additional or substituted work is the same in character, conditions and quantity to items in the contract bills, then bill rates or prices are to be used to value the variation.
2. Where the additional or substituted work is the same in character, but is executed under different conditions or results in significant changes in quantity, then the bill rates or prices are to be used as a basis for valuing the variation. These are known as pro-rata rates.
3. If the additional or substituted work is different from those items in bills, then a fair method of valuation is to be used, often known as star rates.
4. Omissions are valued at bill rates unless the remaining quantities are substantially changed, in which case a revaluation of these items will become necessary using method 3 above.

If any percentage or lump-sum adjustments have been made in the contract bills – for example, for the correction of errors (see clause 14) – then these will

Note: Omitted work at bill rates unless the remaining work changes substantially in quantities, in which case a revaluation of these items becomes necessary.

Fig. 16.1   Valuation of variations

need to be adjusted accordingly. Also, if it can be shown that the value of preliminary items have changed as a result of variations, then this will require adjustment.

If the varied work cannot be properly measured or valued, then the contractor or subcontractor is to be paid for the work on a daywork basis. The schedule, 'Definition of Prime Cost of Day work carried out under a Building Contract' and issued by the Royal Institution of Chartered Surveyors and the Building Employers Confederation, together with the percentage additions determined by the contractor in the bills, should be used. Alternatively, if the work is within the province of any specialist trade, defined as either electrical or heating and ventilating, then their appropriate definition for daywork together with the percentages inserted by the contractor in the bills should be used. Vouchers showing the daily time spent on the work, the workmen's names and the plant and materials employed should be verified. This is recommended to be done weekly by the architect's representative and this is interpreted to be the clerk of works. It should be noted here that the verified voucher is an agreed record only; it does not mean that the method of valuation adopted will be daywork. This is a matter for the quantity surveyor to determine.

Amendment 7 issued in July 1988 extended these rules to cover approximate quantities in bills of quantities. This change is a result of the introduction of SMM7 as the method of measurement which should be used with JCT 80. If

Fig. 16.2 Effect of changes in quantities in approximate quantities (JCT Amendment 7, of July 1988)

the quantity surveyor has included some approximate quantities in the contract bills and these have a close resemblance to the actual quantities as executed, then the rates inserted by the contractor at the time of tender will be used to value them. If the approximate quantities are not a reasonable forecast then the rates used in the bills will only be used as a basis for revaluation. At the extremes, i.e. where the approximate quantity does not change or where it differs by, say, 100 per cent then the above rules can easily be applied. In the 'grey' areas in between these extremes then the test of reasonableness will need to be applied by the parties concerned. This principle only applies where the work as executed is not altered or modified other than by quantity alone. The architect does not need to give specific instructions in respect of the execution of work for which an approximate quantity is included in the contract bills. This principle is also extended to cover nominated subcontractors' work where this is appropriate.

The valuation of a provisional sum follows a similar process to the valuing of the main contractor's work described in the bills. For example, if a provisional sum had been included in the bills for 'repairs to timber staircase', and it was agreed that daywork should apply, then the above rules for valuing daywork would be used. The term 'provisional sum' has also taken on a redefined meaning in accordance with the provisions of SMM7. This is a sum provided for work being identified as defined or undefined. The above (Fig. 16.2) General Rule 10 from SMM7 should be noted in this context.

The valuation of performance specified works follows the similar procedure valuing work generally. It may, however, include the preparation of drawings, schedules and other documents.

10. Procedure where the drawn and specification information required by these rules is not available

10.1
Where work can be described and given in items in accordance with these rules but the quantity shall be given and identified as an approximate quantity.

10.2

Where work cannot be described and given in items in accordance with these rules it shall be given as a Provisional Sum and identified as for either defined or undefined work as appropriate.

10.3

A Provisional Sum for defined work is a sum provided for work which is not completely designed but for which the following information shall be provided:

(a)   The nature and construction of the work.

(b)   A statement of how and where the work is fixed to the building and what other work is to be fixed thereto.

(c)   A quantity or quantities which indicate the scope and extent of the work.

(d)   Any specific limitations and the like identified in Section A35.

10.4

Where Provisional Sums are given for defined work the Contractor will be deemed to have made due allowance in programming, planning and pricing Preliminaries. Any such allowance will only be subject to adjustment in those circumstances where a variation in respect of other work measured in detail in accordance with the rules would give rise to adjustment.

10.5

A Provisional Sum for undefined work is a sum provided for work where the information required in accordance with rule 10.3 cannot be given.

10.6

Where Provisional Sums are given for undefined work the Contractor will be deemed not to have made any allowance in programming, planning and pricing Preliminaries.

The contractor in pricing the work at tender stage will be deemed to have made due allowance in pricing for the preliminary items. If the execution of any of this work is subject to variation then an adjustment may need to be made to the value of the preliminary items. The repayment of any direct loss or expense resulting from a variation issued by the architect would be reimbursed and discussed under clause 26.

Variations often necessitate either remeasurement on site or from drawings. Clause 13.6 gives the contractor the right to be present at the time that such measurements are taking place.

Variation instruction -- Contractor's quotation in compliance with the instruction (clause 13A)

The valuation of variations will normally follow the procedures of clause 13.4.1 unless the architect's instruction states that the treatment and valuation of the variation should be dealt with under clause 13A (clause 13.2.3). This new clause was added to the form of contract through Amendment 13 which was issued in January 1994. Clause 13A can also apply to instructions that may be given to nominated subcontractors.

The application of this clause will only apply to an architect's instruction where the contractor agrees with this method of valuation. Where the contractor disagrees, then this must be notified in writing to the architect within 7 days of receiving the instruction. Valuation rules 13.4.1 will then be used as the basis for valuing the variation.

Clause 13A allows the contractor to provide a quotation for a variation, in advance of the work being carried out. The quotation should be based upon:

- where relevant, the rates and prices contained in the contract bills;
- where appropriate, the adjustment of preliminary items;
- any adjustment in time required for completion of the works;
- any amount paid in lieu of direct loss and expense under clause 26.1;
- a fair and reasonable amount in respect of preparing the quotation.

The architect's instruction may also require the contractor to identify any additional resources that may be required and the method of carrying out the variation. The quotation should provide sufficient information to allow the work to be properly evaluated on behalf of the employer.

If a quotation has been requested and the work is then not proceeded with in this way, then the contractor is to be allowed to add to the contract sum the reasonable costs involved of preparing the quotation.

Where a clause 13A quotation has been accepted, then any subsequent variations issued by the architect that may affect this work, will then be valued by the quantity surveyor on a fair and reasonable basis and not by using the rules of clause 13.5.

The effect of the valuation of variations is that such sums are either added to or deducted from the contract sum.

Contract sum (clause 14)

The contract sum is assumed to have been calculated on the basis of the quality and quantity of work as described in the bills of quantities. A part of the quantity surveying process on any project is to establish the correctness of the contract sum both arithmetically and technically. This means that the bills should have been checked to see that the item costs have been extended correctly, that page totals add up and that the various collection sheets and summaries have been correctly completed. The adequacy of the contractor's rates should also have been examined in order to avoid difficulties that could arise in the agreement of the final account. Failure, however, on the part of the quantity surveyor to perform these duties efficiently will not provide the contractor with any redress against the building owner. It is the contractor's responsibility to determine the sufficiency of the tender, with no alternative but to honour the pricing should any errors occur at a future date during the contract. Any errors discovered by the quantity surveyor or the contractor prior to the signing of the contract can be corrected by using one of the alternative methods described in the code of procedure for selective tendering (see Chapter 8). It is prudent, therefore, on the part of the quantity surveyor to be satisfied on the nature of the prices prior to the signing of the contract.

The only errors that can be corrected are those made by the quantity surveyor during the preparation of the contract bills (clause 2.2). These may have occurred because of errors in the quantities or descriptions or because items have been omitted. If the bills depart from the method of measurement stated, and this has not been brought to the contractor's notice, then this will also be deemed to be an error that will need to be corrected.

Materials and goods unfixed or off site (clause 16)

Materials and goods which have been delivered to the site or placed on or adjacent to works, and are intended for the works, must not be removed from the site unless written consent has been received from the architect. Once the value of these goods and materials has been included in an interim certificate and paid for by the employer they become the property of the employer. There has been considerable case law on this point. However, the main contractor will still be responsible for any loss or damage they may suffer and for the insurance of the same, as long as clauses 22A and 22B are in operation. Although the employer becomes the true owner of the materials and goods concerned, the contractor's insolvency may raise the question of whether the contractor was the reputed owner. The employer would need to ensure that the contractor's title to the goods was not defective.

Where the value of any materials or goods intended for the works, but stored off site, has been included in an interim certificate and paid for by the employer, then these materials will also become the property of the employer. The contractor must not remove these items from the premises except to the project for which they are intended. The contractor, however, continues to be responsible for any loss or damage that may occur, and for their insurance in accordance with clauses 22A and 22B. In these circumstances the architect has exercised an option under clause 30 to pay for materials off site. This clause has particular relevance and importance to factory manufactured components, used with industrialized buildings. In these situations the contractor may be loath to bring to site items of manufactured joinery until their incorporation in the works is imminent. The option of paying for these materials will assist the contractor's cash flow, and should cause no problems if the provisions of clause 30 are properly complied with.

Damages for non-completion (clause 24)

If the contractor fails to complete the works by the completion date, then the architect must issue a certificate accordingly. This certificate allows the employer to deduct from monies due to the contractor, the liquidated and ascertained damages at the rate stated in the Appendix. The amount of damages claimed is based upon the period between the completion date and the date of practical completion. If there is an insufficient amount owing to the contractor by which to offset the damages, the employer is able to recover the balance as a debt.

The amount stated in the Appendix for liquidated and ascertained damages must be a realistic sum related to possible actual damages suffered by the employer. If the amount stated is shown to be a penalty, then the courts will set a fair, but smaller amount, as damages payable by the contractor.

If the architect subsequently fixes a later completion date, then any amounts deducted by the employer are to be adjusted and repaid to the contractor as necessary.

Loss and expense caused by matters materially affecting regular progress of the works (clause 26)

The main purpose of this clause is to reimburse the contractor in those circumstances where loss and expense have been suffered, and will not be reimbursed elsewhere under the terms of the contract. The loss and expense claim must be directly attributable to matters that have substantially affected the regular progress of the construction of the project.

In order for the contractor to claim for reimbursement a written application must first be made to the architect. In this correspondence it must be stated that direct loss and expense have been, or are very likely to be, incurred during the execution of the works, and that adequate reimbursement will not be made under any other provision of the contract. The basis of claim is that the regular progress of the works has been disturbed and this has resulted in the loss and expense. Loss in this context means that the contractor has been inadequately reimbursed for work carried out. Expense implies that additional resources were necessary to complete the works.

The conditions of contract list various matters that could affect the regular progress of works. The contractor must cite one or more of the following items in support of his claim for loss and expense:

1. Delay in the receipt of instructions (including the expenditure of provisional sums), drawings, details or levels from the architect. The contractor must have requested this information in writing from the architect, and have allowed sufficient time to elapse prior to its use on site.
2. Opening up of work for inspection or testing of materials and for their

consequential making good. This is providing the items were in accordance with the work specified.

3.   Discrepancies between the contract drawings, contract bills and numbered document.

4.   Work being carried out by firms employed directly by the employer. This also includes the supply of materials and goods by the employer for the project.

5.   Postponement of any of the work to be executed under the provisions of the contract.

6.   Failure on the part of the employer to give ingress to or egress from the works by the appropriate time.

7.   Variations authorized by the architect under clause 13.2 or the expenditure in regard to provisional sums for defined work.

8.   The execution of work for which an approximate quantity is included in the contract bills which is not a reasonably accurate forecast of the quantity of work required.

Upon receipt of the correspondence from the contractor the architect must then assess whether the claim is justified. First, it will be necessary to assess that the regular progress of the works had been disturbed by one or more of the eight matters listed above. Reference will need to be made to the contractor's master programme for this purpose. The mere fact that the project is running behind schedule may also be due in part to the contractor's inability to perform the works adequately. Some allowance on the period of delay may therefore need to be taken for this assumption. Second, either the architect or the quantity surveyor will need to ascertain the amount of the loss and expense incurred by the contractor. In practice the architect may agree that the contractor has a valid argument, but leave the settlement of the financial sum to the quantity surveyor.

The contractor's written application should be made as soon as it is apparent that the regular progress of the works has been affected. Relevant information should be submitted to the architect in support of the claim that will help the architect form an opinion. The contractor should also provide some indication of the amount of loss and expense that has been suffered. If any extension of time has already been agreed by the architect under the appropriate items of clause 25, then the contractor shall be informed accordingly. This may affect the calculation and assessment of the contractor's claim.

A nominated subcontractor can also submit a claim for the loss and expense caused by the disturbance of the regular progress of the subcontract works (JCT form of subcontract, clause 13.1). Such a claim must first be submitted to the contractor. If it is appropriate, then the contractor will in turn submit it to the architect. This claim will then follow a similar process, as described above.

Any amounts that the architect agrees should be paid to the contractor for a claim under this clause are to be added to the contract sum. If they can be agreed during the progress of the works, they can then be included in the next valuation.

The inclusion of this clause within the form of contract provides only one remedy for the contractor. Other courses of action are therefore open to the contractor in the event of the regular progress of the works being affected. Other actions the contractor may wish to take, if they are to succeed with the payment of damages, must not be too remote in the eyes of the law. The loss of profit is, however, a reasonable claim to be made under this heading. The provisions of clause 26 are without prejudice to any other rights and remedies which the contractor might possess.

Certificates and payments (clause 30)

Interim valuations are generally prepared by the client's quantity surveyor (clause 30.1.2) in agreement with the contractor's surveyor. Although these may be required at more frequent intervals by the architect (clause 30.1.2), the Conditions of Contract will stipulate a maximum period for interim certificates. The Appendix to the form of contract, which needs completing individually for each project, recommends this period to be one month, although the parties do have the option of stating any period that they desire. The ICE Conditions of Contract also stipulate that the valuation must achieve a minimum amount (to be stated in the contract) before any monthly payment will be made. There is no comparable condition in JCT 80, although if this was desirable then it could be inserted as a supplementary condition. The purpose of such a recommendation is to attempt to ensure that the contractor is making regular progress of the works. On very large contracts it may be necessary to provide approximate valuations on a weekly basis in order to satisfy the contractor's cash flow. More accurate payments would continue to be made at the monthly interval. This may be required at peak construction periods, for example during the summer months on mass earthmoving contracts. In some contracts, stage payment system (clause 30.2) may be used as a preference.

Valuations will be prepared on a monthly basis (or on whatever basis has been stated in the Appendix) until the certificate of practical completion is issued. If the work has been accurately valued at this point, then only retention monies will be outstanding and these can therefore be released with the final certificate. There will therefore be no requirements to issue a certificate between these two certificates. The certificate of practical completion has therefore often been referred to as the penultimate certificate, although there is nothing in the contract to prohibit the issue of further certificates beyond this one. In a real contract situation it is often not possible to value accurately the works at completion, and this therefore results in further certificates being issued.

The final certificate is referred to as the certificate of completion of making good defects, and is issued either at the end of the defects liability period or once the defects have all been made good, whichever date is the later. The certificate of practical completion of the works includes the release of one moiety (one-half) of the retention monies, the remainder being released with the certificate of making good defects.

One further point that needs some consideration is the effect of the NEDO formulae on valuations. Using the traditional method of price fluctuation – i.e. increased cost sheets – these were quite independent from the value of the measured works. The interim valuation of the contract works was also looked upon as a means to an end, and as long as it was reasonably correct overall that was all that mattered. The contractor needed to be paid a reasonable sum for the work carried out, and the employer needed to be satisfied that certificates were not extremely high. The introduction of the NEDO formulae has, however, meant that interim valuations must be much more accurate since the appropriate percentages used to calculate the increases (or decreases) use the valuation amounts in their computation. Although at interim valuation time the indices may only be provisional, the work valued must be actual, to closely resemble the work completed. Using the traditional method for calculating price increases, it was generally accepted that it was in the best interest of the contractor to overvalue the works wherever possible, as this helped to improve the contractor's cash flow. The adoption of the formulae method will usually result in a higher payment should the contractor wait as long as possible before including the work in his valuation.

In practice, the contractor's surveyor often prepares the valuation since they are more often on site, and therefore more familiar with the progress of the works. The quantity surveyor will then visit the site at the appointed date to examine, approve and agree the amount of the valuation. Should there be any dispute between these parties on the amount to be paid, the client's quantity surveyor's assessment will be used. The valuation is then forwarded to the architect with the provision that the work included is in accordance with the architect's requirements. The quantity surveyor should not knowingly include in a valuation work that does not conform to the contract, but the question of quality control is not really the quantity surveyor's prerogative. If, however, there are any doubts over an item, this should be brought to the notice of the architect. The architect will generally accept the valuation and use it for the preparation of his certificate. This is sent to the employer with a copy to the contractor, and should be paid within the 14 days stipulated in the contract. If it is not, then the contractor can determine the contract under clause 28.

Amounts due

The amount stated as due in an interim certificate is the gross valuation agreed between the parties and certified by the architect. In order to calculate the amount payable to the contractor, deductions in the form of retention and payments made under previous certificates are made. The gross valuation includes the following, which are *subject to retention* as stated in the Appendix:

1.   The total value of work properly executed by the contractor including

variations carried out and agreed in terms of their financial consequences but excluding any restoration, replacement or repair or loss or damage and removal and disposal of debris which in clauses 22B.3.5 and 22C.4.4 are treated as if they were a variation.

2. Any adjustments to these values arising as a result of the application of the price adjustment formulae under clause 40.

3. The total value of materials and goods delivered to the site. This, in practice, often only includes those items of a major financial importance. The materials on site will only include those items that are reasonably, properly and not prematurely delivered to site. The inclusion, in the valuation, of sanitary ware that is already on site at the start of the contract may be refused because they have been prematurely brought to the site. The client, when paying for materials on site, will need to be satisfied in every respect regarding their safety from damage or theft. Materials on site for long periods are more susceptible to these occurrences. The provision for payment may also require adequate protection from the weather as a prerequisite condition. This clause also applies in respect of materials from nominated suppliers.

4. The value of any materials off site as agreed with the architect as long as they conform to the requirements of the contract as described in clause 30.3.

5. The amounts of any nominated subcontractor's work that have been properly executed. Included with the subcontractor's invoice may be materials on or off site as appropriate and agreed by the architect. It is normal practice to include these amounts only where the subcontractor supplies an invoice. In addition, in some circumstances the architect or quantity surveyor may require proof that previous payments have been made to nominated subcontractors.

6. The profit of the contractor in respect of nominated subcontractors' invoices. The rates (percentages) stated in the bill of quantities are used. Should nomination be the result of a provisional sum, then these rates will be used as a basis. The contractor's profit on nominated suppliers' accounts is presumably covered with the supply of the materials under items 3 and 4 above, and would be added as appropriate. Attendance items are properly the main contractor's work and come, therefore, within the definition of 1 above.

In addition the following items are to be included which are *not subject to retention*:

1. Items which adjust the contract sum resulting from changes in fees and charges (clause 6.2), opening up for inspection and testing of the works where found to be correct (clause 8.3), royalties or patent rights resulting from an architect's instruction (clause 9.2), certain insurance matters (clause 21.2.3) and failure of the employer to insure the works (clauses 22B.2 and 22C.2)

2. Loss and expense agreed under clauses 26.1 or 34.3 or in respect of any restoration, replacement or repair or loss or damage and removal of and disposal of debris which in clauses 22B.3.5 and 22C.4.4 are treated as if they were a variation.
3. Where final payment has been secured to a nominated subcontractor under clause 35.17.
4. Any increased payments in respect of contributions, levies and tax fluctuations under clauses 38 and 39.
5. Any amounts of a similar nature to those described above relating to nominated subcontractors' works.

The following items are not subject to retention but are to be deducted from interim certificates:

1. Amounts in respect of levels and setting out of the works (clause 7); work, materials or goods which although not in accordance with the contract have been allowed to remain (clause 8.4.2); any defects, shrinkages or other faults which have been allowed to remain in the works (clauses 17.2 and 17.3) or any amounts allowable by the contractor to the employer in respect of fluctuations (clauses 38 and 39).
2. Any similar allowance in respect of a reduction in nominated subcontractors' payments.

Off-site materials or goods

The amount stated as due in an interim certificate may, at the discretion or option of the architect, include the value of such items prior to delivery to the site. There are a number of stipulations that the contractor must comply with before payment may be made for such goods and materials.

1. The materials are intended for incorporation within the works. This would normally be interpreted to mean that the materials or goods concerned were 'special' to this contract. Common bricks or quantities of standard sized timber which could be used on any project would not normally therefore be allowable items to be included.
2. Nothing remains to be done to the materials prior to their incorporation within the works. This also eliminates the standard type materials and goods that could have been provided by the contractor for any type of contract. The items envisaged therefore assume some form of prefabrication for the project concerned, either at the contractor's workshops or the workshops of a subcontractor.
3. The materials have been set apart from other materials at the place of storage. They must be clearly and visibly marked by letters to identify the employer and the name of the project for which they are intended.
4. If the materials are ordered from a supplier by the contractor or subcontractor, then the supply must be in writing and the goods must pass unconditionally to the contractor or subcontractor.

5. If the materials are manufactured or assembled by a subcontractor, then these similar conditions must also apply.
6. The materials must be in accordance with the contract.
7. The contractor must also provide the architect with reasonable proof of his ownership of the goods and materials.
8. The contractor must show that these goods and materials are properly insured in accordance with the terms of the contract both whilst they remain in storage and also during their transportation to the site.

Retention

The contractor is not paid the full amount of the valuation, but this is subject to a deduction in the form of retention. Retention is applied to work that has not reached practical completion and to materials and goods referred to above, including nominated works. The purpose of this retention is to provide some incentive for the contractor to complete the works, and it also provides some security should the contractor default in construction. The employer has only a fiduciary interest in the retention. In this respect the retention is held on trust only, and need not therefore be invested to accrue interest.

The amount retained by the employer under this clause is recommended as 5 per cent, although a lower rate can be agreed between the parties. It would appear that higher rates of retention are not envisaged under this contract. The percentage amount of retention is shown in the Appendix. Where the size of the project exceeds a contract sum of £500,000 then the recommendation of this contract is that the amount retained should be limited to 3 per cent. This would imply a 3 per cent retention throughout, rather than a 5 per cent retention with a limit of 3 per cent of the contract sum. Retention is applied to all those items of work and materials described in clause 30.2.1.

The retention is released to the contractor as follows. One-half of that which is retained by the employer at the certificate of practical completion of the works, and the remainder with the issue of the certificate of making good defects.

At the date of each interim certificate the quantity surveyor must prepare a statement of retention. This should show the amount of the contractor's retention and the retention for each nominated subcontractor. This statement should be issued by the architect to the employer, contractor and each nominated subcontractor concerned.

The employer may exercise the right to pay a nominated subcontractor direct, because of the contractor's default. The contractor must be informed of this action and its subsequent effect upon the retention.

Final account

Either during the contract period or within 6 months after practical completion of the works, the contractor shall provide all the documents necessary for the preparation of the final account. These documents should include the appropriate details from nominated subcontractors and nominated suppliers. When this has been complied with, the quantity surveyor must prepare a statement of the final valuation under clause 13. The architect must send a copy of this to the contractor and to each nominated subcontractor. The quantity surveyor should within 3 months of receiving the information from the contractor ascertain any loss and expense under clauses 26.1, 26.4.1 and 34.3 and also prepare a statement of all contract sum adjustments as follows. The following items are to be deducted from the contract sum:

1. Prime cost sums, which include the contractor's profit and attendance items where appropriate. This also includes the value of any work by a nominated subcontractor, whose employment has been determined in accordance with clause 35.24 which was not in accordance with the relevant subcontract but which has been paid or otherwise discharged by the employer.
2. Provisional sums and provisional work (approximate quantities) in the contract bills.
3. Amounts omitted by reason of variations caused by architect's instructions.
4. Amounts deducted or deductible under clause 7 (Levels and setting out of the works), clause 8.4.2 (Materials and goods which although not in accordance with the contract have been allowed to remain), clauses 17.2 or 17.3 (Defects, shrinkages or other faults which have been allowed to remain). It also includes amounts allowable to the employer under clause 38 (Contributions, levy and tax), clause 39 (Labour and materials cost and tax fluctuations) and clause 40 (Use of price adjustment formulae).
5. Any other amount which is required by this contract to be deducted from the contract sum, such as liquidated damages.

The following items are to be added:

1. Nominated subcontract sums as finally adjusted or ascertained under the relevant provisions of subcontract NSC/4.
2. The tender sum properly adjusted against prime cost sum items which have been undertaken by the contractor.
3. Nominated suppliers' accounts adjusted within the terms of the contract.
4. The profit and attendance items on nominated subcontractors' and nominated suppliers' items where appropriate and including cases where nomination arises through the expenditure, for example, of provisional sums.
5. Additional payments authorized by the employer in respect of
    (a) fees and charges (clause 6.2);
    (b) opening up of the works for inspection and testing where the work complies with the contract (clause 8.3);
    (c) royalties and patent rights (clause 9.2);
    (d) insurance (clause 21.2.3).

6. Variations authorized or approved by the architect.
7. The expenditure associated with provisional sums and approximate quantities in the contract bills.
8. Loss and expense ascertained under clauses 26.1 or 34.3.
9. Amounts under clauses 22B and 22C (Insurances by the employer) which the contractor is entitled to add to the contract sum.
10. Increases in contributions, levies and taxes under clauses 38, 39 or 40.
11. Any other amount which is required to be added to the contract, such as the agreement of the contractor's claims.

If it is practicable, but at least 28 days before the issue of the final certificate, the architect should issue an interim certificate which should include the amounts of the subcontract sum for all the nominated subcontractors adjusted and ascertained under all the relevant provisions of the contract.

The architect must issue the final certificate and inform each nominated subcontractor of its issue within 2 months of the last of the following events:
1. End of defects liability period.
2. Date of issue of certificate of making good defects.
3. Agreement of the final account.

The final certificate must state:
1. The amounts already paid to the contractor under interim certificates.
2. The contract sum adjusted within the terms of the contract.
3. The difference expressed as a debt to either the employer or the contractor.

The final certificate is conclusive evidence that:
- The quality of materials and standards of workmanship are to the reasonable satisfaction of the architect.
- The contract sum has been properly adjusted within the terms of the contract.
- Relevant extensions of time have been given under clause 25.
- Reimbursement of direct loss and expense is in final settlement of any contractor claims.

However, if there has been any accidental inclusion or exclusion of work, or arithmetical errors in computation, these are able to be corrected. The same principle applies in the case of fraud.

If any arbitration or other proceedings have been commenced by either party before the issue of the final certificate, then the final certificate shall have effect as conclusive evidence as provided in clause 30.9.1 after either:
- such proceedings have been concluded and the final certificate is subject to the award or judgment that has been made, or
- after a period of 12 months in which neither party has taken further steps to solve the problem, whichever is the earlier.

If arbitration is commenced within 28 days after the final certificate has been issued, the final certificate shall still remain conclusive evidence other than in respect of the matters relating to the proceedings.

No other certificates can be interpreted as conclusive evidence that either the works, goods or materials or performance specified works are in accordance with the contract.

Note

It should be noted at the time of going to publication of this book, that the JCT are in the process of issuing an amendment to the form of contract, in respect of the conclusiveness of the final certificate. This is having regard to a judgment in the Court of Appeal, *Crown Estate Commissioners* v. *John Mowlem & Co. Ltd 1994*. When available this issue will be covered in Amendment 15 to JCT 80. Similar amendments will also be made at that time to the other JCT form contracts.

Chapter 17

Time factor of construction

Several clauses in the Conditions of Contract are of relevance and importance in respect of the time factor. These have been grouped together for commentary purposes.

Clause 17   Practical completion and defects liability.
Clause 18   Partial possession by employer.
Clause 23   Date for possession, completion and postponement.
Clause 25   Extension of time.
Clause 27   Determination by employer.
Clause 28   Determination by contractor.
Clause 28A   Determination by employer or contractor.

These clauses describe the start and finish of the project and the implications associated with these dates. The difference between these is, of course, the contract period. The distinction between completion date and date for completion should be carefully noted. This is described in clause 1 under the general rules of interpretation and definitions. Should the contractor fail to complete the works by the completion date then the architect must issue a certificate of non-completion of the works as described in clause 24, and damages are then payable by the contractor. Upon the practical completion of the project the contractor is relieved of most of the contractual obligations. The contractor is, however, still responsible for defects that may arise due to bad workmanship. This responsibility continues until the end of the defects liability period, which the JCT form recommends should extend for 6 months after practical completion. Currently there is some debate on whether this responsibility should extend further, for some aspects of work, up to 10 years (see Chapter 11). In some circumstances the contractor may be able to secure an extension of the contract period for one of the reasons listed in clause 25. The advantages of this course of action to the contractor is either the reduction or elimination of liquidated damages. The date for completion is stated in the Appendix and any approved extension of time which is added to this provides the later completion date. The completion date cannot occur prior to the date of completion stated in the Appendix, unless the contractor agrees to such a revision. In some extreme circumstances the works may be postponed, perhaps indefinitely, and clause 23 allows for this eventuality. The works may also offer partial possession in the case of a phased project awarded as a single contract.

In this case phased completion is treated almost as a separate project as far as time is concerned. Finally, circumstances can, and sometimes do, arise where either the employer or the contractor feels that the contract should be terminated. This usually results because of a breach by the other party. The procedures and position of each party are described accordingly in clauses 27, 28 and 28A.

Practical completion and defects liability (clause 17)

Practical completion

When in the opinion of the architect the works become practically complete, the certificate of practical completion of the works must be issued. In practice this certificate may be issued even though minor items of work still need to be carried out within the terms of the contract. This does not presume that these items are either irrelevant or need not be completed. The date of practical completion often coincides with the handover date, and this latter consideration may have resulted in this certificate being issued even though the works are only 'almost' complete. Prior to the issue of this certificate the architect needs to be satisfied that:

1. The work has been carried out in accordance with the contract documents and the architect's instructions.
2. The building is in an appropriate state to be taken over and used by the employer.

Usually, where the employer wants to occupy the building, the certificate should be issued.

The date of practical completion is important since the following take effect automatically:

1. The start of the defects liability period (clause 17).
2. The beginning of the period of final measurement (clause 30).
3. The release of the first moiety of the retention fund (clause 30).
4. The ending of the insurance of the works (clause 21).
5. The end of any liability to liquidated damages by the employer (clause 24).
6. The opening of matters referred to arbitration (article 5).
7. The removal of the liability to frost damage (clause 17).

Many of these items also occur to those parts of a project affected by partial completion (clause 18). Upon achieving practical completion, the contractor is no longer obliged to accept instructions from the architect in respect of additional work since the works are now complete. The contractor may choose to do this work on the basis of a fresh agreement. For example, in connection with the payment for this work, bill rates and interim certificate periods, etc. will no longer apply.

Defects liability

The contractor is responsible for the making good of defects, shrinkages or other faults which appear within the defects liability period. These must be due to materials and workmanship which are not in accordance with the contract, or to frost damage occurring before the practical completion of the works. If defects occur because of the inadequacy of the design, the contractor is not obliged to make these good. The architect cannot also issue a variation order after the issue of the certificate of practical completion in order to remedy design faults. Items which 'appear' during the defects liability include those presumably that were unnoticed during the contract period. These items must be included on a schedule of defects not later than 14 days after the expiration of the said defects liability period. The length of the defects liability period must be inserted in the Appendix to the conditions, although 6 months is the recommended length. The making good of the contractor's defects should be done within a reasonable time and entirely at his own expense.

When, in the opinion of the architect, the defects requested have been made good, and the defects liability period has expired, the certificate of making good defects will be issued. The issue of this certificate releases the remainder of the retention monies due to the contractor, and removes the defects obstacle that would prevent the issue of the final certificate. Contractors, however, are not totally released from the responsibility of defective work since they will still be affected by the statute of limitations.

Contractors will never be responsible for making good, at their own expense, damage by frost which occurs after the issue of the certificate of practical completion of the works. Should damage of this nature be found there may be some difficulty in practice of deciding when it occurred.

Partial possession by employer (clause 18)

The employer, with the agreement of the contractor, may decide to take possession of a section of the works. This is particularly appropriate where the contract concerned may be in two distinct parts – for example, alterations and extension, two extensions to an existing building or a housing scheme where numbers of units are released at various different intervals. The architect shall issue to the contractor, on behalf of the employer, a written statement identifying the parts of the works taken into possession and the date when the employer took possession. This certificate has the same effect on the part completed, as the certificate of practical completion has on the whole. Items 1–7 under 'Practical completion' above apply equally to this part of the works that are now complete, and have received the aforementioned certificate. (See sectional completion supplement to JCT form of contracts.)

Date for possession, completion and postponement (clause 23)

The date for possession of the site by the contractor is stated in the Appendix to the conditions of contract. Failure on the part of the building owner to provide the site by this date will result in a breach of contract. There is, however, provision in JCT 80 to allow the employer, without being in breach of contract, to defer giving the contractor possession of the site for a period not exceeding 6 weeks. The deferment of the date of possession is referred to in the Appendix and the period of deferment should be stated if less than 6 weeks. The contractor must start the project and 'regularly and diligently' proceed with the project to the date of completion or the completion date if this has been extended. Failure on the part of the contractor to make regular progess with the works will also result in a breach of contract, this time on the part of the contractor. The employer is able to determine the contractor's employment on the works for this reason (clause 27.1.2).

The completion date is the date at the start of the defects liability period. It is also the date, should the contractor fail to complete by this time, of the starting point of the provisions relating to liquidated damages. It should be noted that the date for completion is the date written into the contract. The completion date is this date amended to take into account any extra time allowed under an extension of time or for the repair of war damage.

The architect can postpone the work for a short period of time or indefinitely. Where postponement exceeds the period of delay stated in the Appendix, the contractor can determine the contract. In circumstances where the postponement is a relatively short period of time the usual redress for the contractor is to claim an extension of time under clause 25 and loss and expense under clause 26.

The employer, with the consent of the contractor in writing, may use or occupy the site or the works for the purpose of storage of goods or otherwise before the date of practical completion. Before the contractor gives this consent the provisions of the insurers should be obtained. If an additional insurance premium is required and the employer continues to use the site then the premium will be added to the contract sum.

Extension of time (clause 25)

Once the main contractor realizes that the progress of the works is likely to be delayed the architect should be informed in writing, giving the reasons for the cause of the delay. Where the delay includes reference to a particular nominated subcontractor, this firm should also be given details of the delay. The effect of the successful application of this clause by the contractor is to reduce or eliminate any damages that may be suffered due to non-completion of the works by the agreed date. The initiative to be taken in seeking either an extension of time or a further extension of time must come from the contractor.

The contractor, in giving notice to the architect, should where possible provide particulars of the expected effects of the delay, and also estimate the extent in respect of completion of the works. If the answers to these questions are not known to the contractor, the architect should nevertheless be informed of a probable delay, and be provided with this information at a later date.

Upon receipt of the notice of delay, the architect shall decide whether any of the events listed are relevant. If, in the architect's opinion, these are not considered to be a reasonable basis for an extension of time, the extension to the contractor should be refused.

If the reasons listed by the contractor are accepted as a relevant event by the architect, then the architect should write to the contractor giving details of:
1. The events that, in the opinion of the architect, are relevant in these circumstances for an extension of time.
2. A new completion date that has been estimated to be fair and reasonable. (If variations of omissions have been issued since the fixing of a previous completion date, then these can be taken into account in the fixing of a new date.)

The new completion date fixed by the architect must be at least 12 weeks from the receipt of the notice, or at the earliest the previously agreed completion date. The architect can therefore bring forward the completion date where the contract work has been significantly reduced. However, reasonable notice must be given to the contractor of this intention (12 weeks) and in any case it must be shown to be a fair and reasonable action. The architect must also notify the contractor in writing where it is not considered to be fair and reasonable to fix a later date as a completion date.

The architect must, within 12 weeks from the date of practical completion of the works, write to the contractor to fix a completion date. This date may be fixed as follows:
1. The completion date as previously fixed or stated in a confirmed acceptance of a 13A Quotation.
2. A later completion date, in order to take into account any extension of time that in the opinion of the architect is justifiable.
3. An earlier completion date, if in the opinion of the architect the construction work has been significantly reduced. This date, however, cannot be fixed earlier than the date for completion stated in the Appendix to the form of contract.

The architect can revise the completion date as necessary. It is not necessary to wait until the contractor suggests that the works will be delayed. If, however, the contractor does not request an extension of time, the architect is not bound to take any action or to attempt to enforce a later completion date than is otherwise stated in the contract.

The contractor must always, using the best endeavours, try to prevent any delay in the progress of the works. The contractor must also, to the satisfaction of the architect, proceed with the regular progress of the works.

The following are the relevant events referred to in clause 25:

1. *Force majeure.* The meaning of this phrase is imprecise, but it is generally accepted to mean 'exceptional circumstances beyond the control of either of the parties of the contract'.

2. *Exceptionally adverse weather conditions.* These are weather conditions that could not normally be expected at the time of the year in the location of the building works. For example, heavy rainfall during the winter months would not fit within the definition of exceptional unless it was abnormal. In the winter of 1978/79 the total rainfall was 579 mm compared to the average for this period over the preceding years of 452 mm (Manchester Weather Centre). This may have been considered exceptional, but such a decision may rest with the courts of law if the parties cannot agree upon an interpretation.

3. *Loss or damage occasioned by any one or more of the specified perils.* The perils referred to in this clause are generally those items which are an insurable risk, such as fire, lightning, explosion, storm, tempest, etc. The full list of the specified perils are described under 'Definitions' in clause 1.3.

4. *Civil commotion, etc.* This is also included as one of the specified perils. It includes both local and national strikes, and lock-outs by management of any of the trades employed upon the works. It is also extended to similar actions in the preparation, manufacture or transportation of the goods and materials.

5(i) *Compliance with architect's instructions* – in respect of:
   (a) discrepancies in or divergences between documents (clauses 2.3 and 2.4.1);
   (b) an instruction requiring a variation (clause 13.2) (except for a confirmed acceptance of a 13A Quotation);
   (c) the expenditure of provisional sums (clause 13.3) except provisional sums for defined work; or a provisional sum for performance specified work (clause 13A.4.1);
   (d) the postponement of any work (clause 23.2);
   (e) the finding of antiquities on the site (clause 34);
   (f) nominated subcontractors' work (clause 35);
   (g) nominated suppliers (clause 36).

5(ii) If the main contractor is required to open up work for inspection or testing, and if the work complies with the contract, then this becomes an admissible event. If the work is not in accordance with the contract any delays ensuing will not be grounds for an extension of time.

6. *Delay in the receipt of instructions, drawings, details or levels from the architect.* If this is to be accepted as a relevant event the contractor must have requested the information beforehand from the architect. The contractor must also use some foresight in respect of when the details are required. The architect must be given reasonable notice so that the

information can be prepared and provided by the requisite time. In practice the contractor, by reference to the programme of works, should be able to ask for such information well in advance. The clause does not, however, assume that the architect will only work at the 'direction' of the contractor, but that the architect will be diligently preparing the information that the contractor will require anyway. In the event of this assumption being invalid, the contractor could be involved in preparing the architect's checklist, and then be penalized for doing this inadequately.

7. *Delay on the part of the nominated subcontractors or nominated suppliers.* If the main contractor has taken all practicable steps to avoid or reduce these delays this fulfils this condition for an extension of time.

8. *Delay on the part of works or persons engaged by the employer.* This assumes that if the employer decides to undertake some of the work direct, outside the scope of this contract, then such work should be carried out so as not to cause a delay to the main contract. The main contractor here will have minimal control. It is up to the employer, therefore, to take the necessary steps to ensure as little inconvenience as may be expected. This clause also covers the supply by the employer of materials and goods which the employer has agreed to provide for the works.

9. *Government intervention.* If, once the contract has been signed, the government restricts the availability or use of labour which is essential to the carrying out of the works, then the contractor may apply for an extension of time. In the case of war, for example, the government may call up all 'able-bodied' men to the armed services thus removing tradesmen from the labour market. In other circumstances it may commandeer the essential building materials. On other occasions it may restrict the use of fuel or energy resulting in limited working, as occurred in 1973 with the three-day working week. Two points are, however, worthy of note. First, the government intervention must restrict the essential supplies of men, materials, fuel or energy. If the work can be easily performed in some other way, without detriment to the project, then no claim for an extension of time will be permitted. Second, the government intervention must occur after the signing of the contract. If the contractor knew or should have known before entering into the contract that the government would introduce certain restrictive measures, this cannot be claimed as a basis of defence.

10. *Contractor's inability to secure labour and material.* The foregoing comments on government intervention apply equally to this relevant event. For example, a sudden unexpected upturn of the construction industry in a certain area may starve some sites of the essential supplies of labour and materials.

11. *Work by local authorities or statutory undertakings.* Although these may be part of the contract, the contractor may have severe difficulties in

attempting to control them. In some circumstances the contractor may be delayed waiting for statutory inspections by local authorities. The contractor must, however, have taken all reasonable steps to avoid difficulties occurring in these circumstances.

12. *Failure on the part of the employer to give access.* If the employer is unable to give to the contractor, by the stipulated dates stated in the contract, proper ingress to or egress from the works as defined in the contract documents, then the contractor will be entitled to an extension of the contract period.

13. Where clause 23.1.2 is stated in the Appendix to apply, the deferment by the employer of giving an extension under this clause.

14. *Inaccurate forecast of an approximate quantity.* Where such work is executed by the contractor then it must be a reasonably accurate forecast.

15. Delays which the contractor has taken all practical steps to avoid due to changes in statutory requirements which necessitate some alteration or modification to performance specified work.

16. The use or threat of terrorism and the actions of the authorities in dealing with such threats.

It should be noted under clause 25 that the matters discussed relate only to an extension of the contract period. The relevant events listed will form a good reason on the part of the contractor to this contractual provision. It must not be assumed to be an automatic result following any one of these events. In any case the agreement for an extension of time could result, in some cases, in only a matter of a few days.

Another important factor connected with this clause, is the aspect of any financial adjustment to the contract sum either in connection with damages for non-completion (clause 24) or the loss and expense to the contractor resulting from the delay (clause 26). These matters are discussed more fully with those appropriate clauses.

One further point that needs to be considered is that an extension of the contract period, for any reason, may be unacceptable to the employer. The architect may therefore reasonably expect the contractor to take appropriate action to save time. The contractor may also reasonably expect to be paid for the costs involved in such action. There is, however, no obligation under the contract for the contractor to take such action.

Determination by employer (clause 27)

In certain circumstances the employer is rightfully allowed to terminate the employment of the contractor. If the contractor defaults in one of the following ways the architect may issue a notice to the contractor accordingly. This notice must be delivered by registered post or recorded delivery specifying the default. The reason why the notice must be delivered in this manner is to avoid any claim by the contractor that it was not received.

1. The contractor unreasonably suspends the carrying out of the works. This is for the architect to decide.
2. The contractor fails to carry out the works in a regular and diligent manner. This may also put the contractor in breach of clause 23.
3. The contractor fails to comply with an instruction from the architect to remedy defective work, and this results in further damage to the works. (It should be noted that the failure to comply with other instructions merely results in the architect issuing the instructions to another firm, and recouping the necessary amount from the contractor.)
4. The contractor has either assigned or sublet a portion of the works without permission (clause 19).

In the case of a default the contractor should be asked to remedy the contract, perhaps unofficially at first. If the contractor continues to ignore the warning from the architect then the notice of determination should be sent to the contractor. The contractor, upon receipt of the notice, has then 14 days in which to rectify the problem. The employer may then within 10 days after this date, assuming that the contractor is still in default, issue a notice that effectively terminates the employment of the contractor. The employer must ensure that the issue of the notice is a reasonable course of action to take, and should not be given solely to annoy the contractor (clause 27.2.4).

If the contractor ends the specified default or the employer does not determine the contract on this occasion, this can nevertheless be proceeded with later should the contractor default on some other issue.

If a contractor becomes insolvent, or arranges with creditors for voluntary winding up (Companies Act 1985 and Insolvency Act 1986 and Fig. 17.1), then the employment of the contractor is automatically terminated. There is, however, provision in the contract for this employment to be reinstated where both the employer and the contractor, or liquidator, agree. In practice, there are immense disadvantages to the employer where bankruptcy of the contractor occurs. It is therefore in the best interests to retain the services of the contractor, where this has been previously satisfactory. The liquidator is also in a position of wishing to continue with those contracts that are likely to be profitable and quick to execute. Contracts that are nearing completion are therefore likely to be retained, whilst those in their earlier stages of construction may be dispensed with.

The employer is also entitled to terminate the contractor's employment in cases of corruption. This can be extended to all contracts between the employer and the contractor where an irregularity of this nature has occurred on only one contract. The contractor may, for example, be already undertaking several different contracts on behalf of the employer. A bribe might be used to secure further work. Where this is proved, then all the contractor's work may be terminated. Corruption may result from the method of obtaining work or from the execution of the contract. Corruption can also occur where one of the contractor's employees offers favours which are neither known nor sanctioned

Position as it should have been

		£
Contract sum		500,000
Value of variations		25,000
Theoretical Final Account		525,000

Position at determination

Value of work executed at time of liquidation		340,000
Interim payments	300,000	
Less retention	−15,000	
	285,000	
Nominated subcontractors paid after determination	30,000	
	315,000	315,000
Amount outstanding at determination		25,000

Position at final account

Paid as above, at determination	315,000
New completion contract	250,000
Employer's loss and expense	25,000
	590,000
Less as it should have been	525,000
Cost of determination/bankruptcy	£65,000

Fig. 17.1   Example showing calculation at contractor's insolvency

by the contractor. The offences would usually come within the remit of the Prevention of Corruption Acts 1889 to 1916. Although corruption is generally well understood, it is often difficult to draw a line between the actions that may be classified as such. For example, many would regard the offer of a bottle of spirits at Christmas time as quite acceptable, and not as a bribe or offered in return for a favour. A crate of spirits would probably prove to be a different situation!

The respective rights of the employer and contractor, upon the termination of the contractor's employment, are as follows:

1.   The employer may engage another firm to complete the project. This firm is to be allowed to use all the temporary buildings, plant and equipment until completion free of charge.

2.   Unless the termination occurs because of bankruptcy, the contractor must, without payment, assign to the employer any benefits for the supply of goods and materials or for the execution of subcontracts. In practice, the contractor could encourage bad relations to develop in order to deprive the employer of these benefits.

3.   Where insolvency has not occurred the employer may pay any supplier for materials or goods, or a subcontractor for work executed, who have not previously received payment. The employer may also use discretion for paying nominated subcontractors, who should have been paid previously under certificates. The employer will then try to recover these sums from the contractor. In practice, those who should have been paid, but have not been because of a default on the part of the contract, may be unwilling to carry on their work unless they receive a payment. The employer may

therefore be forced into this situation, in order to see progress in the works, and then try to recover the amounts from the contractor.

4.   The contractor must remove temporary works and other items within a reasonable time after receiving an instruction from the architect. Where the contractor fails to do this, the employer shall remove and sell the items, and after deducting costs, pass on the proceeds for the benefit of the contractor.

5.   If the employer suffers any loss or expense because of this termination then this will become a debt of the contractor.

6.   The employer is not bound to make any further payments to the contractor until the project has been properly completed and the accounts agreed for the project as a whole.

If after the determination of the contractor, the employer chooses not to proceed with the works, then the contractor must be notified. The total value of work that has been properly executed is calculated, less any reasonable costs and expenses borne by the employer. The difference is then expressed as a debt or credit to the contractor.

Determination by contractor (clause 28)

A number of situations can arise which can give the contractor the legal right to terminate the contract. If the contractor decides that this is an appropriate course of action to follow then a notice in writing must be sent to the employer specifying the default that has caused this to take place. The notice should be sent by registered post or recorded delivery (clause 28.1.1). It must not be sent simply to annoy either the employer or the architect (clause 28.2.5). However, this does not imply that a contractor should take into account the peculiar state of the employer in respect of, for example, the employer's temporary shortage of funds due to a cash flow crisis.

However, in a majority of cases this course of action suits no one. It is therefore introduced as a last resort measure. The contractor will already have attempted to solve the dispute that caused the determination in other ways. Also whilst a contractor may be completely innocent, damage may nevertheless be suffered in terms of reputation or financial loss. Determination usually results from a series of actions rather than a single misdemeanour on the part of the employer. This might, for example, result from a repetition of one of the events listed below. Determination usually occurs for one of the following reasons.

Financial

The employer:

1.   Does not discharge in accordance with the contract the amount properly due in respect of a certificate or VAT in pursuant of the VAT Agreement.

2.   Interferes or obstructs the issue of any certificate.

If the employer fails to pay a certificate within 14 days (clause 30) and continues to default for a further 7 days, then the contractor can issue a notice of intention of termination. The first time that this occurs, the contractor is more likely to approach the architect regarding the absence of the payment. The certification of monies due is not a matter of debate by the employer. Where an employer has misgivings about the performance of the contractor, then this should be brought to the attention of the architect. Also the employer cannot deduct sums of money from a certificate that has already been authorized by the architect. This is the most usual circumstance that results in determination by the contractor because the employer fails to honour the conditions of an interim certificate.

Assignment and subcontracts

If the employer fails to comply with the provisions of clause 19.1.1 and attempts to assign a part of the contract to another, without the contractor's permission, then this can give rise to determination by the contractor.

Suspension of the works

The project has been suspended by the architect, employer or someone else such as a local authority. The period for such a delay is entered in the Appendix to the form of contract, and is normally one month. Suspension of the works may arise because of:
1. The contractor not having received in due time the necessary instructions, drawings, details or levels from the architect, for which the contractor has made a specific request in writing. Such requests must, of course, allow the architect sufficient time to provide this information.
2. The compliance with an architect's instructions issued under clauses 2.3 (discrepancies between documents), 13.2 (variations) or 23.2 (postponement), unless caused by the contractor.
3. Delays caused by persons employed directly by the employer.
4. Failure on the part of the employer to give in due time ingress to or egress from the site of the works through or over any land or buildings.

Insolvency of the employer

The employer shall inform the contractor in writing where this situation arises. Determination shall take effect upon the date of receipt of such notice.

Effects of determination by the contractor

The effects of determination by the contractor results in the following financial arrangements with the following sums being paid by the employer:

1. The reasonable costs of the removal of any temporary buildings, plant, tools, equipment and goods, including subcontractors. This must be done within a reasonable period of time, taking precautions to prevent possible injury, death or damage.
2. The payment of any retention monies within 28 days.

The contractor shall within a reasonable time prepare an account setting out the following:

1. The value of work already completed and the value of work under construction, that have been properly authorized by the architect.
2. Any sum resulting from loss and expenses under clause 26.
3. The reasonable cost of removal in pursuing this course of action.
4. The direct loss and expense resulting directly from this determination.
5. The costs of other materials and goods already ordered and provided for the works.

The respective procedure, therefore, following determination by the contractor is as follows. The contractor will clear the site, the employer will pay for the work completed to date including materials and goods for the works and retention amounts. In addition the contractor will be paid for loss and expense to cover this premature action by the employer.

Determination by employer or contractor (clause 28A)

This clause results from the tribunal's decision that those grounds in clause 28.1.3, under which the contractor could give notice to determine the contract and which were not acts or defaults of the employer, should be withdrawn from this clause. They are in effect neutral events caused by neither the employer nor the contractor. They should thus be given as grounds for determination by either party. The events listed relate to the suspension of the works and are:

1. *Force majeure.*
2. Loss or damage to the works occasioned by any one or more of the specified perils.
3. Civil commotion.
4. Architect's instructions issued under clauses 2.3 (discrepancies or divergencies between documents), 13.2 (instructions requiring a variation) or 23.2 (architect's instructions – postponement).
5. Hostilities in the UK, whether or not war has been declared.
6. Terrorist activity.

Either the employer or contractor may give notice in writing to the other party by registered post or recorded delivery. The notice will deemed to have been received within 48 hours of posting. If after a further 7 days the suspension of the works has not ended, then the contract will be determined. In this situation presumably neither party wants the contract to end, but this has occurred due to events beyond the control of either party.

The contractor will not be allowed to give notice under clause 28A.1.1.2, where the loss or damage was due to the contractor's own negligence or default.

The consequences of this determination are as follows. The removal from the site of the contractor's temporary buildings, plant, tools, equipment, materials and goods, including site materials. This must be done within a reasonable length of time and with precautions to prevent injury, death or damage. This applies also to subcontractors working on the site. The employer will release half of the retention monies within 28 days of the notice.

Within a further 2 months, the contractor must provide the necessary documents to prepare the final account for the project. This is to be calculated as follows:

1. Total value of works at determination.
2. Sum ascertained in respect of direct loss and expense under clauses 26 (loss and expense generally) and 34.3 (antiquities).
3. Reasonable cost of removal under clause 28A.3.
4. Cost of all materials and goods ordered for the works, which then become the property of the employer.
5. Any direct loss or damage caused by the determination.

This amount together with any outstanding retention sums should be paid to the contractor within 28 days. This could include loss due to one of the specified perils that might have been caused by the negligence of the employer. Nominated subcontractors will also be informed of this situation.

Chapter 18

Works by other persons

The following group of clauses relate to those parts of the works that are done by firms other than the main contractor. In some examples the main contractor has no choice in the matter, other than a reasonable objection to such firms or persons on the works.

Clause 19   Assignment and subcontracts.
Clause 29   Works by employer or persons employed or engaged by employer.
Clause 35   Nominated subcontractors.
Clause 36   Nominated suppliers.

The first of these clauses allows the main contractor to appoint domestic subcontractors. The number of subcontractors employed will depend on the overall facilities provided by the main contractor. On some projects the contractor may work in a co-ordinating and organizing role only, after subcontracting the whole of the work. The architect must approve all these subcontractors, and in any event the main contractor's responsibilities within the terms of the contract are not diminished. The assignment of these responsibilities to another firm is generally not acceptable to the architect or building owner.

Clause 29 provides the right to allow the employer's own contractors to be engaged upon the works during the normal contract period. These firms may be of a very specialized nature, such as sculptors, and the employer may wish, therefore, to retain a more direct control over their work.

Clause 35 is one of the longer clauses of JCT 80, and deals with the provision for nominated subcontractors. The clause is subdivided into 26 subclauses, as follows:

35.1–2   General.
35.3–35.12   Procedure for nomination.
35.13   Payment of nominated subcontractors.
35.14   Extension of period for completion of nominated subcontract works.
35.15   Failure to complete nominated subcontract works.
35.16   Practical completion of nominated subcontract works.
35.17–35.19 Early final payment of nominated subcontractors.
35.20   Position of employer in relation to nominated subcontractors.
35.21   Position of main contractor.
35.22–35.23 Limitation of liability of nominated subcontractors.

35.24   Circumstances where renomination is necessary.
35.25–35.26 Determination of employment of nominated subcontractors.

Nominated subcontractors include statutory undertakings, although these are special subcontractors since neither the client, the architect nor the main contractor has any choice in their appointment.

The work to be executed covered by classes 35 and 36 are written into the bill of quantities as prime cost sums, and are subject to adjustments under the terms of the contract.

Assignment and subcontracts (clause 19)

Neither the employer nor the contractor shall, without the written consent of the other, assign the contract. The contractor must also, prior to subletting any portion of the works, obtain the written consent of the architect. The consent must not be unreasonably withheld. The terms of the contract accept that the main contractor will probably not undertake all the trades, but that some of the work will be done by subcontracting firms. The subcontractors whom the main contractor chooses to employ are known as domestic subcontractors. In order that the architect can have some influence over domestic subcontractors, it is necessary to know who they will be in order that they can be approved. This approval would only be withheld where the architect considered them to be unreliable or where they performed a poor standard of workmanship. The architect may have previously worked with them on other contracts or be dissatisfied with their standards of sample work.

Subletting occurs where the contractor chooses to enter into a subcontract with other firms for some part or even the whole of the contract, whilst still maintaining the existing relationship to the employer in all respects. Assignment occurs where another firm takes over the contractual rights of the contractor, and for all purposes the contractor to whom the project was contracted ceases to exist. Although subletting occurs, to some degree, on all construction projects, assignment is extremely unusual.

Where the main contractor intends to sublet some of the work, the names of the firms together with work to be sublet, should be annexed to the contract bills. The contractor must list at least three suitable firms for each section that may be sublet. The architect and the contractor are also entitled, with the consent of each other, to add additional firms to these lists at any time prior to the execution of a binding subcontract agreement.

If for any reason the main contractor's employment is determined under the contract, then the employment of these domestic subcontractors will also cease.

Where subletting occurs, then all the conditions in the contract between the main contractor and the employer must apply equally to the subcontract. The main contractor will, of course, have to ensure that these arrangements are written into the subcontract agreement otherwise conditions will apply to the contractor that will not be able to be enforced on the subcontractor.

The contractor's tender will be based upon the subcontractors' prices and quotations. However, since the subcontractors are subject to the approval of the architect, this adds some risk to the contractor, if they are not subsequently approved. Other subcontractors will then have to be invited to tender for the subcontract works, and presumably at a higher price. The approval of domestic subcontractors by the architect should therefore be sought prior to the signing of the main contract.

The main contractor has no responsibility to supply and fix materials or goods or to execute work that in the documents was intended to be carried out by nominated subcontractors (clause 19.5).

Works by employer or persons employed or engaged by employer (clause 29)

This clause used to be described as 'Artists and Tradesmen'. It envisages that the employer may choose to employ some trades directly. This work may be of a relatively minor nature or concerning items which are only loosely related to the building industry. The clause is required to secure the right to the site for such persons or firms. The contractor, knowing that these will require entry to the site, can organize and allow for any possible inconvenience or disruption. This knowledge will also give the opportunity to the contractor of including for any expense that may thus be incurred. If there is any delay on the part of their work the contractor has some redress by an extension of time (clause 25), or loss and expense (clause 26) or determination (clause 28).

If the execution of work under this heading is an afterthought on the part of the employer, the contractor must be prepared to give the same reasonable access to the works. It should be noted that the employer is responsible for their proper organization and control, because they will not fall within the jurisdiction of a subcontractor, nor the authority of the main contractor.

Nominated subcontractors (clause 35)

Works which are required to be carried out by nominated subcontractors are included in the bills of quantities as a prime cost sum. These subcontractors may supply and fix materials or goods or execute work. The Standard Method of Measurement of Building Works, seventh edition, provides for the inclusion of such items. In addition, works undertaken by nomininated subcontractors may arise from the following situations:
1. The expenditure of provisional sums.
2. An instruction from the architect requiring a variation. This is providing that such work is an extra to the contract, and that it is similar in content to other work already being carried out by nominated subcontractors.
3. By agreement between the contractor and architect on behalf of the employer. It should be noted, however, that the architect does not have the

power under the contract to omit contractor's work and award this to a nominated subcontractor (clause 13.1.3). The creation of prime cost sums can only be formed with the agreement of the main contractor.

It is the architect's prerogative to nominate firms to undertake the above work. The firms selected should meet the approval of the contractor. The nomination, however, may still proceed in certain cases where the main contractor believes that there are reasonable grounds for refusing such an approval. In these circumstances it may be unwise on the part of the architect to proceed with the nomination of such a firm. If the contractor has a reasonable objection to a proposed nominated subcontractor the architect should be informed, preferably in writing, as soon as possible. This obviously needs to be done prior to actual nomination, but also in sufficient time to enable the architect to nominate others without any delay occurring in the contract programme.

The main contractor may also wish to carry out work for which a prime cost sum has been included in the contract documents. It is sometimes usual to supply, with the tender form, both a list of the main contractor's domestic subcontractors and also a list of prime cost sums for which the contractor desires to tender. Both of these forms are often required to be returned with the contractor's tender. The following conditions from clause 35 will generally apply regarding such prime cost sums:

1.   The contractor, during the ordinary course of business, must directly carry out this work. This does not preclude subletting if agreed by the architect.
2.   The contractor must give notice of this intention as soon as possible. This is in order to pre-empt a contract being awarded to another firm. The architect may at the tender stage have already received quotations for this work.
3.   The architect must be willing to allow the contractor to tender. Refusal to tender, or to accept the contractor's lowest tender should this be the case, will usually mean that the architect prefers a specialist firm to do the work.

If the main contractor is allowed to submit a tender for this work, then the invitation to submit a price must make it absolutely clear on items such as the contractor's discounts, profit and attendances. Where the price is submitted in competition, then the importance of these items may influence the choice of the successful tender. An obvious way is to treat the main contractor's quotation in the same way as each of the other subcontractors. Problems in practice may, however, favour a composite price from the main contractor inclusive of all these items.

Procedure for nomination of a subcontractor

The following documents relate to nominated subcontractors. These are based upon a new system of nomination introduced in 1991.

The Standard Form of Nominated Subcontract Tender – NSC/T

Part 1 – The architect's invitation to tender

Part 2 – Tender by a subcontractor

Part 3 – Particular conditions (to be agreed by a contractor and sub-contractor)

The Standard Form of Articles of Nominated Subcontract Agreement between a Contractor and a Nominated Subcontractor – Agreement NSC/A

The Standard Conditions of Nominated Subcontract – NSC/C

The Standard Form of Employer/Nominated Subcontractor Agreement – NSC/W

The Standard Form of Nomination Instruction for a Subcontractor – NSC/N

The following procedures are used for the nomination of a subcontractor:

1. The architect issues an instruction to the contractor on Nomination NSC/N, nominating the subcontractor. This is accompanied by:

    (a) NSC/T Part 1, completed by the architect and NSC/T Part 2 completed and signed by the subcontractor and by the architect or the employer as approved. It includes a copy of the numbered tender documents listed in and enclosed with NSC/T Part 1 together with additional documents or amendments approved by the architect.

    (b) NSC/W, Agreement completed by the employer and subcontractor.

    (c) NSC/T Part 1, confirming any alterations to:
    item 7: obligations or restrictions imposed by employer
    item 8: order of works: employer's requirements
    item 9: type and location of access.

2. A copy of the instructions are then sent by the architect to the subcontractor together with a copy of the completed Appendix for the main contract.

3. The contractor upon receipt of this instruction then completes the NSC/T signed by both the contractor and the subcontractor and executes the Agreement NSC/A with the subcontractor.

4. A copy of NSC/A and NSC/T Part 3 is sent to the architect.

5. If the contractor after using the best endeavours has not within 10 working days complied with clause 35.7 (executing the Agreement NSC/A) then the architect must be informed in writing stating:

    (a) the date when such compliance is expected to be done, or

    (b) the reasons for the non-compliance, which might include; discrepancy in or divergence between the numbered tender documents or a discrepancy or divergence between the numbered tender documents referred to in clauses 2.3 to 2.3.4.

6. The architect may then:

    (a) if appropriate fix a later date for the contractor's compliance,

    (b) disagree that the matters identified are of relevance in which case the contractor must then comply with the nomination, or

(c)   accept that the matters are relevant and issue a further instruction or
       nominate a new subcontractor.

Payment of a nominated subcontractor

Before any nominated subcontractor's work can be included in a valuation,
invoices must be made available for inspection by the quantity surveyor. The
invoice signifies that the subcontractor concerned requires payment. The
quantity surveyor should check the invoice against the quotation. The rates, the
prices, and the arithmetic should be checked; and a check should also be made
to ensure that the quantity of work has been properly executed. Although it is
not the quantity surveyor's duty to inspect the quality of the materials and
workmanship, work should nevertheless not be included that is obviously
defective. If there are any doubts the matter should be brought to the attention
of the architect. The approved invoices are then included in the quantity
surveyor's valuation of the work as per clause 30.2, and subsequently in the
architect's certificate.

Upon the issue of each interim certificate, the architect must inform the
contractor of the amount that has been included for each nominated
subcontractor. It must also be clearly stated whether these amounts are
interim or final payments due to the subcontractors. The architect will also
inform the individual subcontractors accordingly. The main contractor must
then make these payments as directed. Deductions cannot be made for contra-
charges unless these are agreed by the subcontractor concerned. Before the
issue of each certificate, the contractor must provide some evidence that the
appropriate amounts shown on previous certificates have been paid. Such
evidence for example, might include a receipt for the amount listed. The
absence of this evidence will not automatically assume that the subcontractor
has not been paid, but before proceeding to issue another certificate the
architect must be reasonably satisfied that this is not the case.

The form of contract provides a remedy for paying the subcontractor direct,
in those cases where the main contractor defaults in payment. In circumstances
where adequate proof is unavailable to the satisfaction of the architect, the
architect shall issue a certificate accordingly together with a copy to the
nominated subcontractor. The employer is now able to pay the subcontractor
direct and to deduct these amounts from future payments to the contractor. If,
however, it is known that the main contractor is shortly due to enter into
liquidation, such a direct payment will not be made by the employer. In no
circumstances does the employer want to be placed in a position of having to
pay a subcontractor twice. Unfortunately situations do, however, occur where
this may be necessary in order to secure the services of a particular
subcontractor, without which the project would not be completed.

There are also provisions in the form of contract (clause 35.13) to allow an
employer to pay a nominated subcontractor for design work, materials and

goods prior to the issue of an instruction of nomination. Such direct payments are ignored in computing interim and final certificate payments.

Time

The main contractor is not able to give a nominated subcontractor an extension of time (this being an extension of the period in which the subcontract works are to be carried out) without the written consent of the architect. It is up to the architect to operate the relevant provisions of the subcontract, namely clause 11 in this respect.

If any nominated subcontractor fails to complete the subcontract works within the period allocated on the contract programme, or any revision thereof, then the contractor should inform the architect of this event. The architect should then send a certificate to the contractor accordingly. A duplicate copy of the certificate should be forwarded to the nominated subcontractor concerned. The certificate must be sent within 2 months of the date of notification to the architect.

When, in the opinion of the architect, a nominated subcontractor achieves practical completion of the works, a certificate should be sent to the contractor to this effect, with a duplicate copy to the nominated subcontractor.

Defects and early final payment

Final payment can be made to the nominated subcontractor prior to that of the main contract. Twelve months must elapse before this payment can be made from the date of the subcontractor's certificate of practical completion. The subcontractor concerned must, however, have remedied any defective work, and sent through the contractor to the quantity surveyor the necessary documents for the final adjustment of the contract sum.

If upon discharge by the contractor to the nominated subcontractor, the subcontractor fails to rectify those items which are the subcontractor's responsibility then, in accordance with the contract, the architect will issue an instruction to others to rectify the work. The employer in these circumstances will take the necessary steps to recover the amounts of this remedial work. If the employer is unable to recover these sums from the subcontractor, then the main contractor must provide for the necessary payments.

The main contractor will, however, be responsible for any defects to the nominated subcontractor's work from the date of the subcontractor's completion up to the issue of the final certificate for the project as a whole. Before the subcontractor is therefore released from the contract, the main contractor will require some form of indemnity against the possibility of defects occurring and the costs of their making good.

The existence of clause 35, or even other clauses within the conditions of contract, will not render the employer liable in any way to a nominated subcontractor. The only exception to this rule may be by way of the terms and agreement set out in clause NSC/Agreement. Bills of quantities often state that once the formal process of nomination has been completed such subcontractors are not dissimilar to the domestic subcontractors in contractual terms.

Design works

The main contractor is not liable to the employer in any way regarding the nominated subcontract works for any design responsibility that may be undertaken by the nominated subcontractor. The main contractor in general undertakes no design responsibility. However, the contractor is responsible for the carrying out of the work in order to ensure that it complies with the design and that the materials and workmanship are in accordance with the specification.

Liability

The liability of the main contractor to the employer cannot exceed the liability of the subcontractor to the main contractor in respect of subcontract works.

Renomination

Renomination of a nominated subcontractor is necessary if the following conditions arise:

1. If the architect is of the opinion that the nominated subcontractor has made a default regarding items in 7.1.1.1 to 7.1.1.4 of the subcontract. The main contractor must have informed the architect of the alleged default together with any observations. The architect must be of the opinion that the subcontractor has made the default.
2. If the nominated subcontractor becomes insolvent or makes an arrangement with creditors for the winding up of the company, voluntary or otherwise. This is with the exception of amalgamation or reconstruction.
3. If the nominated subcontractor has determined the contract under clause 7.7 of the subcontract.
4. The contractor has been required by the employer to determine a subcontractor's employment under clause 7.3 of the subcontract.
5. Work properly executed has to be re-executed as a result of compliance with an architect's instruction and the nominated subcontractor does not agree to carry out the work.

Where any of the above five events occurs, then the following are to apply:

1. The architect must issue an instruction to the main contractor to give to

the nominated subcontractor the notice specifying the default. The instruction may also require the contractor to obtain a further instruction prior to determining the employment of the nominated subcontractor.

2. The contractor must inform the architect, following the issue of the notice, if the employment of the nominated subcontractor has been determined. If the second instruction under this clause has been given, then the contractor must confirm the determination to the architect.

3. Once the architect has been finally informed of the determination of the nominated subcontractor, renomination is made as necessary. Where such determination has occurred because of the failure of the subcontractor to remedy the defects, the main contractor must be given the opportunity to agree the price to be charged by the substituted nominated subcontractor.

The architect must renominate as necessary in the case of the subcontractor's insolvency. If, however, the architect reasonably believes that the appointed receiver is prepared to continue to completion, then the architect may postpone a renomination. This is as long as the relevant subcontract does not detrimentally affect any other person involved in the works.

If the subcontractor has reasonably determined the contract, then the architect must renominate as necessary. Any excess price of the substituted nominated subcontractor over that of the originally nominated subcontractor may be recovered by the employer from the contractor. The reasonableness of this charge against the contractor is because, in this case, determination is a result of the contractor's default.

All amounts payable to the renominated subcontractors must be included in the interim certificates and added to the contract sum.

The contractor cannot determine the contract of any nominated subcontractor without an appropriate instruction from the architect. If the determination is made under the subcontract then the architect must direct the contractor with regards to any amounts due in an interim certificate.

Nominated suppliers (clause 36)

Goods and materials which are required to be obtained from a nominated supplier, are to be included in the contract bills as a prime cost sum. Where the architect knows the name of the supplier, this should be stated in the description. The fixing of these items will be undertaken by the main contractor or a domestic subcontractor where this is approved. The costs associated with fixing generally include all those items from the point of delivery to the site. The right of nomination is solely that of the architect. The nomination of firms to supply materials or goods may arise in the following ways:

(a) by the inclusion of a prime cost sum in the contract bills for the supply of goods or materials;

(b) where a provisional sum is included in the contract bills, and an architect's instruction names the supplier of any goods or materials involved;

(c) where a provisional sum results in an architect's instructions to a sole source of supply of such goods or materials;

(d) where a variation made by the architect specifies goods or materials for which there is only a single source of supply.

In the conditions of contract a nominated supplier must be covered by a prime cost sum. The naming of a supplier as part of the contractor's work – even where this is a sole supplier of goods and materials – will not therefore always result in a prime cost sum. Work can therefore be measured in the contract bills as supply and fix, even where only one supplier is known.

The architect must issue instructions for the purpose of nominating a supplier, for the works that are covered by a prime cost sum in a bill of quantities.

The amounts properly chargeable to the employer in respect of nominated suppliers' accounts, include the following items as appropriate:

1. A cash discount to the contractor of 5 per cent, where the contractor makes the necessary payment within 30 days of the end of the month during which delivery of the materials or goods are made. Any discount offered in excess of this must be passed on for the benefit of the employer. Where no discount has been included, the main contractor is allowed to add one-nineteenth to the net cost of the invoice. Quotations should be checked with regard to the discount offered prior to their acceptance.

2. Any tax or duty that is recoverable under this contract. This excludes value added tax which is capable of being treated as an input tax by the contractor (see clause 15).

3. The net cost of appropriate packaging, carriage and delivery charges. The main contractor should return the empty packing to the supplier for any credit that may be available. The credit is for the benefit of the employer. The cost of such carriage should be identified on the quotation.

4. The charges incurred for any adjustment in price, in accordance with clauses 38–40.

5. If, in the opinion of the architect, the contractor incurs additional expense for which there is no proper reimbursement, then such an amount may be added to the contract sum. Such an amount may arise as a direct charge made to the contractor by the supplier.

The architect should only nominate firms as suppliers of goods and materials where the following conditions apply. The contractor can refuse to enter into a contract of sale, where they do not.

1. The quality of the materials and goods must conform to the standards specified. This is largely a matter for the architect to determine, but they may affect the overall quality of the works and the method of fixing undertaken by the contractor.

2. The nominated supplier must make good any defects, in the materials or goods, which appear before the end of the defects liability period. The supplier should also reimburse the contractor for any costs that may be incurred – for example, in refixing or returning the defective materials to the suppliers. Any extra costs might also presumably include loss and expense caused by delays. Reimbursement of the contractor's costs will only be paid in the following circumstances:
   (a) where a reasonable examination of the goods by the contractor would not have revealed their defects;
   (b) where the goods have been properly stored and not misused before, during or after their incorporation in the works.

3. The delivery of the materials or goods, including unloading, is done in accordance with the instructions of the supplier, or agreed between the supplier and the contractor, or undertaken in a reasonable manner by the contractor. The supplier must also be prepared to accept the contractor's programme as far as delivery is concerned. If the supplier is unable to meet this, then the contractor can reasonably expect the architect to nominate an alternative supplier, because they may be crucial to the overall contract programme. The programme may only be varied on the following grounds:
   (a) *force majeure*;
   (b) civil commotion;
   (c) any instruction of the architect under clause 13.2 (variations) or clause 13.3 (provisional sums);
   (d) failure on the part of the architect to supply information at the due time;
   (e) exceptionally adverse weather conditions.

4. The nominated supplier must make the appropriate allowance for the cash discount of 5 per cent.

5. The nominated supplier will not usually deliver goods to the site after the contractor's determination, unless they have already been paid for by the employer.

6. The main contractor must pay the required amount within 30 days of the end of the month during which delivery is made.

7. The ownership of the materials or goods will pass to the contractor upon delivery to site by the nominated supplier, regardless of whether payment has been made. This may be a difficult clause to substantiate in practice, particularly if some of the components or materials supplied have a defective title.

8. If differences in opinion exist between the supplier and the contractor, they must first agree to take their differences to arbitration.

9. The conditions of sale, often printed on the reverse side of suppliers' quotations and invoices, will not override the conditions as described above.

Of course, in practice, if the supplier can persuade the architect or the contractor to waive any of these conditions, this can be done by agreement. Good advice, recommended elsewhere, is that the standard clauses should not be tampered with except in extreme circumstances. If, however, the architect wishes to appoint a firm whose contract of sale excludes a condition listed above, then the architect must also be prepared to relieve the contractor of this same obligation towards the employer.

Chapter 19

Injury and insurance of the works

The definition of 'insurance' is that one party (the insurer) undertakes to make payments to or for the benefit of the other party (the assured) upon the occurrence of certain specified events. The insurance contract between these parties is generally contained in a document called an insurance policy. The consideration, which is necessary to make such a contract binding, is provided by the assured in the way of a premium.

An insurance contract is said to be *uberrimae fidei*: that is, it is based upon good faith between the parties. The assured must therefore make a full disclosure of every material fact that is known. A material fact is information which, if disclosed, would influence the judgement of the insurer. Filling in the proposal form incorrectly can make the policy voidable by the insurer, even where an innocent mistake occurs. The insurance policies are usually printed on standard forms by the company issuing its own terms. Each policy must, however, be clear on the terms of insurance, and be accompanied by certain exclusions of liability.

If a situation occurs that may result in a claim by the assured, this must be notified to the company within a reasonable time of the event. The claim is often forwarded by the insurance company to a loss adjuster. This is the general procedure involving sums of even a relatively minor amount. The loss adjuster will then assess the amount of damage and the sum payable in respect of the insurance policy. Although the loss adjusters work on behalf of the insurance company, they will try to achieve an equitable settlement between the parties. In some circumstances the employer or contractor may employ a loss adjuster on their behalf in order to negotiate with the insurance company's own loss adjuster.

The following clauses are examined in this section:

Clause 20   Injury to persons and property and indemnity to the employer.
Clause 21   Insurance against injury to persons and property.
Clause 22   Insurance of the works.
Clause 22A   Erection of new buildings. All-risks insurance of the works by the contractor.
Clause 22B   Erection of new buildings. All-risks insurance of the works by the employer.

Clause 22C   Insurance of existing structures. Insurance of the works in or extensions to existing structures.

Clause 22D   Insurance for employer's loss of liquidated damages.

Injury to persons and property and indemnity to the employer (clause 20)

The contractor is liable for, and must indemnify the employer against, any expense, liability, loss, claim or proceedings of any nature. These may arise because of statute legislation or at common law. They are in respect of personal injury to, or the death of, anyone caused by the carrying out of the works by the contractor or others employed, such as subcontractors. The contractor's liability does not extend to any act of negligence either by the employer or persons directly under the employer's control, such as the employer's own contractors (clause 29). Indemnity in this circumstance means the protection that one party gives to another in respect of claims by a third party. Mainly because the contractor may be forced into liquidation, the contract provides for insurance under clauses 21 and 22 of these conditions. If, however, for some reason the insurance fails, this does not relieve the contractor of the indemnity.

The contractor is also liable for, and must indemnify the employer against, injury to property. The injury applies to any type of property and must be as a result of the carrying out of the works. The two exceptions to this liability are the same as for personal injury, viz. employer's negligence and the employer's own directly employed contractors.

The employer does, however, have the option of accepting some of the risks where one of the alternatives of clauses 22B or 22C is selected. Also, the contractor will not be responsible should damage occur because of an inappropriate or false design, but must ensure that even in these circumstances all reasonable precautions during the execution of the works have been taken. Where loss or damage does occur the contractor's main area of defence is to point any negligence in the direction of the employer, architect or other agents working on behalf of the employer.

Insurance against injury to persons and property (clause 21)

The main contractor under clause 20 has a liability to indemnify the employer against injury to persons and property. The main contractor is responsible for the whole works, including that of subcontractors. The contractor should therefore seek to ensure that all subcontractors maintain insurances to cover the liability of the contractor in respect of all of those items in clause 20. If, however, a subcontractor fails to provide the appropriate insurance cover, this will not remove the overall liability of the main contractor to the employer. The contractor is only exempt in the case of negligence caused by the employer or persons for whom the employer is directly responsible.

Insurance is required against claims submitted by third parties for injury to persons and property. These third parties will include the owners and the occupiers of adjoining properties and the general public. It will also include all those who visit the site or who have lawful entry to the works. A public liability policy will protect the contractor against claims arising through negligence or mistake. There may also be occasions when a third party will be able to substantiate a claim even when negligence cannot be proved. The policy must therefore include clauses to guard against such claims. A major risk with constructional work is the danger of subsidence to adjoining property. It is equally important to ensure that the contractor's public liability policy also covers this event.

The contractor will also be required to provide an employer's liability insurance for workmen employed by the contractor. Although the National Insurance provides for compensation of employees for injury, the employer will still be liable at common law to compensate the employee for injury due to negligence, whether through the fault of the individual concerned or that of another employee. The premiums paid are often calculated on the basis of the annual wage bill.

The employer can at any time request the contractor, or any subcontractor, to produce for inspection, documentary evidence that the insurances are properly maintained. This will usually require the appropriate policies being produced at least some time during the early stages of the contract. The employer can, however, require them to be produced at other reasonable times, as long as this is not done simply to irritate the contractor.

If the contractor or a subcontractor fails to insure properly or continue to insure the works as requested, then the employer may insure on their behalf. The employer will pay the necessary premiums and deduct these amounts from sums due to the contractor. The amounts recoverable from the contractor are those amounts that the employer actually pays, rather than any amount inserted by the contractor in the bills. Because this problem is more likely to occur at the beginning of the contract, the employer can deduct the appropriate amounts from interim certificates.

In some circumstances a provisional sum may be included in the bills of quantities for insurances. The contractor should then maintain in the joint names of the employer and contractor, insurances to the appropriate amount as stated in the contract bills. Such indemnity shall cover damage to property other than the works caused by collapse, subsidence, vibration, weakening or removal of support, or lowering of ground water, unless the damage occurs because of:
(a)   contractor's liability under clause 20.2;
(b)   errors in the design of the works;
(c)   damage that is likely to be inevitable having regard to the nature of the works, which is almost an uninsurable item;
(d)   where the employer has accepted responsibility for the insurance of the works under clause 22c;

(e)   war risks or excepted risks.

Any insurance required for the above should be placed with insurers approved by the employer. The contractor must also provide proof of the policy and that the premiums have been paid. The inclusion of a provisional sum may mean that some of these items are difficult to insure.

In no circumstances will the contractor be liable either to indemnify the employer or to insure against personal injury or death of any person, or damage, loss or injury caused to the works or site materials, work executed, the site, or any property, by the effect of an excepted risk. The excepted risks are defined in clause 1.3 and are as follows:

(a)   ionizing radiations;
(b)   contamination by radioactivity from any nuclear fuel or from any nuclear waste from the combustion of nuclear fuel;
(c)   radioactive toxic explosive;
(d)   other hazardous properties of any nuclear assembly or component;
(e)   pressure waves caused by aircraft;
(f)   other aerial devices travelling at sonic or supersonic speeds.

The amount of insurance cover required for any one occurrence or series of occurrences arising out of one event, in respect of injury to persons and property, is to be stated in the Appendix to the form of contract. The employer may need to seek expert advice in connection with this sum, but in any event the contractor may well wish to maintain third party policies at a much higher level.

Insurance of the works (clause 22)

The responsibility for the cost of making good any damage to the works, during the period of construction under JCT 80 allows for one of three choices to be made by the employer. Two of these should therefore be deleted. The conditions do not envisage, in any circumstances, the contractor being responsible for insurance beyond the period of practical completion of the works. They assume that the date of handover of the project will become the entire responsibility of the employer as far as the insurance items are concerned.

The three choices available for the insurance of the works are as follows:

22A   Erection of new buildings. All-risks insurance of the works by the contractor.
22B   Erection of new buildings. All-risks insurance of the works by the employer.
22C   Insurance of existing structures. Insurance of the works in or extensions to existing structures.

Where the project is comprised of two separate parts, one being new works and the other being alterations, it is possible to use both clauses 22A and 22C. Confusion might occur regarding the common stock of materials and the apportionment of the preliminaries costs. From a procedural point of view, the events would be governed by the alternative invoked when a particular incident occurred. A further clause 22D has also been added, to cover the insurance for employer's loss of liquidated damages under clause 25.4.3.

Essentially two kinds of policy are available for property insurance. The first type is known as an indemnity policy. 'To indemnify' means not only to protect against harm or loss and make financial compensations, but also to secure legal responsibility. The payments made by the insurance company are based upon the damage that occurs less any depreciation in the value of the property. The alternative policy has a reinstatement clause which commits the insurers to paying the full cost of replacement, no account being taken of depreciation. If property is insured for less than its true value, the policy holder then will be paid an average sum based upon a ratio of insured to true value. For example, if the property is only insured at half the true amount then whatever the size of the claim only half of it will be reimbursed. Some property owners choose to carry a part of the risk themselves, and in these circumstances the insurance company will then only be responsible for a proportion of the loss. In other circumstances an excess clause may be included to avoid claims for trivial amounts of damage. In addition to the cost of reinstatement the insured could be put to further expense as a result of the incident, such as the provision of alternative accommodation. This is known as consequential loss and a clause to cover this should be included in the policy.

Clause 22 is largely concerned with definitions, for example, all-risks insurance – defined as insurance which provides cover against any physical loss or damage to work executed and site materials but excluding the cost necessary to repair, replace or rectify:

1. Property which is defective due to wear and tear, obsolescence, deterioration, rust or mildew.
2. Materials or workmanship which are defective in terms of their design or executed work which relied upon the support or stability or work which was defective.
3. Loss or damage caused by or arising from:
   (a) any consequence of war, invasion, act of foreign enemy, hostilities (whether or not war has been declared), civil war, rebellion, revolution, insurrection, military or usurped power, confiscation, commandeering, nationalization or requisition or loss or destruction of or damage to any property by or under the order of any government *de jure* or *de facto* or public, municipal or local authority;
   (b) disappearance or shortage if such disappearance or shortage is only revealed when an inventory is made or is not traceable to an identifiable event;
   (c) an excepted risk (as defined in clause 1.3).
4. If the contract is carried out in Northern Ireland:

(a)   civil commotion;

(b)   any unlawful, wanton or malicious act committed maliciously by a person or persons acting on behalf of or in connection with an unlawful association. Reference is made here to the Northern Ireland (Emergency Provisions) Act 1973.

The contractor where clause 22A applies and the employer where either clause 22B or 22C applies, shall insure the works in the joint names of both the employer and the contractor. The joint names policy must provide for either recognition of each nominated subcontractor or include a waiver by the relevant insurers of any right of subrogation which they might have against any such nominated subcontractor in respect of loss or damage by the specified perils where applicable. The specified perils are defined in clause 1.3 and include fire, lightning, explosion, storm, tempest, flood, bursting or overflowing of water tanks, apparatus or pipes, earthquake, aircraft or other aerial devices or articles dropped therefrom, riot and civil commotion, but excluding the excepted risks defined above.

Erection of new buildings -- all-risks insurance of the works by the contractor (clause 22A)

The contractor should take out and maintain a joint names policy for all-risks insurance as defined in clause 22.2. The insurance to be provided by the contractor is to be for the full reinstatement value including professional fees, the percentage for which is as stated in the Appendix. The policy shall be maintained up to the issue of the certificate of practical completion or up to any date of determination under clauses 27, 28 or 28A. This is regardless of whether the validity of determination has been contested.

The joint names policy must be taken out with insurers approved by the employer. The contractor must send to the architect, for deposit by the employer, a copy of the policy and the receipt for the premiums paid. Where the contractor fails to provide adequate insurance cover in respect of the contract, the employer may insure against the risks described. The employer cannot extend the policy to cover other risks, but can deduct the premiums from amounts owed to the contractor under interim payments. If, however, the contractor maintains an all-risks policy as the normal pattern of business efficiency, then this may be accepted as an alternative to the joint names policy outlined above. It will be subject to the endorsement of the employer's interest on the policy, and evidence that it is appropriate and being maintained and that the necessary premiums have been paid. The architect, on occasions, may also wish to inspect the policy and the contract provides for this possibility. The annual renewal date, as supplied by the contractor, of this insurance is stated on the Appendix. The provisions outlined previously in regard to any default by the contractor in taking out and maintaining insurances apply equally in this case.

If the necessity for an insurance claim arises then the contractor shall proceed as follows:

1. Inform both the architect and employer in writing of the nature, extent and location of the claim.
2. Allow for inspection by the insurers.
3. Diligently restore any work which has been damaged, replace or repair any site materials which have been lost or damaged, remove and dispose of any debris and proceed with the carrying out and completion of the works.

The insurance monies received for this work will be paid to the employer. The contractor will be paid for the rectification of this work by instalments under certificates of the architect on a similar basis to that of interim certificates. The sums received for professional fees will be paid to parties concerned. The contractor will not be paid anything extra to cover the restoration of the damaged work other than that received from the insurers. Before proceeding 'with due diligence' the contractor should make sure that the insurers have accepted the claim. Unless it is necessary for safety reasons this part of the works should not be disturbed until the company's loss adjusters have inspected the damage. The final amount received by the contractor and the employer for professional fees may be inadequate since the nature of the damages may not be pro-rata in either situation.

Erection of new buildings -- all-risks insurance of the works by the employer (clause 22B)

Under this clause the employer is responsible for insuring the works and a similar procedure to the above is adopted. The insured roles of the two parties are reversed and the principles of providing documentary evidence by the employer, or a subsequent failure to insure the works can be rectified by the contractor. In this case the amount of the premiums are added to the contract sum. The procedure to be followed by the contractor in the event of an insured claim also follows the pattern outlined above. The value of rectifying the damaged work may be on the basis of bill rates, but agreement with the insurance company's loss adjusters will be necessary to determine the actual amount to be paid to the employer. Whether the insurer's basis of payment is the same as that of the contract basis is a matter which must remain at the employer's risk.

Insurance of existing structures -- insurance of the works in or extensions to existing structures (clause 22C)

The employer is responsible for insuring the existing works under this clause in a joint names policy, with the same contractual risks occurring as with clause 22B. The procedure for notifying both the architect and the employer follows that of clause 22A. A similar pattern of reinstatement by the contractor and payment by the insurance company occurs as under clause 22B. One assumes that in this case, the contractor will be paid the full cost of reinstatement, in accordance with the contract and valuation rules. Any shortfall between that received by the employer from the insurance company and that paid to the contractor would thus be borne entirely by the employer. The insurer may, however, pay for reinstatement on the basis of the contractor's estimate for making good. Under this section, however, the occurrence of loss or damage by a specified peril may result in determination of the contract by the employer or the contractor. Presumably the damage could be so extensive as to make reinstatement of the existing building unwise as far as the employer is concerned. The contractor may also wish to terminate because the damage could result in a project that has become too complex to contemplate.

Insurance for the employer's loss of liquidated damages (clause 22D)

The Appendix to the form of contract identifies to the contractor whether or not this clause will be applied. Once the contract has been signed then the contractor may be requested to obtain a quotation for such insurance. This will be on an agreed basis of a genuine pre-estimate of the damages which may occur as the result of any delay and at the rate stated for liquidated and ascertained damages included in the Appendix. The amounts expended by the contractor to take out and maintain this insurance are added to the contract sum.

Chapter 20

Fluctuations in costs

Contracts are often described as either fixed price or fluctuating price contracts, the essential difference being that the former expects the contractor to have allowed for any changes to the contract sum for items such as inflation, etc., and the latter does not. The relevant provisions are contained in the following clauses:

Clause 37 Fluctuations
Clause 38 Contributions, levy and tax fluctuations.
Clause 39 Labour and materials costs and tax fluctuations.
Clause 40 Use of price adjustment formulae.

Fluctuations (clause 37)

Fluctuations can be dealt with in the conditions of contract in one of three ways:

1. *Clause 38*. This allows only for the adjustments in price of contributions, levies or taxes. This technically is therefore described as the 'firm price' contract.
2. *Clause 39*. The assessment of labour and materials costs and tax fluctuations, using the traditional method of calculation.
3. *Clause 40*. The calculation of price fluctuations by the formulae method.

Only one of these clauses may apply and this clause should be stated in the Appendix. If this has been omitted then it is presumed that clause 38 will be used. The three fluctuation clauses are contained in a separate booklet detailing the various provisions of each clause. In the approximate quantities version, clause 38 cannot apply. It should be noted that a strictly firm price version is not now available, since each of the choices allow for fluctuations in cost, at least caused by changes in government legislation.

Contributions, levy and tax fluctuations (clause 38)

The contract sum is deemed to have been calculated as detailed by this clause. The adjustments that may therefore be necessary will occur where differences eventually arise because of the following provisions.

Clause 38.6 includes the following definitions that are appropriate both to this clause and to clause 39:

1. *Base date.* In the first edition of JCT 80 this was described as the date of tender which was defined as 10 days before the date fixed for the receipt of tenders. Representation to the tribunal suggested that this did not provide a firm enough date because employers infrequently revised the tender date so necessitating recalculation and causing uncertainty. A firm date is now written into the Appendix and called the base date, which brings the terminology in line with the Formula Rules for Price Adjustment. The necessity for the date is to avoid contractors having to make last-minute adjustments to their tenders.

2. *Materials and goods.* This excludes consumable stores, plant and machinery, but can include timber used in formwork, electricity, and fuels if this has been specifically stated in the bills.

3. *Workpeople.* Persons whose rate of wages are governed by rules, decisions or agreements of the National Joint Council for the Building Industry or some other wage-fixing body. Foremen, for example, who work as tradesmen will be assumed to be tradesmen for the purpose and application of this clause. It should be noted that workpeople not only include those employed by the contractor on the project, but also those who may work off site in the contractor's workshops, e.g. joinery shop.

4. *Wage-fixing body.* A body which lays down recognized terms and conditions of workers as under the Employment Protection Act 1975.

The prices in the contract bills are based upon those contributions that are current at the base date. Should these change or the contractor's status be revised, then adjustment will become necessary. Although this clause is one of the trio of increased cost provisions, money may need to be repaid to the employer where the contributions decrease. It should be noted, however, that levies payable under the Industrial Training Act 1964 are expressly excluded from any adjustment (clause 38.12).

To enable the contractor to claim fluctuations in the costs of labour, the following provisions must apply. Each employee must have worked on the project for a minimum of 2 working days in any week for which the claim is applicable. The aggregation of days and parts of a day do not therefore apply. The highest properly fixed tradesman's rate must be used, provided that such a tradesman is employed by either the contractor or a domestic subcontractor. The clause is applied in the context of the Income Tax (Employment) Regulations 1973 (the PAYE regulations) under section 204 of the Income and Corporation Taxes Act 1970.

Where any of the tender types or tender rates change, then the net actual amount of an adjustment must be calculated. This sum is then paid to or allowed by the contractor. The change is measured as the difference between monies actually expended and those that were appropriate at the base date. It has already been noted that some changes are based upon a theoretical adjustment. For example, where a foreman works as a craftsman any adjustments that may be due are based upon the craftsmen rate adjustment.

In other circumstances where the workpeople are contracted out within the meaning of the Social Security Pensions Act 1975, the method of adjustment is on the basis that they are not contracted out employees.

The contributions, levies and taxes which are subject to adjustment are those which result because of an Act of Parliament or because of a change in an Act of Parliament. They are the amounts that a contractor must pay as a result of being an employer of labour, and therefore include sums such as the statutory insurances against personal injury or death. Originally the Standard Form of Building Contract (1963 edition) allowed only for fixed price and fluctuation price contracts. Either the contractor was eligible to claim for increased costs because of, for example, pay rises, or these were deemed to be included in the fixed price tender. The mid-1960s saw the introduction of taxes such as selective employment tax, and strictly in the way the fixed price contract was calculated this sum could not be recovered. Because of the expected further intervention by future governments the clause was changed so that all contracts would not include the minimum provision of dealing with these items.

The contract sum is deemed to have been calculated in the following manner in respect of materials, goods and fuels (cluase 38.2):
1. The prices contained in the contract bills are based upon the types and rates of duty and tax applicable at the base date (other than VAT). These include amounts payable on the import, purchase, sale appropriation, processing or use of the materials, goods, electricity and, where specifically mentioned in the bills, fuels.
2. If any types or rates of duty, in the context of the above, are altered, then the net difference between that actually paid by the contractor and what was presumed to have been allowed in the bills must be calculated. This sum will then be either paid to the contractor or refunded to the employer.

Where the main contractor has chosen to subcontract some of the works to domestic subcontractors the following should apply. The subcontract must incorporate provisions to provide the same effect as clause 38 of the main contract (clause 38.3), together with any percentage that may be appropriate (clause 38.7). These adjustments will be paid to the contractor or refunded to the employer.

The contractor must give a written notice to the architect of the occurrence of any of the events regarding the following provisions, for the purposes of this contract:

Clause 38.1.2   Tender types and rates, and workpeople.
Clause 38.1.6   Tender types and rates, and refunds.
Clause 38.2.2   Tender types and rates, and materials.
Clause 38.3.2   Domestic subcontractors' fluctuations.

The written notice is a condition with which the contractor must comply in order to recoup any increased costs. The notice must be sent within a reasonable time, so that the architect is aware that further expenditure is likely. Presumably this also gives the architect the opportunity of rejecting a spurious claim that is outside the scope of these conditions. The quantity surveyor and the contractor will calculate and agree the amount of fluctuation appropriate to each notified event. Any amounts that have been agreed are then added to or deducted from the contract sum. They will also be taken into account when calculating the contractor's determination payments under clause 28. The contractor must provide the quantity surveyor with the necessary evidence, in order that the amounts of fluctuations may be calculated. This must be done within a reasonable time. The incentive necessary for the contractor to do this is that payment will be received within the interim certificates once they are agreed (clause 30.2). When a fluctuation is claimed in respect of employees other than workpeople, the necessary evidence must include a certificate signed on behalf of the contractor each week, certifying the validity of the evidence (clause 38.4.5). Fluctuations are always net under this clause, exclusive of any profit to the contractor (clause 38.4.6).

Where the contractor is in default over completion, the fluctuations will not be adjusted in line with actual expenditure. The amount of fluctuations will be technically frozen at the level applicable at completion date. The contractor will therefore still be eligible for increases, but not at the true level of expenditure. If the architect has already awarded an extension of time in accordance with clause 25, or subsequently does so, then the actual increases will be reimbursed to the contractor (clause 38.4.7).

These fluctuation provisions are not applicable in respect of:

(a)   Dayworks, because these will have been valued at current rates and therefore take into account the appropriate adjustments (clause 13.5.4);

(b)   specialist works carried out by nominated suppliers or nominated subcontractors as all fluctuations will be dealt with by their invoices;

(c)   a contractor acting as a nominated subcontractor, where the above provision will apply;

(d)   changes in VAT, because these are exempt under this clause.

The percentage stated in the Appendix must be added to fluctuations paid or allowed by the contractor. The percentage stated can only be recovered on certain defined fluctuations covered by clauses 38.1.2, 38.1.3, 38.1.6 or 38.2.2. The tendering documents will stipulate the percentage to be added. Although JCT discussed a figure of 20 per cent, the typical amount inserted is nil.

Labour and materials costs and tax fluctuations (clause 39)

This is the traditional full fluctuation clause, and therefore the provisions of clause 38 are included. The contractor is thus able to claim for increases in the costs of employing labour and the costs of purchasing materials in addition to the other statutory increases. The definitions of clause 39.7 are identical to those described in clause 38.6.

Labour

The contract sum is deemed to have been calculated as follows. The prices in the bills are based upon the rates of wages, and any changes will result in an adjustment to the contract sum.

1. The adjustment is in respect of workpeople on site and of those employed directly upon the works in the contractor's workshops.
2. The rules or decisions of the National Joint Council for the Building Industry (NJCBI) or other appropriate wage-fixing body as applicable to the works will be used.
3. The rates of wages also include other emoluments and expenses, such as holiday credits and insurances.
4. Only wage changes unknown at the base date are eligible for adjustment. Promulgated changes are those that have already been agreed, and must therefore have been allowed for in the tender, even though they may not come into operation until some time after the contract has started. The actual amount of the changes must, however, be known. Proposed unagreed rates are therefore not promulgated within this definition.
5. Incentive schemes or productivity agreements under the rules of the NJCBI are subject to adjustment. For example, changes in the amount of the guaranteed bonus payment would be eligible. Independent incentive schemes operated by the contractor on site – for example, where a contractor agrees to pay the workmen an arbitrary increase – are not allowed to be reclaimed under this clause.
6. If the terms of the public holiday agreements change during the duration of the project, then the appropriate costs of these can also be included under the heading of fluctuations. If such changes were promulgated at the time of tender, then these are assumed to have been covered by the contractor.
7. The contributions and levies of the CITB, for example, are excluded from adjustment and the contractor must therefore bear the costs of all increases. In practice, considerable time is generally notified in respect of the future increases in these payments.
8. Promulgated wage rate increases known before the base date would also mean that the contractor should have allowed for increases in the respective liability insurance. Only increases that are unknown at the base date can be claimed. Because the employer's liability insurance is often based upon the wages bill of the firm, this would be an accepted adjustable item in other circumstances. However, should the employer choose to provide a more expensive insurance this claim would not be valid. Increases because of changes in the wages bill or because of inflation are therefore allowable where they were unknown at the time of tender.
9. Increases in the cost of productivity bonuses resulting from increases in standard rates of wages are recoverable. Thus, where the appropriate wage-fixing body agree upon an increase in the basic rate, the contractor

would be able to reclaim this similar proportion paid by way of his productivity agreement.

10. The contractor's employees, who are outside the scope of workpeople but who are engaged on the works, are subject to fluctuations as if they were craft operatives. A foreman working as a bricklayer would be reimbursed accordingly.

11. The prices in the bills are based upon basic transport charges as submitted by the contractor and attached to the contract bills. Provision is therefore made for increases in travel allowances payable to workpeople under a joint agreement, including increased costs of employer's transport where used, or public transport fares.

12. Clause 39.2 is largely a reproduction of the appropriate parts of clause 38, applicable to contributions, levies and taxes.

Materials

The contract sum is deemed to have been calculated in the following manner:

1. The prices contained in the contract bills are based upon the market prices of materials, goods, electricity and, where specifically stated in the bills, fuels which were current at the base date.

2. The above market prices are referred to as basic prices, and are included on a basic price list for these items. In practice, only the major cost items are listed. This may be done by the quantity surveyor in which case the list is determined at the time of tender, or alternatively, the contractor is asked to prepare a list together with prices.

3. Any changes in the market prices of these items are then subject to fluctuations and adjustments of the net changes. Only the items included on the basic price are subject to adjustment.

4. Market price changes include any changes in duty or tax (other than VAT) on the import, purchase, sale appropriation, processing or use of goods, materials, electricity or fuels as specified.

5. In order to avoid contention later, the quantity surveyor must approve of the basic prices shown on the list. These are usually supported by invoices from a single supplier. It is usual then for the contractor to obtain the actual materials from this supplier. Any changes, therefore, between quotation and invoice can be easily calculated. Where it is necessary for the contractor to use an alternative supplier, the change in price may be calculated between the invoice and the price on the basic price list and adjusted for any changes due to the use of a different supplier.

Domestic subcontractors

The provisions relating to domestic subcontractors correspond generally to the provisions of clause 38.3, but of increased scope to cover wage fluctuations.

The remaining clauses 39.5–39.8 generally also correspond to the similar provisions included under clause 38. The following briefly are those provisions:

Clause 38.5.1 Written notice of fluctuations required from the contractor.

Clause 39.5.2 Notice must be provided within a reasonable time after the occurrence of any price change.

Clause 39.5.3 Agreement of amount payable to be determined between the contractor and the quantity surveyor.

Clause 39.5.4 Amount of fluctuations to be added to the contract sum.

Clause 39.5.5 The contractor must provide the evidence for the computations.

Clause 39.5.6 Fluctuations must not result in any alteration to the contractor's profit.

Clause 39.5.7 Increased costs occurring after completion will only be paid for on the basis of those prevailing at the completion date. This may result in those circumstances where the contractor has defaulted over completion.

Clause 39.5.8 Percentage addition to be included in the Appendix where appropriate.

Use of price adjustment formulae (clause 40)

The traditional method of calculating fluctuations has many drawbacks. These may be summarized as:

(a) disagreements over what is allowable;
(b) shortfall in recovery;
(c) delays in payment;
(d) extensive work in documenting and checking claims.

An alternative procedure has therefore been developed, based upon the idea of using index numbers. This method is known as the Formulae Method of Price Adjustment and is based upon rules published by the Joint Contracts Tribunal. The indices which are used are those provided by the National Economic Development Office and the method has thus become known as the NEDO formulae. The rules are given contractual effect by incorporation in the main contract or subcontract. Two series have been devised:

1. 34 work category indices, dated March 1975.
2. 48 work category indices, dated April 1977 and with 1980 amendments.

The series 2 formulae rates are in three sections:

1. Definitions, exclusions, correction of errors.
2. Operation of work category and work group methods.
3. Application of formulae to main contractor's specialist work.

These have now been consolidated in the 'Formulae Rules 1987'. In addition there are formulae rules for subcontracts.

The use of clause 40 prescribes that the contract sum will be adjusted by use of the formulae rules. The date of tender is chosen as the base date to which the indices will apply. Since the contract sum is exclusive of VAT, the operation of this clause will in no way affect the VAT agreement and clause 15.

The following definitions from rule 3 of the formulae rules are to apply to clause 40:

1. *Base date*. This is defined in the same way as clause 38.
2. *Index numbers*. Obtained from the monthly *Bulletin of Construction Indices* published by the Property Services Agency through HMSO.
3. *Base month*. Normally the calendar month prior to the date when the tenders are returned.
4. *Valuation period*. The date of the valuation and the mid-point of the period when the fluctuations are calculated.
5. *Work categories*. The 34 (series 1) or 48 (series 2) classifications of the contract work.
6. *Work groups*. The less detailed classification which may be used in preference to item 5 above. It operates by aggregating work categories into larger units. It reduces the number of calculations but may make the results untypical of the work being measured.
7. *Balance of adjustable work*. Some sections of the bills, e.g. preliminaries, are excluded from the work categories and are valued on the basis of averaging the index numbers which are used.
8. *Non-adjustable element*. A proportion of the value of work may be excluded from the operation of the formulae under the local authorities edition of the JCT form.

The formula calculation adjustment is added to each valuation on the basis of the work carried out that month. Unlike the calculation of increased costs in clause 39, the amount determined under this clause is subject to retention. Initially the amount will be calculated using provisional indices, and eventually 3–4 months later these will be firmed up, when the final indices can be determined.

Some articles may be manufactured outside the United Kingdom, and it would therefore not be realistic to apply the formulae rules in such cases. If any variation in the market price occurs, then they will be subject to fluctuation adjustment using similar provisions to those of clause 39.

The method of adjustment to nominated subcontracts depends upon the instructions, tender and agreement reached between the subcontractor and the architect. The available methods using a formula calculation are as follows:

1. Electrical, heating and ventilating, air-conditioning, lifts, structural steelwork and catering. The relevant specialist formula, rules 50, 54, 58, 63 and 69.
2. Where none of the specialist formulae applies, the formulae in part 1 of section 2 of the formulae rules and one or more of the work categories set out in Appendix A to the formulae rules.
3. Some other appropriate method.

If the contractor decides to sublet any portion of the works these provisions must be incorporated into the subcontract as appropriate.

The quantity surveyor and the contractor have the power to agree any alteration to the methods and procedures for the formula fluctuations recovery. This is presumably to help to reduce the number of tedious calculations where an agreeable amount can be ascertained. The amounts calculated are then deemed to be the formula adjustment amounts. This is provided that such sums are a reasonable approximation to those that would have been calculated by the operation of the formulae rules.

Where the contractor does not complete the works by the completion date, the following procedure is to be adopted. The value of work completed after that date is subject to formulae adjustment on the basis of the indices applicable at the relevant completion date. Where a contract is therefore running behind schedule, the employer will consistently month by month be paying higher amounts than would otherwise be the case. If the architect has, however, granted an extension of time and fixed a later completion date, then formulae adjustment will continue to run at the current dates.

Chapter 21

Financial matters

Two clauses have been included under this heading dealing with matters relating to financial legislation:

Clause 15   Valued added tax – supplemental provisions.
Clause 31   Finance (No. 2) Act 1975 – statutory tax deduction scheme.

Value added tax – supplemental provisions (clause 15)

Value added tax (VAT) was introduced to the construction industry through the Finance Act 1972. It is administered through HM Customs and Excise. During the Chancellor's annual Budget statement there is the opportunity to amend both the extent and rate of this tax. This has been done many times since 1972.

Building work is either standard-rated (currently 17.5 per cent) or zero-rated. Examples of zero-rated works are residential buildings which include: children's homes, old people's homes, homes for rehabilitation purposes, hospices, student living accommodation, armed forces living accommodation, religious community dwellings and other buildings that are used for residential purposes. Certain buildings intended for use by registered charities may also be zero-rated. Buildings which are specifically excluded from zero-rating include hospitals, hotels, inns and similar establishments. The conversion, reconstruction, alteration or enlargement of any existing building are now always standard-rated, although this was not always the case when the tax was first introduced. All services which are merely incidental to the construction of a qualifying building are standard-rated, such as architects', surveyors' and other consultants' fees and much of the temporary work associated with a project. Items which may be typically described as 'furnishings and fittings' (fitted furniture, domestic appliances, carpets, free-standing equipment, etc.) are always standard-rated irrespective of whether the project may be classified as zero-rated. The VAT guides provide further information.

The contract sum referred to in article 2 and clause 14 of JCT 80 is exclusive of VAT. Adjustments to the contract sum will also be exclusive of the tax, since the conditions specifically state that VAT will not be dealt with under the terms of the contract. If after the date of tender the goods and services become exempt from VAT, then the employer must pay the contractor an equal amount to the loss of the contractor's input tax. This will then equate with the amount that the contractor would otherwise have recovered.

The supplemental provisions are included into the contract by clause 15.1. The employer agrees to pay the appropriate tax to the contractor that is chargeable by the Customs and Excise office. The employer must therefore pay to the contractor the appropriate amount in respect of any positively rated items in the contract. The procedure for this payment is as follows:

1. The contractor gives to the employer a written provisional assessment of the respective values of any goods and materials which have been included in a payment, and are subject to VAT.
2. This should be done not later than the date for the issue of each interim certificate.
3. The contractor must specify the rate of tax chargeable on these items. The rate is fixed by the Customs and Excise but it could change, and several different rates could be introduced.
4. The employer, on receipt of the provisional assessment from the contractor, must calculate the amount of tax due.
5. This amount is then included with the amount of the interim certificate and paid to the contractor.
6. If the employer has reasonable grounds for objection to the provisional assessment, the contractor must be informed in writing within 3 working days of receipt.
7. The contractor must then either withdraw the assessment, and thereby release the employer from the obligations, or confirm the assessment.
8. When the certificate of making good defects has been issued, the contractor must then prepare a written final statement of the respective values of all the supplies of goods and materials. The contractor must specify the respective rates of tax on these items.
9. This final statement can be issued either prior to or after the issue of the final certificate. For practical purposes it is advantageous to issue the statement after the final certificate has been accepted.
10. The employer, on receipt of the final statement, must calculate the tax that is due. The balance to the contractor is paid within 28 days of receipt of the statement. In those circumstances where the employer may have overpaid the contractor in respect of VAT, a refund of the appropriate amount will be due to the employer.
11. The contractor must issue to the employer receipts under the certificates for the appropriate amount of tax that has been paid. These receipts must comply with regulations 2(2) of the VAT Regulations (1972), including the particulars as required by regulation 9(1), taking into account any of the amendments or re-enactments.
12. The employer must disregard any set-off in respect of liquidated damages when calculating and paying the amounts of VAT due to the contractor. The contractor in a similar manner must ignore contra-charges of

liquidated damages by the employer.

13. If the employer and contractor disagree it may require the decision to be made by the VAT commissioners. This should be done before the payment becomes due. The employer can also request the contractor to appeal further to the commissioners, should there still be disagreement with their findings. In these circumstances the contractor would be able to claim any costs or expenses involved from the employer. Before the appeal can proceed, the employer must pay to the contractor the full amount of the tax that has been charged.

14. The commissioners' appeal decision is final and binding, unless they subsequently introduce a correction to the tax that has been charged.

15. Arbitration is not applicable to VAT assessments by the commissioners.

16. If the contractor fails to provide a receipt for the tax paid by the employer, then the employer is not obliged to make any further payments. This applies only if the employer requires a validated receipt for tax purposes, or where the employer has paid tax in accordance with the provisional assessments.

17. If the employer has determined the contractor's employment, any additional tax which the employer may have to pay as a result of the determination may be set off against any payments to be made to the contractor.

Finance (No. 2) Act 1975 -- statutory tax deduction scheme (clause 31)

The purpose of this legislation is to deal with the problems of tax evasion by subcontractors, particularly the labour-only 'lump' subcontractors. Machinery is established whereby the main contractor collects tax on behalf of the Inland Revenue from those subcontractors who do not hold a tax certificate. Those subcontractors who hold the 714 certificate are eligible for full payment on the basis that they deal with the Inland Revenue direct.

The following definitions are included within this clause:

Act – Finance (No. 2) Act 1975.

Regulations – Income Tax (Subcontractors in the Construction Industry) Regulations 1975, SI No. 1960.

Contractor – A person who is a contractor for the purpose of the Act.

Evidence – That required by the regulations to be produced for the verification of a subcontractor's tax certificate.

Statutory deduction – Referred to in Section 69(4) of the Act.

Subcontractor – Any person who is a subcontractor for the purposes of the Act and Regulations.

Tax certificate – A certificate issuable under section 70 of the Act.

In the Appendix to the form of contract the employer needs to be stated as either 'a contractor' or 'not a contractor'. Where the former applies, the employer is responsible for making the statutory deduction. Where the employer is 'not a contractor', the appropriate deductions must be made by the main contractor. If the responsible party fails to make the necessary deduction they may find themselves liable to the authorities for the tax. The status of the employer for tax deduction purposes is also referred to in the fourth recital. An employer may automatically be a 'contractor' to cover a wider statutory position, for example, in the case of local authorities. In the case of private employers it will largely depend upon whether the employer is engaged in 'construction operations'. These are defined very broadly in the legislation.

At least 21 days before the issue of the first certificate the main contractor must either:

(a) provide the employer with the evidence that the contractor is eligible to be paid without deduction; or

(b) inform the employer in writing and also send a duplicate copy to the architect that such a deduction should be made.

The onus is on the contractor to provide this information and presumably until this is done condition (b) will apply. The employer, however, needs to be extremely careful, since a failure to make the necessary deduction may result in a liability for the tax. Alternatively, if amounts are deducted without the necessary authority to do so this may result in a breach of contract. The employer must also attempt to make sure that the evidence is valid, and if there are any doubts appropriate deduction will continue to be made. If the status of the contractor changes within the terms of this clause during the progress of the works, then it is up to the contractor to inform the employer accordingly in order that the alternative arrangement can be made. The contractor must immediately inform the employer in writing if the current tax certificate is cancelled, and also give the date of such cancellation. Where the employer is of the opinion that the contractor's tax position has changed then the contractor must be informed accordingly. The contractor must inform the employer if this is not the correct situation.

When the employer is required to make the statutory deduction, this amount must exclude the cost of any materials. The clause is only concerned with income tax deductions for labour. The contractor must provide the employer with this information, but should this not be done then the employer will make a reasonable estimate of the amount. If errors or omissions do occur in the calculation there is provision for their correction.

The importance of this clause is illustrated in clause 31.8. Clause 31 takes precedence over the other clauses of the conditions of contract to such an extent that non-compliance with another clause may be envisaged. The interpretation of this clause may cause differences of opinion to occur, and these should be dealt with at arbitration. If, however, a particular Act suggests a method of resolving the difficulty, then this will override any arbitration proceedings.

Chapter 22

Clauses of a general nature

The following clauses from JCT 80 have been grouped together because they appertain to matters of a general nature:

Clause 1   Interpretations, definitions, etc.
Clause 2   Contractor's obligations.
Clause 4   Architect's instructions.
Clause 5   Contract documents.
(Clause 19A Fair wages – deleted.)
(Clause 32   Outbreak of hostilities – deleted.)
(Clause 33   War damage – deleted.)
Clause 34   Antiquities.
Clause 41   Settlement of disputes – arbitration.

Clauses 1, 2, 4 and 5 deal with matters of a broad nature that set the scene for the contract in general. Clause 1, for example, provides a considerable list of definitions which are then used throughout the contract. The inclusion of these avoids undue confusion both in the interpretation of the clauses and the use of the contract in practice. Clause 2 defines very briefly the contractor's obligation in connection with the works and clauses 4 and 5 together cover those matters established as contractual and the procedures and provisions for instructions from the architect.

Clause 19A has now been deleted from the local authorities edition (since July 1988).

The following three clauses deal with events that may never happen. Clauses 32 and 33 are more likely to occur in today's society than 20 years ago. They detailed the procedures to be followed in the event of such happenings that could have occurred. The discovery of antiquities (clause 34) may seem a more remote possibility, since a number of finds have been made in recent years. It may be every builder's dream to unearth a unique Roman vase in one piece, but the value of such stays strictly with the landowner. Clause 41 is a new clause which embraces arbitration good practice.

Interpretations, definitions, etc. (clause 1)

The Articles of Agreement, the Conditions and the Appendix are to be read as a whole, and together they form the Standard Form of Building Contract. They cannot therefore be used independently, and in many instances they have a bearing upon each other. For example, the details completed in the Appendix will generally override the specific requirements indicated in each clause. The Appendix will make recommendations for the contract, but the parties have some liberty on the amounts or times that they wish to insert against the appropriate clause.

A selection of definitions appertaining to the contract are included in clause 1.3. The definitions listed generally also refer to appropriate clause references, and these are discussed in detail where necessary. These include:

Conditions: clauses 1–37, either clause 38, 39 or 40, clauses 41 and 42 and the supplemental provisions (the VAT Agreement) annexed to the Articles of Agreement.

Contract bills: the bills of quantities referred to in the first recital which have been priced by the contractor and signed by or on behalf of the parties to the contract.

Contract documents: the contract drawings, contract bills, the Articles of Agreement, the Conditions and the Appendix.

Contract drawings: the drawings referred to in the first recital which have been signed by or on behalf of the parties to the contract.

Date for possession: the date stated in the Appendix under reference to clause 23.1.

Date for completion: the date fixed and stated in the Appendix.

Completion date: the date for completion as fixed and stated in the Appendix or any date fixed either under clause 25 or in a confirmed acceptance of a 13A quotation.

Defects liability period: the period named in the Appendix under the reference to clause 17.2.

Specified perils: fire, lightning, explosion, storm, tempest, flood, bursting or overflowing of water tanks, apparatus or pipes, earthquake, aircraft and other aerial devices or articles dropped therefrom, riot and civil commotion, but excluding excepted risks.

Clause 1.4 has been added to reinforce the responsibilities and obligations of the contractor under the terms of the contract. This states that regardless of any obligations that the architect may have towards the employer or whether or not the employer appoints a clerk of works, the contractor will nevertheless be responsible for carrying out and completing the works in accordance with clause 2.1. This is so, irrespective of whether the architect or clerk of works inspects the works, workshops or any other place where work is being prepared. The architect is not made responsible under JCT 80 for the supervision of the works which the contractor is to carry out and complete. The contractor's responsibility for work is in no way reduced by the conditions which allow for an architect or clerk of works' inspection.

Contractor's obligations (clause 2)

The contractor will carry out and complete the works in accordance with the:
(a)   contract drawings;
(b)   contract bills;
(c)   Articles of Agreement;
(d)   Conditions of Contract;
(e)   Appendix to the Conditions of Contract;
(f)   numbered documents (subcontract agreements).

Collectively the above are known as the contract documents. The contractor must use the materials and workmanship that have been specified. The approval of the quality of materials or standards of workmanship will be decided by the architect. These are to be to a reasonable satisfaction. The architect can, however, only require that standard described in the contract documents. In the selection of materials and the assessment of workmanship the architect and the documents must be precise. Although objectivity may achieve the appropriate and desired standards, some subjective analysis and interpretation by the architect will also be necessary.

The contract bills cannot override or modify either the application or the interpretation of these conditions of contract, with the exception of the rules for measurement. Unless it has been previously stated, JCT 80 assumes that SMM7 will have been used for the preparation of the bills. If other methods of measurement are preferred and have been used, this must be clearly stated in the contract bills. If the quantity surveyor chooses to measure items not in accordance with SMM7, this too must be stated. Any errors subsequently found in the contract bills resulting from their method of preparation must be corrected. The correction of these errors is automatic and does not require a variation instruction to be issued by the architect. The errors referred to cover descriptions, quantities or omission of items. They are errors made by the quantity surveyor. Errors in pricing resulting from mistakes made by the contractor do not come within this definition, and will therefore not be corrected once the contract has been signed. A procedure for their correction prior to the contractor's tender being accepted is described in Chapter 8, describing the code of procedure for selective tendering.

If the contractor finds any discrepancies or divergences between or within the following documents, the architect should be informed of the differences.
1.   Contract drawings.
2.   Contract bills.
3.   Architect's instructions.
4.   Additional drawings or documents.
5.   Nominated subcontracts NSC 4 and NSC 4a.

The architect must then give instructions to the contractor in order to clarify the discrepancy or divergence, so that the works can proceed. The contractor cannot assume, for example, that the drawing will automatically take preference over the bills. However, it can be reasonably assumed that the Conditions of Contract will always take preference unless there is some clause to the contrary (clause 2.2.1). It should further be noted that the Conditions of Contract are not one of the documents capable of discrepancy, as listed above.

Discrepancies or divergences between the statement in respect of performance specified work and an architect's instruction may also occur. If this occurs after the issue of the contractor's statement, then the architect must be informed in writing in order that appropriate instructions can be given. If the contractor or architect find any discrepancy in the contractor's statement, the contractor must correct the statement to remove any discrepancy and inform the architect in writing of the correction that has been made. In this situation there will be no cost to the employer.

The conditions do not imply that the contractor must go looking for differences in the documents. If the compliance with the drawings later revealed that the bills were different but correct, then the architect would need to issue further instructions for the correction of this work, if that was so desired. The contractor should, however, take all reasonable steps to avoid the occurrence of this situation.

Architect's instructions (clause 4)

The contractor must comply with all instructions issued by the architect, unless a reasonable objection in writing is made regarding the non-compliance. A reasonable objection may include the refusal to accept the nomination of a subcontractor, where an unsatisfactory relationship has existed on a previous contract. The contractor may also challenge the architect's authority to issue certain instructions. In these circumstances the architect may be requested to specify in writing the provision in the contract which empowers the issue of the particular instruction. The architect must comply with this request. If the two parties cannot agree upon this point, the matter may be referred to arbitration for a decision. If the contractor complies with the instruction on the basis of the architect's reply, then this shall be assumed to be an instruction under the terms of the contract.

The architect may write to the contractor requesting the immediate compliance with an instruction. If after 7 days of receipt of this notice the contractor does not comply, the employer may employ other firms to execute the work. The costs involved with this will be deducted from monies due to the contractor, or they may be recoverable as a debt by the employer. In more severe cases, particularly where the contractor persistently fails to comply with a written instruction, the employer may terminate the contractor's employment under clause 27.

All architect's instructions must be in writing to have any contractual effect. If, however, oral instructions are given by the architect, the following procedure should be adopted:

1.   Confirmation should be given in writing within 7 days by the contractor to
      the architect.
2.   Unless the architect dissents in writing within a further 7 days the
      instruction shall be accepted as an architect's instruction within the terms
      of the contract.
3.   Alternatively, if the architect confirms in writing the oral instruction
      within 7 days, then the contractor needs only to accept this as an
      architect's instruction.
4.   If neither the architect nor the contractor confirms the oral instruction, but
      the contractor executes the work accordingly, then it may be confirmed by
      the architect at any time prior to the issue of the final certificate.

Contract documents (clause 5)

The contract documents using the JCT 80 form of contract with quantities are as
follows:
1.   *Contract drawings*. These are the drawings which have been signed by or
      on behalf of the parties.
2.   *Contract bills*. These are the bills of quantities which have been priced by
      the contractor and signed by or on behalf of the parties.
3.   *Form of contract*. JCT 80 duly completed where required.
      Where bills of quantities have not been prepared, either a specification or a
schedule rates may become a contract document. In these circumstances the
form of contract, without quantities, is used. When the contract has been signed
the architect must provide the contractor with:
(a)   a copy of the documents certified by the employer;
(b)   two further copies of the contract drawings;
(c)   two copies of the unpriced bills of quantities.
      Within a reasonable period of time the architect should then supply the
contractor with further information, which might include descriptive schedules
and further drawings to amplify the contract drawings. These additional
documents are not allowed to impose further obligations beyond those
described in the contract documents.
      The contract drawings and contract bills are to remain in the custody of the
employer but must be available at all reasonable times for the inspection of the
contractor. The contractor must also keep one copy of the contract drawings,
one copy of the unpriced bills and other schedules, documents and drawings on
the site for reference by the architect or the architect's representative at all
reasonable times. Copies of all the information provided by the architect for the
construction of works should be retained on site by the contractor for use by the
contractor and the architect.
      It is the contractor's responsibility to provide the architect with two copies of
the master programme. If this requires updating because of an extension of
time, then the contractor must supply a further copy of the revised master

programme. A copy of the master programme should be retained on site for reference purposes. There is no requirement under the clause for the contractor to indicate the progress of the works.

When the contractor has received the final payment under the terms of the contract, request may be made to return all drawings, details schedules and other documents which bear the architect's name to the architect. The copyright of the design is vested in the architect. If the building owner or the contractor wish to repeat the design, then the architect can request a further fee. None of the documents mentioned must be used for any purpose other than this contract. The contractor's rates must not be divulged to others, or be used for any purpose other than this contract. Of course, where permission is sought from the architect or contractor, as appropriate, the contractual information may be reused for other purposes.

Any certificates that the architect issues shall be sent to both the contractor and the employer concurrently.

Before the date of practical completion, the contractor, without charge, should supply the employer with drawings and other information that relate to the performance specified work. This will show the work as built and also include maintenance and operating schedules, where appropriate.

Fair wages (clause 19A)

Clause 19A was, originally in 1980, only included in the local authorities edition. This particular clause is now a matter for the history books, at least for the time being. Amendment 6 which was issued in July 1988 deleted this clause in its entirety from this edition. The provisions of the clause could no longer be operated in view of the provisions contained in the Local Government Act 1988. The clause was concerned with rates of wages, hours of work, conditions of employment, trade union representation and covered both operatives on site and those in workshops as well as those employed by subcontractors.

Outbreak of hostilities (clause 32)

This clause was deleted in July 1992 with the provisions added to insurance provisions of the relevant clauses dealing with insurance provision.

War damage (clause 33)

This clause was deleted in July 1992 with the provisions added to insurance provisions of the relevant clauses dealing with insurance provision.

Antiquities (clause 34)

Antiquities include fossils and other items of interest or value which may be found on the site or during the excavation part of the works. These items become the property of the employer, and if such finds occur:

1. The contractor shall use the best endeavours not to disturb the object and, if necessary, cease construction operations within the vicinity until instructions are received from the architect. Where there is any reasonable doubt about a discovered object this procedure should be followed as a precaution.
2. The contractor shall take all necessary precautions in order to preserve the condition of the objects from possible damage until they can be dealt with by experts if necessary.
3. The contractor shall inform either the architect or clerk of works of the discovery and its precise location on site.

The architect must issue instructions regarding the removal of antiquities. This may involve a third party, such as an archaeological society, examining, excavating or removing the object. Such a party will not be described as a subcontractor but as persons directly employed by the employer.

If in the opinion of the architect the above instructions involve the contractor in direct loss or expense, for which reimbursement is not provided elsewhere under the contract, the architect or quantity surveyor shall ascertain the amount of such loss or expense. This amount will then be added to the contract sum. If the architect considers that an extension of the contract is appropriate, then the removal of the antiquity becomes a relevant event under clause 25.

Settlement of disputes -- arbitration (clause 41)

This clause was inserted into the form of contract in July 1987. It replaces much of what was included in article 5 of the form. If any of the following disputes or differences occur, as referred to in article 5, then the matter shall be referred to arbitration:

(a) any matter or thing left by the contract to the discretion of the architect;
(b) withholding by the architect of any certificate due to the contractor;
(c) adjustment of the contract sum;
(d) rights and liabilities of the parties in respect of determination by the contractor or employer;
(e) unreasonable withholding of consent or agreement by the employer or the architect or by the contractor.

If the disputes or differences which are to be referred to arbitration raise issues which are substantially the same as, or connected with, issues in a related dispute between the following, then the employer and contractor agree that the same arbitrator shall be used:

(a) employer and nominated subcontractor;
(b) contractor and nominated subcontractor;
(c) contractor and/or employer and nominated supplier so long as the contract of sale provides for such an arrangement.

Clearly if the employer or architect considers that the appointed arbitrator is not appropriately qualified to determine the dispute then a different arbitrator must then be appointed. These clauses will apply unless they have been deleted in the Appendix.

Arbitration usually arises after the practical completion, termination of the contractor's employment or the abandonment of the works. It may be commenced earlier as long as the employer, architect and contractor agree and put this consent in writing. There are, however, some circumstances which can be dealt with as and when the dispute occurs, such as the following:

(a)   whether or not the issue of an instruction is empowered by the conditions;
(b)   whether or not a certificate has been improperly withheld;
(c)   whether a certificate is not in accordance with the conditions;
(d)   whether a determination under clause 22C.4.3.1 will be just and equitable;
(e)   any dispute or difference regarding the issue of architect's instructions in regard to a reasonable objection by the contractor (clause 4.1);
(f)   work, materials and goods in compliance with the contract (clauses 8.4 and 8.5);
(g)   partial possession by employer (clause 18.1);
(h)   use and occupation of the works by the employer (clause 23.3.2);
(i)   extensions of time (clause 25).

The arbitrator has the power to direct such measurements and valuations which in the arbitrator's opinion are desirable in order to determine the rights of the respective parties who are in dispute. The arbitrator can ascertain and award any sum which ought to have been included in any certificate. The arbitrator can open up works, review and revise certificates, opinions, decisions, requirements or notices in order to determine the matters that are in dispute. These are subject to the provisions of the following clauses:

Clause 4.2   Provision of architect to issue instructions.
Clause 30.9   Effect of final certificate.
Clause 38.4.3   Agreement of fluctuations by the contractor and the quantity surveyor.
Clause 39.5.3   Similar provisions to clause 38.4.3.
Clause 40.5   Similar provisions to clause 38.4.3.

The arbitrator's award is final and binding on both parties. Unless it is subsequently amended, all arbitrations in England apply under the Arbitration Acts of 1950 and 1979. The parties may appeal to the High Court on any question of law arising out of an award or in the course of a reference, and the parties agree that the High Court should have jurisdiction to determine any such question of law.

If before making the final award, the arbitrator dies or ceases to act as an arbitrator then the employer and contractor must appoint a new arbitrator within 14 days. If this is not done, then either the employer or contractor may request the person named in the Appendix to appoint a further arbitrator. Such an appointee may not disregard any direction given by a previous arbitrator except that the previous arbitrator had powers so to do under the contract, with the agreement of the parties concerned or by the operation of law.

The Appendix to the form of contract allows for an appointer to be stated. This can be either the President or Vice-President of:

(a)   Royal Institute of British Architects;

(b)   Royal Institution of Chartered Surveyors;

(c)   Chartered Institute of Arbitrators.

If none is stated then the appointer will come from the RIBA.

Chapter 23

JCT nominated subcontracts documentation

Introduction

At the request of a number of its constituent bodies, the Joint Contracts Tribunal has reviewed the procedure for the nomination of subcontractors, that was set out in the original version of JCT 80. It has done this in order to simplify the process that is involved. A new set of documentation was issued for this purpose in 1991.

The introduction of JCT 80 originally included two procedures, known as the basic method and the alternative method. The revised procedures have replaced these with a single method. The review has changed only the procedures involved with nomination. It has not changed in any way the liabilities of the various parties arising out of such a nomination. The new procedures are outlined in *Revised Procedure for Nomination of a Subcontractor* (Joint Contracts Tribunal, 1991). This documentation provides a comprehensive set of information together with guidance notes.

Documents

The following documents relate to revised procedures for the nomination of subcontractors:

NSC/T – The Standard Form of Nominated Subcontract Tender

    Part 1 – The invitation to tender which is issued by the architect to prospective subcontractors.

    Part 2 – The form of tender to be submitted by each subcontractor invited to tender.

    Part 3 – The particular conditions to be agreed by the contractor and each subcontractor prior to entering into a nominated subcontract.

Agreement NSC/A – The nominated subcontract agreement to be entered into by the main contractor and each nominated subcontractor, subsequent to the latter's nomination by the architect.

Conditions NSC/C – The conditions of subcontract. This was derived from the

Part 5

Subcontract conditions

Nominated Subcontract NSC/4. It is applicable to a subcontract entered into on Agreement (NSC/A) which conditions are incorporated by reference in such agreement.

Agreement NSC/W – The employer and nominated subcontractor agreement entered into between the employer and a nominated subcontractor. This was derived from the previous agreement NSC/2.

Nomination NSC/N – It is essential that the architect uses this form when nominating a subcontractor in accordance with the main contract conditions.

Action

The following action is required by each of the participants under the 1991 procedure.

The architect

1. Completes the Invitation to Tender (NSC/T Part 1) and sends a copy with the Agreement (NSC/W) with page 1 completed, to each of the subcontractors from whom tenders are requested. These are submitted on Tender NSC/T Part 2 together with drawings, specifications, bills of quantities, etc. (the numbered tender documents) as appropriate, that describe the work for which tenders are being sought, and the Appendix to the main contract as it is anticipated it will be completed.

2. When it is intended to nominate a subcontractor the architect:
   (a) arranges for the employer to sign the applicable subcontractor's tender as approved and enters into the Employer/Subcontractor Agreement.
   (b) issues the nomination instruction on form NSC/N and sends this to the contractor together with a copy of:
      (i) invitation to tender and the nominated subcontractor's tender, i.e. the completed parts NSC/T Parts 1 and 2;
      (ii) the numbered tender documents including any amendments;
      (iii) the Employer/Subcontractor Agreement as entered into;
   (c) sends a copy of the nomination instruction to the subcontractor together with a copy of:
      (i) the Employer/Subcontractor Agreement as entered into;
      (ii) the completed Appendix to the main contract.

3. When the subcontract has been entered into, the contractor will submit a copy of the applicable documents for record purposes.

4. If the contractor and subcontractor are unable to enter into a subcontract within 10 working days of receipt of the nomination instruction, then the contractor is to advise the architect of the reasons involved:
   (a) if there are no fundamental reasons, then the architect may extend the time for completing the formalities of entering into the subcontract;

(b) if there are fundamental reasons, then the architect has the options outlined in clause 35.9.2 of the Conditions of Contract;

(c) if the reasons are not valid, then the architect can insist upon a subcontract being formed.

5. If before issuing the nomination instruction the architect wishes a proposed subcontractor to undertake design, ordering of materials or fabrication of components then this can be arranged as long as the Employer/Subcontractor Agreement has been signed.

The subcontractor

1. On receipt of the Invitation to Tender (NSC/T Part 1), the Agreement (NSC/W) and the numbered documents (drawings, specifications, bills of quantities), the subcontractor:

(a) completes the Tender on NSC/T Part 2;

(b) enters into the Agreement (by signing or as a deed) and returns it to the architect.

2. If the subcontractor is unaware of the main contractor when submitting a tender, then such a tender may be withdrawn within 7 days after such notification, without any reasons being given.

3. Upon receipt of a copy of Nomination (NSC/N) and a copy of the Appendix from the main contract, a subcontractor:

(a) agrees with the contractor on the matters set out in NSC/T Part 3 and signs to signify such an agreement, and

(b) checks that any differences between the Appendix to the main contract and the Invitation to Tender are acceptable, and

(c) enters into a subcontract with the contractor on Agreement NSC/A.

4. Where the subcontractor cannot agree with the matters set out in NSC/T Part 3 then the main contractor should be informed in writing of the reasons involved.

5. Upon receipt of the Employer/Subcontractor Agreement, the subcontractor may be instructed to proceed with design work, ordering of materials or fabrication of components prior to being nominated. Arrangements are available for payment for this work prior to the issue of the nomination instruction, where this is desirable.

The contractor

1. Upon receipt of the nomination instruction (NSC/N) and the accompanying documents from the architect, the contractor:

(a) agrees with the subcontractor the matters set out in NSC/T Part 3 and signs in agreement;

(b) enters into a subcontract on the Agreement (NSC/A).

2. If the contractor wishes to make a reasonable objection to the appointment

of a subcontractor then this must be done within 7 working days from receipt of the nomination instruction.

3. If the contractor is unable to enter into a subcontract within 10 working days from the receipt of the nomination then the architect must be advised of the reasons why this has not been done. The contractor must then subsequently follow any instructions that are issued by the architect.

Tender NSC/T: Part 1

This is the architect's or contract administrator's invitation to tender that is sent to a proposed subcontractor. The three schedules provide the full details of the subcontractor's offer. These agreed terms, together with the other subcontract documents (drawings and bills of quantities or specification) will constitute the subcontract. The tender is the formal response to an enquiry by the architect. The subcontractor agrees to carry out the works in accordance with these documents for:

- a VAT exclusive subcontract sum (clause 15.1) or
- a VAT exclusive tender sum (clause 15.2), where the work will be completely remeasured upon completion.

In both cases a 2.5 per cent cash discount is allowed to the main contractor. The offer is subject to the nomination procedures being completed. If either the main contractor or a subcontractor fail to agree upon the terms of the agreement, with good reasons, then the contract will not be formed. Where this situation arises then the employer may be faced with paying a subcontractor for design work, pre-ordering of materials or the fabrication of some components, as instructed and agreed by the architect.

Part 1 provides the essential and general information relating to both the main contract and the subcontract conditions. The details of the main contract Appendix are also provided, appropriately completed. Part 1 provides the following information:

- Numbered tender documents; e.g. drawings, specification, bills of quantities, schedule of rates.
- Main contract works and location.
- Names and addresses of employer, consultants and the main contractor.
- Main contract information.
  1 Form of main contract
  2 Main contract alternative provisions
  3 Any changes made to the standard form
  4 Whether the main contract is executed under hand or as a deed
  5 Facility for inspection of the main contract documents
  6 Main contract Appendix, to be attached
  7 Any obligations or restrictions imposed by the employer that are not covered by the main contract conditions
  8 Order of works; employer's requirements

9   Type and location of access

10   New completion date where this has been altered from the original date for completion stated in the main contract conditions

11   Other relevant information relating to the main contract

12   Subcontract; reference to clause 35.7 of the main contract; issues of retention and execution under hand or deed

13   Main contract Appendix and entries therein

14   Earliest and latest starting dates

15   Income and Corporation Taxes Act 1988, statutory tax deduction scheme

16   Attendance items: provided by the main contractor free of charge to a subcontractor

General attendance: use of contractor's temporary roads, pavings and paths, standing scaffolding, standing power operated hoisting plant, provision of temporary lighting and water supplies, clearing away rubbish, provision of space for the subcontractor's own offices and for the storage of their plant and materials and the use of messrooms, sanitary accommodation and welfare facilities.

Other attendance: This is in addition to the requirements for general attendance by the main contractor. The other attendance is specified separately for each individual subcontractor and may include:

1   special scaffolding or scaffolding additional to the contractor's standing scaffolding

2   the provision of temporary access roads and hardstandings in connection with structural steelwork, precast concrete components, piling, heavy items of plant, etc.

3   unloading, distributing, hoisting and placing in position, giving in the case of significant items the weight and size

4   provision of covered storage accommodation including lighting and power

5   power supplies, giving the maximum loads

6   maintenance of specific temperature or humidity levels

7   any other attendance

17   Fluctuations;

    4A   Contributions, levy and tax fluctuations

    4B   Labour and materials cost and tax fluctuations

    4C   Formula adjustment

Tender NSC/T: Part 2

This represents the tender, or offer, by a subcontractor. It states that the subcontractor will carry out and complete, as a nominated subcontractor, the subcontract works that form a part of the main contract works referred to in NSC/T Part 1. These will have been identified in numbered tender documents listed in Tender NSC/T Part 1 and may also include entries that the subcontractor may have made in the tender. The amount stated by the subcontractor is exclusive of VAT, either as a contract sum or tender sum (see above). The tender should include a schedule of rates or prices for the measured work and daywork percentages for labour, materials and plant relevant to a particular daywork definition, e.g. RICS/BEC (see Chapter 6). Reference is also made to the fluctuation provisions and the attendance to be provided by the main contractor.

Other matters to be included with the tender include the earliest and latest starting dates, the periods required for the submission and approval of all necessary subcontractor's drawings, etc., the execution of any work off site prior to commencement of the work on site and the period required for notice to commence work on site. Also covered are matters relating to insurances, VAT, special conditions or agreements on the employment of labour, limitation of working hours, etc. and the statutory tax deduction scheme.

Particular conditions NSC/T: Part 3

This covers any particular conditions agreed between the contractor and subcontractor. If, for example, any changes or additions to the information given in NSC/T Part 1:

item 7: obligations or restrictions imposed by the employer
item 8: order of works: employer's requirements
item 9: type and location of access

may cause a subcontractor to reconsider a tender that has been submitted.

Agreement NSC/A

This is the standard form of articles of nominated subcontract agreement between a contractor and a nominated subcontractor. It includes seven recitals and four articles. These are as follows.

Recitals

These recite all of the matters, beginning with the architect's invitation to tender.

First. The subcontractor has been invited to submit a tender on NSC/T Part 1 by the employer and architect (or contract administrator) and has submitted an offer on NSC/T Part 2 to supply and fix materials or goods or to execute work in accordance with the particulars that are set out in the numbered tender documents.

Second. The subcontract works are to be executed as part of the main contract works.

Third. The architect has selected the subcontractor's tender for carrying out the works in pursuant of clause 35.1 of the main contract conditions.

Fourth. The employer and subcontractor have entered into the Agreement NSC/W.

Fifth. Under clause 35.6 of the main contract conditions the architect has issued an instruction on nomination NSC/N with a copy to the subcontractor.

Sixth. The contractor and subcontractor have agreed NSC/T Part 3 which has been signed by each of them.

Seventh. The subcontractor's offer is on the basis of a subcontract on the Standard Form of Articles of Nominated Subcontract Agreement NSC/A.

Articles

Article 1. The subcontract consists of:
- the Articles of Agreement
- the completed NSC/T, Part 1, Part 2 and Part 3
- the numbered documents
- the Standard Conditions of Nominated Subcontract (NSC/C)

Article 2. The subcontractor's obligations, which are to carry out and complete the works.

Article 3. Payment, which shall be either a VAT exclusive contract sum or a VAT exclusive tender sum.

Article 4. Settlement of disputes. These shall be referred to arbitration.

Nomination instruction NSC/N

This is a form that is used for the final nomination of subcontractors, after all of the preliminary procedures have been complied with. It is prepared under clause 35.6 of the main contract conditions.

Agreement NSC/W

This is the agreement between a nominated subcontractor and an employer. In the JCT nominated subcontract form, the above agreement is a separate but integral part of the documentation. Whereas the bulk of the documentation is between the main contractor and the nominated subcontractor, the Agreement NSC/W is an agreement between the employer and subcontractor. It is made in accordance with clauses 35.3 – 35.9 of the Standard Form of Building Contract (JCT 80).

When the architect has issued the preliminary notice of nomination and the conditions have then been signed by the respective parties, the Agreement NSC/W is then issued. In the Agreement NSC/W, the nominated subcontractor warrants the employer that reasonable skill and care will be taken in:

- the design of the subcontract works, where the design has been undertaken by the subcontractor;
- the selection of the kinds of materials and goods for the subcontract works where these have been selected by the subcontractor;
- the satisfaction of any performance specification or requirement where appropriate.

The subcontractor may, prior to nomination, be requested by the architect to proceed within the agreement with any design work, the ordering of materials or the fabrication of components for the works. The employer may agree to pay for this work in advance of nomination, in which case the materials become the property of the employer.

The obligations of the employer to the subcontractor are largely financial:

- an agreement to notify the subcontractor of the amount included in interim certificates;
- the possible early final payment under clause 35.17 of the main contract;
- payment to the subcontractor direct, should the main contractor fail to honour a certificate.

The employer must be indemnified where payments are made direct to a subcontractor, after the insolvency of the main contractor.

The Agreement NSC/W includes eleven clauses. These clauses cover the following information:

- completion of the subcontract and the subcontractor's obligations;
- design, selection of materials, satisfaction of performance specification;
- subcontractor's warranty and liabilities;
- architect's or contract administrator's instructions;
- interim and final payments;
- delay in the supply of information by a subcontractor;
- default in performance by the subcontractor;
- renomination;
- assignment;
- conflicts between the tender and agreement;
- arbitration.

Subcontract conditions NSC/C

These are described more fully in Chapter 24.

JCT Nominated Subcontract Conditions (NSC/C) 1991 edition

Introduction

This form of subcontract is intended to be used for nomination of sub-contractors when JCT 80 is used as a main contract. It supersedes the existing standard form of subcontract (NSC/4) that was issued at the same time as main contract form in 1980. The different subcontract forms (BEC, FASS and CASEC), the 'green' form for nominated subcontracts and the 'blue' form for domestic subcontracts are still available and used to a limited extent in the industry (see Chapter 6).

The 'new' JCT form of subcontract was introduced in 1991, and is referred to as NSC/C. Whilst this covers the provisions and requirements set out in the main contract form JCT 80, its format and numbering are considerably different. Main contractors must ensure that the obligations and responsibilities placed on them by the employer, are appropriately and adequately transferred to the various nominated subcontracts. The form (NSC/C) is subdivided into eight sections, 1–9 (section 8 is not used). The form is intended to be read and used in conjunction with the other NSC documents that have been described in Chapter 23. In order for the subcontract to be binding on the parties it must be properly signed by completing the attestation, by the different parties concerned.

Reference should also be made to clause 35 of the main contract conditions (JCT 80), that provide for nominated subcontractors under the main contract.

Section 1: Intentions of the parties

Interpretations, definitions, etc.

This section outlines the different documents that are referred to in the conditions NSC/C (clause 1.1). It also provides a series of definitions (clause 1.4), many of which are similar and refer to the definitions that are included in the main contract (JCT 80). There are also a wide range of definitions, as one would expect, that relate to subcontracts and subcontractors. The various nominated subcontract documents are listed for reference purposes (see Chapter 23).

The subcontract

Clauses 1.5–1.8 define the subcontract documents as the Agreement (NSC/A), the (numbered) documents attached and the subcontract conditions. Clause 1.6 refers to the hierarchical nature of contract documents, making it clear that in the cases of differences, the terms of the main contract will overrule those of the subcontracts. Where any discrepancies occur then a subcontractor should write to the contractor specifying the discrepancy or divergence. The contractor then informs the architect under clause 2.3 of the main contract conditions.

A subcontractor may be required to enter into a sub-subcontract for goods and services, with, for example, other suppliers. This is described as a sub-subcontract. If the sub-subcontract in any way restricts, limits or excludes the liability of such a supplier, then the subcontractor must inform the contractor in writing of the limitation, exclusion or restriction. Under these circumstances, the subcontractor's liability will not be expected to exceed the terms of the sub-subcontract.

Execution of the subcontract works

A subcontractor's obligations are to carry out and complete the subcontract works in compliance with the subcontract documents and in conformity with all reasonable directions and requirements of the main contractor (clause 1.9). All materials and goods, so far procurable, should be:
• of the kinds and standards described in the subcontract documents;
• to the reasonable satisfaction of the architect.
All workmanship should be:
• of the standards described in the subcontract documents;
• be appropriate to the subcontract works;
• to the reasonable satisfaction of the architect;
• carried out in a workmanlike manner.

Subcontractor's liability under incorporated provisions of the main contract

A subcontractor must also observe, perform and comply with the provisions of the main contract, where these relate to the subcontract works. Subcontractors should also indemnify the contractor against and from, any breach, non-observance, non-performance or any act or omission of their workmen or agents. However, subcontractors are not liable for any defaults by the employer or contractor (clause 1.10).

Bills of quantities

If bills of quantities are provided as a subcontract document then these should have been prepared in accordance with SMM7 (clause 1.12).

Benefits under the main contract

The main contractor will request the subcontractor to obtain any rights or benefits of the main contract as they apply to the subcontract works (clause 1.13).

Strikes

The main contract or subcontract works may be affected by a local combination of workmen, strike or lock-out affecting those employed in any capacity with the project (clause 1.14). These include tradesmen on site and those engaged in the preparation, manufacture and transportation of goods and materials. Under the terms of the subcontract:

- Neither party will be able make claims on the other party.
- The contractor will try to ensure that the site is kept open for a subcontractor.
- The subcontractor will take all practical steps to continue with the subcontract works.

Section 2: Commencement and completion

Subcontract obligation

The subcontractor should carry out the works in accordance with the agreed programme details included in NSC/T Part 3 item 1. Subcontractors should also carry out their parts of the works reasonably in accordance with the general progress of the main contract works. The subcontractor will start work on site in accordance with the notice detailed in NSC/T Part 3 item 1. It is the main contractor's responsibility to give to subcontractors sufficient information on the general progress of the works, to enable them to fulfil their obligations under the terms of the subcontract (clause 2.1).

Delays and extension of time

If it becomes apparent that the regular progress of the subcontract works is likely to be delayed, then the subcontractor should notify the contractor in writing of the circumstances causing the delay. The contractor then informs the architect. The subcontractor will always work through the main contractor, maintaining a correct level of protocol. The subcontractor should also provide details on the expected effects of such a delay, estimate how the delay will affect the programme and generally keep the main contractor informed of any changes that might occur. Similar procedures, as outlined in the main contract, are then followed regarding whether the subcontractor should be granted an extension of the time. The various relevant events that are listed in clause 2.6 follow the same pattern and a similar content to the main contract conditions of clause 25.4.

If a subcontractor feels aggrieved about not being granted an extension of time, the main contractor may be invited to join a subcontractor in arbitration proceedings (clause 2.7) to discuss this matter.

Where a subcontractor fails to complete the subcontract works on time then payment may become due to the main contractor from the subcontractor. This will be equivalent to any loss or damage suffered or incurred by the main contractor, that has been caused by the failure of a subcontractor in this respect.

Practical completion of the subcontract works

A subcontractor must give written notice to the main contractor, when practical completion of the subcontract works has been reached. A copy of this notice is then passed to the architect who decides on the date for the practical completion of the subcontract works. The architect then issues a certificate accordingly (clause 2.11). Clause 2.12 deals with defects that must be made good at the expense of the subcontractor, in accordance with the instructions of the architect, or on the directions of the main contractor. Clauses 17 and 18 of JCT 80 set out the liability of the main contractor in respect of defects. Subcontractors are similarly liable for defects in their work which occur before the end of the defects liability period before the expiry of the main contract. Such work includes defects, shrinkages or other faults due to materials or workmanship that were not in accordance with the subcontract or due to frost damage occurring before the date of practical completion of the subcontract. Defects that arise through the design of the subcontract works are a separate matter between the employer and a nominated subcontractor (Agreement NSC/W).

Subcontractors upon practical completion of their subcontract works should clear the site of any property that belongs to them (clause 2.14).

Main contract conditions with sectional completion supplement

Where the main contract conditions provide for sectional completion of the works (Appendix: Sectional Completion Supplement), then this should be attached to NSC/T Part 1 item 6 and enclosed with the copy of Nomination NSC/N.

Section 3: Control of the works

Instructions of the architect and directions from the contractor

Only the information contained in the subcontract documents imposes obligations on the subcontractor (clause 3.1). The subcontractor should keep on the site a competent person to whom the architect, through the contractor, can issue instructions (clause 3.2). For a typical nominated subcontractor this might mean the foreman of a gang of workpeople employed by the subcontractor.

The architect will further issue instructions to the subcontractor through the main contractor. The contractor must pass on such instructions efficiently in order to avoid the possibility of misunderstandings or delays. Subcontractors must then comply with such instructions, unless they make a reasonable written objection to their compliance. Reasonable objection may arise in connection with variations. For example, if a subcontractor was in the process of fabricating a component, a variation to change the size, shape or materials used may result in the nearly complete component becoming useless and worthless. Due, perhaps, to the subcontractor's other work in progress, time may not permit the manufacture of such a component caused by a variation.

Since instructions are issued through the contractor they follow the principles laid down in JCT 80.

Work not in accordance with the subcontract

Where the subcontract works are not in accordance with the contract then a subcontractor can be given instructions to remove the work (clause 3.5). Alternatively the substandard work can be accepted and an appropriate deduction made from the contract sum (clause 3.6). Provision exists in the subcontract in the same way as the main contract for opening up the works for testing purposes (clause 3.7). The subcontractor is to indemnify the main contractor in respect of any liability and to reimburse the contractor for any loss as a result of direct compliance by the operation of these clauses.

Subcontractor's failure to comply with directions

If a subcontractor fails to comply with an architect's instruction within 7 days after its receipt, then the contractor may, with the architect's permission, employ others to comply with the direction (clause 3.10).

Architect's instructions – statement of authority

Subcontractors are able to object to architect's instructions where they consider that the architect is exceeding the powers granted under the terms of the contract (clause 3.11).

Right of access of contractor and architect

Both the architect and the contractor are to have reasonable access to the workshops of a subcontractor (clause 3.12).

Assignment and subletting

A subcontractor must not assign or sublet any part of the subcontract works without the architect's written consent (clauses 3.13–3.14).

General and other attendance

General attendance is provided to nominated subcontractors free of charge (clause 3.15). The main contractor may, however, have priced this item in the bills of quantities. Other attendance (clause 3.16) is provided individually to each different subcontractor depending upon their requirements and outlined in NSC/T. This will also be provided free to the subcontractor concerned. The costs of other attendance are normally recouped from the employer through pricing the items in the bills of quantities. Attendance items have been described in Chapter 23. Subcontractors should clear away their rubbish into places provided by the main contractor on site (clause 3.15). The eventual removal from site is provided by the contractor under general attendance. Subject to the above clauses subcontractors are responsible for their own temporary workshops, sheds or other temporary buildings on site. The contractor must provide only for the space requirements on site for such buildings, as required by the general attendance requirements.

Contractor and subcontractor not to make a wrongful use or to interfere with the property of the other

The main contractor and the subcontractors should not make wrongful use or interfere with the property of others working on the site (clause 3.19). Theft and the interference with a subcontractor's work can represent a major problem for the many different firms who may be working on a building site at the same time. One of the biggest problems is associated with the 'borrowing' or theft of materials, plant and equipment by others.

Section 4: Payment

Subcontract or tender sum

Either a subcontract sum (clause 4.2), based upon a lump sum, is agreed for work that has been clearly defined, or a subcontract tender sum (clause 4.3) that allows for remeasurement upon completion of the subcontract works. Where adjustments are made to the subcontract sum in preparation of the final account, then once these amounts have been agreed they can be included in the interim payments (clause 4.1).

Valuation of variations

The rules for the valuation of variations (clause 4.4) follow the same principles as the rules in JCT 80. These include variations resulting from architect's instructions, and work executed that was covered by an approximate quantity in the original bills. Work that is changed by the subcontractor can at a later date also become the subject of a variation if accepted by the architect. These rules for the valuation of variations are summarized as follows for work under a contract sum as Agreement NSC/A article 3.1:

- The rates and prices contained in the subcontract documents are used for work that is of a similar character and executed under similar conditions (clause 4.6.1.1).
- Pro-rata rates to those contained in the subcontract documents are used where the work is of a similar character but is executed under different conditions (clause 4.6.1.2).
- Fair rates and prices to those contained in the subcontract documents are to be used for work that is not of a similar character (clause 4.6.1.3).
- The rates and prices contained in the subcontract documents are to be used for reasonably accurate forecasts of approximate quantities (clause 4.6.1.4).
- Pro-rata rates to those contained in the subcontract documents are used where the approximate quantities are not a reasonably accurate forecast of the work (clause 4.6.1.5).
- Work that is omitted from the contract is valued at the rates and prices contained in the documents, provided the remaining work is not affected (clauses 4.6.2 and 4.6.5).
- Allowances can also be made to a reduction or addition in value to the preliminary items in the subcontract documents (clause 4.6.3).
- Work that cannot be properly measured or valued, will use daywork rates (clause 4.6.4).
- If variations to the works substantially change the conditions under which any other part of the subcontract work is executed then this may necessitate revaluation under clause 4.6.

The subcontractor has the right to attend any remeasurement that may be necessary in connection with the valuation of variations (clause 4.8). Where the work is to be entirely remeasured under a tender sum as Agreement NSC/A article 3.2, then the above similar rules of valuation apply (clauses 4.10ff.).

Payment of subcontractor

Interim and final payments to nominated subcontractors are to be made in accordance with the provisions of clauses 4.14–4.25. These clauses incorporate the provisions of the main contract conditions of clause 35. Clause 4.15.1 makes it clear that the subcontractor must apply for payment through the main contractor. This must be done in writing, and whilst a letter will be accepted in practice, for accounting purposes an invoice is preferable. The invoice may include work completed, materials on site and materials off site where the provisions of clause 30.3 of JCT 80 (clause 4.15.3) have been observed. There are also provisions in JCT 80 (clause 35.13) and this is repeated in the Agreement NSC/W (clause 2.2.4), to allow an employer to pay a nominated subcontractor for design work, materials and goods prior to the instruction of actual nomination.

Notification by the main contractor to the subcontractor of the amount included in the certificate must be made within 17 days (clause 4.16.1) of the date of the interim certificate. This notification will also include for the appropriate amount of payment due, less the 2.5 per cent cash discount. The cash discount is allowable from all nominated subcontractors' invoices. Where this has not been allowed for at tender stage, it is usual then to add 1/39th to the total (clause 4.17.2.4). This envisages a cheque being posted to the subcontractor upon receipt of payment to the main contractor from the employer. In practice, where the employer defaults in payment, this will then cause a chain reaction of non-payment by the main contractor to the different nominated subcontractors. The subcontractor must issue a receipt to the contractor which can then be shown as reasonable proof of payment to the architect. Comparable provisions to those included in the main contract to allow an employer to pay a subcontractor direct, or for final payment to be made to a subcontractor, are also included.

Where the value of any of a subcontractor's goods or materials has been included in an interim certificate, and the employer has paid the main contractor for them, then such goods become the property of the employer (clause 4.15.2). The architect must inform the subcontractor of the amount of payment in this respect, in the usual way. This is an attempt to avoid the employer having to pay twice for these items, in the case of default by the main contractor. This issue has, in the past, caused disputes in the courts regarding the ownership or title to such goods.

The contract also provides for an early final payment to subcontractors, where subcontractors are prepared to indemnify the main contractor in respect of any future defects in their work occurring (clause 4.16.2).

The ascertainment of the amounts due under interim and final payments (clause 4.17) contain similar provisions to those of the main contract conditions (clause 30, JCT 80). Amounts in interim certificates are described as being subject to retention or amounts not subject to retention. The subcontractor should ensure that the main contractor has invoices for the work at least 7 days before the date of the interim certificate (clause 4.17). This is to allow time for inclusion in the quantity surveyor's valuation of the works. The gross valuation includes the following:

- value of work that has been properly executed;
- value of materials and goods delivered to the site;
- value of materials off site, where the architect has exercised discretion in this respect;
- amounts in pursuant of clause 4.1, as a result of payments or costs incurred by a subcontractor;
- amounts in respect of restoration, replacement or repair of loss or damage (clause 4.38) and the removal of debris which in clauses 6B.4 and 6C.4

are treated as if they were a variation;
- amounts in respect of fluctuations (clauses 4A or 4B);
- amounts equal to 1/39th of the amounts in the last three items (the first three items will already include this cash discount amount).

Where a subcontractor is not satisfied with the amount of an interim payment, or the failure on the part of the architect to certify any amount, then the subcontractor together with the main contractor can instigate arbitration proceedings (clause 4.20). This may arise where:

- The main contractor has withheld payments under the set-off provision (clauses 4.26ff.), and these have been contested by a subcontractor.
- The employer has failed to operate the provisions for payments directly to a subcontractor, when the main contractor has defaulted in respect of interim payments.

A subcontractor can then choose to suspend the subcontract works until the matter is satisfactorily resolved. Notice must first be given to the employer and contractor of the subcontractor's intention (clause 4.21.1). This right must not be exercised unreasonably or vexatiously (clause 4.21.3).

The main contractor's interest in a subcontractor's retention money is fiduciary, as trustee for the subcontractor (clause 4.22). There is no obligation to invest the amount, i.e. where this is done any interest accruing will be for the benefit of the main contractor only. In some circumstances it may be necessary to provide a separate bank account to hold this money. This principle is the same as that used between the employer and the main contractor.

The adjustment of the subcontract sum or tender sum follows a similar procedure to that of the adjustment of the main contract sum.

Contractor's right to set-off

The main contractor is entitled to deduct amounts from money that has been authorized for a nominated subcontractor (clause 4.26) provided that:

- The amount of set-off has been quantified in detail and with reasonable accuracy by the contractor.
- The subcontractor agrees that the amount is owed to the main contractor.
- The sum has been finally awarded in arbitration or litigation in favour of the main contractor.

The main contractor is also entitled to set-off against any money due to the nominated subcontractor for loss and expense because of a failure on the part of a subcontractor to observe the provisions of the subcontract. The main contractor must be able to prove an actual loss or expense due to a subcontractor's breach of contract. Any amount ascertained in this respect can only be deducted from a subcontractor's outstanding payment on the judgment of an adjudicator, where the two parties cannot agree.

A subcontractor who disagrees with the amount specified in the contractor's notice of the intention to set off must within 14 days of the receipt of such notice send a written statement to the contractor (clause 4.30). This must be done by registered post or recorded delivery, setting out the reasons for such disagreement with the particulars of any counterclaim. At the same time the subcontractor should give notice of arbitration under section 9 of these conditions (clause 4.30.1). The subcontractor should also request the action by the adjudicator (clause 4.30.2).

Matters affecting regular progress

A subcontractor who feels that direct loss or expense will be incurred, for which adequate reimbursement will not be made, must inform the contractor accordingly. This must be done in writing, listing one or more of the reasons offered in clause 4.38.2. These reasons follow those outlined in clause 26.2 of the main contract conditions. A subcontractor's application under this clause should be made as soon as the subcontractor becomes aware that the regular progress of the works is likely to be affected. A subcontractor must then, as soon as possible, provide the main contractor with the details of the loss and expense incurred, in order that the architect and quantity surveyor can assess the likely amount of money that is involved. It is obviously important to the employer that any amounts to be added to the contract sum are known as soon as possible. This will enable the employer to be better aware of the overall financial commitment to the project.

The regular progress of the works may become materially affected because of an act, omission or default of the main contractor or any subcontractor. In these circumstances, the subcontractor must give written notice to the main contractor of any possible claim that might be forthcoming. Any amount agreed therefore becomes a debt recoverable from the main contractor.

In clause 4.40, this represents the opposite position to the above. A nominated subcontractor is at fault and a claim is now due to the main contractor. During the preparation of this claim, the main contractor should also take into account in the calculations any liability towards other subcontractors that may be working on the site.

All of the provisions of clauses 4.38–4.40 are without prejudice to any other rights or remedies that the main contractor or nominated subcontractor may possess.

Section 4A–4B–4C: Fluctuations

This group of clauses follows the same pattern as the main contract provisions (clauses 37–40). Clause 4A (Contribution, levy and tax fluctuations) will apply if no mention is made of either clause 4B (Labour and materials cost and tax fluctuations) or 4C (Formula adjustment). The use of the latter depends upon a suitable analysis of the original contract sum.

Section 5: Statutory obligations

Value added tax

These clauses (5A and 5B) operate in a similar manner to clause 15 of the main contract conditions. The clause therefore provides for the subcontract sum to be exclusive of VAT. This is to be paid as an extra to the subcontract. Main contractors, will in turn, recover any tax that they have to pay as an input tax.

Income and Corporation Taxes Act 1988

Clause 5C refers to the Income and Corporation Taxes Act 1988 and the Income Tax (Subcontractors in the Construction Industry) Regulations 1975. They are concerned with the subcontractors' use of a current tax certificate, commonly referred to as a 714 certificate. They complement the provisions of clause 31 in the main contract conditions.

Section 6: Injury, damage and insurance

Injury to persons and property

A subcontractor is responsible for injury that may be caused to persons or property due to the negligent carrying out of the subcontract works. The subcontractor must therefore indemnify the contractor accordingly in connection with the possibility of this occurring. The indemnity excludes any act or neglect on the part of either the main contractor or another subcontractor working on the site.

The liability for loss or damage excludes injury or damage where clause 6C applies, where the employer is responsible. An employer, for example, is likely to already have the existing premises insured. The liability also excludes the specified perils that have been defined in clause 1.3 of JCT 80.

Insurance against injury to persons and property

The subcontractor is responsible for maintaining such insurances that are necessary to cover liability in respect of personal injury or death and injury or damage to property, that might be caused whilst carrying out the subcontract works. The insurance in respect of personal injury or death should comply with the Employer's Liability (Compulsory Insurance) Act 1969 and any relevant statutory orders.

A subcontractor is not liable to indemnify the contractor or to provide insurance in respect of personal injury or death or damage to the works, materials or property by the effect of an excepted risk. These are defined in clause 1.3 of JCT 80.

Loss or damage to the works or subcontract works

Three options for insurance are offered. These follow the principles outlined in the main contract, JCT 80. The one retained in the subcontract will be the same as the one used on the main contract.

Clause 6A New buildings: contractor arranges joint names policy.
Clause 6B New buildings: employer arranges joint names policy.
Clause 6C Works in or extensions to existing structures: employer arranges joint names policy.

Clause 6A: New buildings (note main contract conditions clause 22A)

The main contractor is responsible for insuring the works and materials against the specified risks (clause 1.3, JCT 80). This responsibility runs until the issue of the certificate of practical completion, and includes the subcontractor's work and materials. Any loss or damage occurring after this date to the subcontract works, unless it is due to negligence, breach of statutory duty, omission or default, is not the subcontractor's responsibility.

The subcontractor is also not responsible for any loss or damage that occurs due to the occurrence of one of the specified perils (clause 1.3, JCT 80). Neither is the subcontractor responsible for any loss or damage that might arise due to the fault of the main contractor or anyone for whom the main contractor is responsible.

Subcontractors are of course responsible for defects or damage caused by their own workmen. They are also responsible for their own temporary buildings, plant, tools and equipment, and will need to insure these accordingly. Subcontractors should also consider whether any insurance should be provided, at their own expense, to cover any other possible risks that are not covered under this clause 6A, such as impact, subsidence, theft, vandalism.

If any loss or damage occurs, either due to a specified peril or otherwise, then a subcontractor must inform the main contractor in writing of the extent, nature and location of the damage. A subcontractor, on the instructions of the architect or contractor, must restore any damaged subcontract works or materials and dispose of any debris that may have arisen. If the loss or damage is not the responsibility of the subcontractor, then these will be treated as a variation. The sum is then recovered from the contractor as a debt, but is not added to the contract sum. The main contractor must then claim the amount from his own insurers.

Clause 6B: New buildings (note main contract conditions clause 22B)

Under these conditions it is the contractor's responsibility to ensure that the employer insures the works in a joint policy that is referred to in clause 22B of the main contract (JCT 80). Subcontractors are either recognized as an insured, under the joint names policy, or the insurers waive the rights of subrogation (i.e.

substitution of one person for another, in regard to a legal claim) they may have against the subcontractor. The same procedures apply as under 6A, except that it is treated as if it were a variation and the amount then added to the contract sum. Employers would then seek to recover the amounts from their own insurers. The subcontractors will continue to insure their own personal effects, such as temporary buildings, plant and equipment and risks that are not otherwise covered by clause 6B, such as impact, subsidence, theft, vandalism.

Clause 6C: Works in or extensions to existing structures (note main contract conditions clause 22C)

These are similar provisions to clause 6B above.

Policies of insurance, production, payment of premiums, default by contractor or subcontractor

The main contractor and the subcontractors, respectively, are all required to have the necessary insurance in compliance with the contract. The provision of such insurance by one party may affect another. There is, therefore, the provision to allow either party, at reasonable times, to inspect the policies or premium receipts of the other. Where the main contractor or a subcontractor fails to properly insure, then the other party may do this on their behalf. The amounts of the premiums are then recovered from the party who is in default.

Subcontractor's plant, etc. responsibility of contractor

Any plant, tools or equipment brought on to the site by a nominated subcontractor are the sole risk and responsibility of the subcontractor. If any negligence, breach of statutory duty, omission or default of the contractor, or others for whom the main contractor has a responsibility, results in damage or loss of these items, the subcontractor can claim from the parties responsible. Subcontractors are, however, responsible for injury to persons and property resulting from the use of their plant or equipment. The main contractor will, therefore, require to be indemnified by a subcontractor against all possible claims and legal proceedings in this respect. Subcontractors are also responsible for any insurances that may be required for their own plant and equipment.

Section 7: Determination

Determination of the employment of the subcontractor by the contractor

One of the remedies that the main contractor may request of the architect, if a nominated subcontractor defaults in one of the following ways, is the determination of the employment of the subcontractor (clause 7.1):

- without reasonable cause the subcontractor suspends the works;
- without reasonable cause fails to proceed with the subcontract works in the manner provided in clause 2.1;
- refuses or neglects written notices from the contractor to remove defective work or improper materials or wrongly fails to rectify defects;
- fails to comply with the provisions of clause 3.13 or 3.14 (assignment and subletting).

It is the contractor's responsibility to first inform the architect that one of the above has occurred. The contractor must also supply the appropriate details. The architect may then instruct the main contractor to issue a notice of the impending determination of a subcontractor. The notice should be issued either by registered post or recorded delivery. The subcontractor has 14 days in which to remedy the default, otherwise the employment is terminated.

In the event of a subcontractor becoming bankrupt or making arrangements to enter liquidation in accordance with the Insolvency Act 1986, then the subcontract is terminated automatically.

If a subcontractor or any person employed, even without the subcontractor's knowledge, offers an inducement or reward in relation to the obtaining or the execution of the subcontract, then the employer may determine the subcontract (clause 7.3). This clause may be extended to subcontracts on other projects being undertaken by the employer. When a subcontract has been terminated under this clause, the following represent the respective rights and duties of the main contractor and subcontractor:

- The subcontractor's temporary buildings, plant and equipment may be used freely by the firm appointed to complete the subcontract works.
- The subcontractor must assign to the main contractor, without any payment, any benefit of any agreement for the supply of materials or goods or for the execution of any of the subcontract works.
- The contractor may be directed by the architect to pay for any goods or materials that have been delivered to site, but not paid for by the subcontractor.
- The subcontractor must remove personal effects such as temporary buildings, plant and equipment when requested to do so by the architect. If the subcontractor ignores this instruction, then the main contractor may within a reasonable time, remove and sell them. The proceeds of such a sale are then held for the benefit of the subcontractor.
- The subcontractor must pay the main contractor for any direct loss or expense that has resulted from the determination.

Determination of employment under the subcontract by the subcontractor

If the main contractor makes a default for one of the following reasons, then a subcontractor can determine their employment under the terms of the subcontract (clause 7.6):

- Without reasonable cause the contractor wholly suspends the works before completion.
- Without reasonable cause, the contractor fails to proceed with the works so that the reasonable progress of the subcontract works is seriously affected.

A subcontractor may then take the following action (clause 7.7):

- Issue a written notice specifying the default, sent registered post or recorded delivery, with a copy to the architect.
- If after 14 days after the notice of default has been given the contractor has not rectified the situation, then the subcontractor may terminate the employment under the subcontract.

The rights and remedies, without prejudice to other accrued rights, or to the subcontractor's liability to the contractor under clause 6 for injury to persons and property, are as follows (clause 7.7):

- The subcontractor removes personal items such as temporary buildings, plant, tools equipment, goods or materials. The subcontractor must do this with care to prevent injury, death or damage to those items for which the subcontractor is responsible under clause 6.
- The contractor must then pay to the subcontractor the following:
    - the total value of work completed at the date of determination, ascertained under clause 4;
    - the total value of any work in progress;
    - any sum ascertained in respect of direct loss and expense under clause 4.39;
    - the costs of any materials or goods properly ordered for the subcontract works of which the contractor is bound to accept delivery;
    - the reasonable cost of removal under clause 7.7.1;
    - any direct loss or expense caused to the subcontractor because of the determination.

Determination of the contractor's employment under the main contract

If the employment of the main contractor is determined under clauses 28 or 28A of the main contract, then the employment of every nominated subcontractor is also automatically determined. The provisions of clause 7.7 will then apply to each subcontractor.

If the main contractor decides to terminate the contract because of one of the reasons listed in clause 28 of the main contract, the subcontracts are also automatically terminated. The main difference is that the subcontractors will receive a share of any payments that become due because of the termination of the contract. These amounts, in respect of subcontractors, are calculated under clause 28.2.2.6 of the main contract. The subcontractors, of course, will necessarily have suffered direct loss and expense, and will need to substantiate their claims to the main contractor. The sums agreed and due to the subcontractors under interim certificates are not affected because of the main contractor's determination under clause 28.

Section 9: Arbitration

This clause (clause 9) incorporates the provisions of the main contract (clause 41, JCT 80) and gives the arbitrator specific powers to rectify a subcontract. The JCT Arbitration Rules (July 1988) are to apply.

Chapter 25

Domestic subcontract conditions

The construction industry changed rapidly during the 1980s in order to become more efficient, effective and economic in its practice. Such changes continue to take place across a whole spectrum of activities. One of the changes that occurred during this period was the widespread use of subcontracting firms to undertake work on behalf of the main contractor. There are now relatively few main contractors who carry out a wide range of different construction trades. The process of change is of course evolutionary in order to meet the demands placed upon the industry by employers and the need for contractors to manage their work in the best possible way. In a few years time, it is likely that the position will have changed again in order to meet new methods of working and contracting generally. It may be that someone will 'discover' the general contractor.

The main contract conditions do not generally recognize the main contractor's own subcontractors. These are often referred to as domestic subcontractors. As far as the contract is concerned, the work that they carry out is deemed to be that of the main contractor. The architect will generally only deal with the main contractor's representative, through, for example, the issue of site instructions. The main contractor must thus inform these subcontractors where these instructions relate to their work. For convenience and expediency the quantity surveyor may choose to remeasure or value the works of subcontractors with them in attendance.

The contractor at tender stage will decide on which work will be carried out by his own workmen, if any. The remainder will then be subcontracted to specialist firms who may undertake just a single trade such as bricklaying or carpentry and joinery. In order to incorporate their prices within the main contract tender, they will in the first instance price the relevant extracts from the bills of quantities or work schedules. Several firms may be invited to submit prices in this way. The main contractor will then use those prices that are the most advantageous, adding profit and overheads where appropriate.

Under the JCT 80 form of contract the main contractor must first seek the approval of the architect before placing a contract with any of these firms (JCT 80, clause 19.2). Unless the architect has a reasonable objection, then the consent should not normally be withheld. If the main contractor's tender is successful, a firm order is then able to be placed with these firms. The main contractor should be satisfied that they are able to carry out the work in accordance with the contract, to the appropriate standards and quality and at the period of time that is shown on the contract programme. Wherever possible the main contractor should be satisfied with their performance on previous and similar projects and that the price they have quoted is reasonable for the work undertaken. A very low subcontractor quotation that may be below cost, can create problems later during the construction of the project.

The terms of subletting will be agreed between the main contractor and the subcontractor. The main contractor may have pre-printed conditions for this purpose. It is more likely that one of the standard subcontract forms will be used. The conditions outlined in these forms provide for fair and reasonable conditions of engagement to both parties and their use is therefore to be encouraged. The use of such forms may also avoid possible friction arising between the main contractor and the subcontractor, where each may have made different assumptions and interpretations of non-standard conditions. Subcontracting can present many difficulties to each party and *ad hoc* arrangements will not help either party, either to achieve satisfaction or in the smooth running of the contract. The use of a standard non-nominated form is therefore recommended.

The following refer to the Subcontract Conditions for use with the Domestic Subcontract DOM/1 Articles of Agreement. The form has largely replaced the existing 'blue' form, referred to in this way because of the colour of paper on which it was printed. The JCT 80 non-nominated form of subcontract comprises the following documents:

Articles of Agreement, for use with JCT 80 – DOM/1
Subcontract Conditions – DOM/1C
Contra-charges and Set-off under DOM/1

The following non-nominated forms are also available for use with other JCT forms:

Articles of Agreement for use with Contractor's Design 1981 – DOM/2
Articles of Agreement for use in connection with IFC 84 – IN/SC
Conditions for use with IN/SC

The above include a range of amendments that are issued from time to time, often in conjunction with amendments with the main forms of contract.

The different domestic subcontract conditions are also available for use with most of the major forms of contract (see also Chapter 6).

The following comments apply only to DOM/1 conditions for use with the Standard Form of Contract.

The Articles of Agreement follow the pattern of those in the main contract conditions. The agreement is in this case between the main contractor and a domestic subcontractor. A separate contract is formed between the main contractor and each of the domestic subcontractors. The name of the employer is provided for the subcontractor's information only. The employer is not a party to this contract and can therefore neither sue nor be sued under the provisions of the contract. There are of course other remedies that either the employer or subcontractor can pursue in the case of a grievance that cannot be settled contractually.

Article 1. This describes the subcontractor's obligation to become familiar with the provisions of the main contract and the overall aims and objectives of the employer. The subcontractor will, however, only be bound by those contract conditions that are written into the subcontract agreement. By becoming familiar with the main contract, the subcontractor will be able to gain a better understanding of any implications that may have an effect upon the tender price submitted and the proposed method for carrying out the works.

Article 2. This states that the subcontract price is to be exclusive of VAT, in line with the main contract conditions. The agreed subcontract sum is entered here in the contract. This sum will include a 2.5 percent cash discount for the main contractor, unless an alternative percentage has been inserted in Part 7 of these conditions. Article 2.1 refers to a subcontract sum where the subcontractor's tender sum is unlikely to be any different from the final account for the work. Where the work is to be remeasured, the subcontractor's tender sum will be inserted into the conditions. Only one of these alternatives is applicable, the other being deleted from the Articles of Agreement.

Article 3. This refers to the settlement of disputes, and the requirement that all matters will be first referred to arbitration and not directly to the courts. The dispute will arise in the first instance because of a difference that may arise between the main contractor and a subcontractor. This may result in arbitration proceedings being instigated by the contractor against the employer. This will occur where the dispute is more of a matter to be resolved by the employer than a dispute directly with the contractor.

Appendix to DOM/1

The Appendix to DOM/1 provides information relevant to the subcontract conditions in fourteen parts.

Part 1

This contains information which is extracted from the main contract conditions, but which is relevant to the subcontract.

Part 1, section A

This includes the following information:
(a)   description of the works;

(b)   form of main contract;
(c)   the main contract documents and where they can be inspected;
(d)   whether the main contract has been executed under hand or under seal;
(e)   which of the main contract conditions are to apply where an alternative is available, e.g. architect or supervising officer, type of insurance for the works;
(f)   any of the standard main contract conditions which have been amended or revised.

Part 1, section B

This contains a copy of the completed Appendix applicable to the main contract.

Part 1, section C

This is subdivided into three separate sections, the first of which deals with any obligations or restrictions that have been imposed by the employers on the project. These will therefore have been covered in the preliminaries section of the bill of quantities. It may include restrictions on working hours, the use of non-union labour, etc. Such matters will, of course, appertain to the contractor's domestic subcontractors. The second section outlines the employer's requirements affecting the order of the works where this is required. The third section covers a description of the location of the site and the mode of access.

Part 2

This describes briefly the particulars of the subcontract works that will be undertaken by this subcontractor. Any relevant documents – such as detailed drawings, specifications or bills of quantities – should be listed for identification and contractual purposes.

Part 3

This requires the subcontractor to insure for personal injury, damage to property and liability. The amount of insurance is to be specified in accordance with clause 7.2 of the subcontract conditions.

Part 4

This includes reference to clause 11.1 of the subcontract conditions regarding the time factor of the subcontract works, and provides for:
(a)   the date for commencement of the subcontract works, which is designated between two calendar dates;

(b)   the subcontract period for this work;

(c)   the period required for notice to commence work on site;

(d)   the period for subcontract works off site and prior to commencement on site;

(e)   any further details that may be appropriate to the time factor.

Part 5

Clauses 16.2 and 17.2 refer to daywork undertaken by the subcontractor. The provisions of the main contract will apply in respect of the definition of prime cost of daywork regarding the analysis of the work. The appropriate RICS schedule will be used depending upon the nature of the subcontractor. Subcontractors have the option of including percentage additions for the daywork sections. The main contractor will, however, only be eligible to reclaim from the employer, where this is appropriate, at the rates which he has inserted in the contract bills. The contractor will therefore endeavour to make sure that they are no higher than those rates.

Part 6

Clauses 19A and 19B deal with the alternative VAT arrangements, one of which should be deleted.

Part 7

This part covers the main contractor's cash discount on the subcontract invoices. The recommended discount is 2.5 per cent. Also listed is the retention percentage to be deducted from interim payments. This is normally in accordance with the provisions of the main contract, and 5 per cent is therefore considered to be the maximum.

Part 8

Clause 24 considers the contractor's claims against the subcontractor and the arrangement for set-off. This includes the same requirements as for nominated subcontractors. The name and address of the adjudicator and the trustee-stakeholder should be provided in accordance with this clause.

Part 9

Particulars of the subcontract's other attendance requirements should be described separately, initialled by the parties and attached to the Appendix. The domestic subcontractor, in common with the nominated subcontractor, is entitled to the free provision of general attendance facilities. The main contractor may, however, make an allowance in his rates inserted in the bills for the appropriate costs associated with such items.

Parts 10–13

These relate to the fluctuation provisions and follow a similar pattern to the main form. Clause 35 will apply if there is nothing to the contrary. Clause 34 expects, however, that one of the alternatives will be clearly identified. Where the formula rules are used the base month appropriate to the subcontractor must be clearly indicated.

Part 14

If the main contractor desires to insist upon other stipulations in connection with a subcontractor, then this should be stated.

The JCT Domestic Subcontract Conditions (DOM/ 1C)

These follow a similar pattern and content to the Nominated Subcontract Conditions (NSC/C). However, the domestic subcontractor is not generally recognized in the same way by the employer as the nominated subcontractor. There are clear advantages in being appointed on the basis of the latter. For example, there are no direct payment provisions by the employer should the main contractor default in paying a domestic subcontractor. Neither is there any provision for an early release of retention. Where a nominated subcontractor feels aggrieved at receiving apparently unfair treatment from the main contractor, there is the possibility of an appeal to the architect to help settle the matter, since it was partially because of the architect that the subcontractor was nominated in the first place. The direct subcontractor does not easily have this redress, since the architect will only be responsible for approving this firm under clause 19 (Assignment and subcontracts) of the main contract conditions. The architect, through the main contractor, will require that the work carried out by a domestic subcontractor meets the general requirements of the contract and is completed to the reasonable satisfaction of the architect. The domestic subcontractor must also comply with all instructions, make good any defective work and allow access for the architect to workshops if this is required. Such instructions will be issued through the main contractor.

Part 6

Other contract conditions

Chapter 26

Agreement for minor building works

The first edition of the JCT Agreement for Minor Building Works was published in 1968, based upon the JCT 1963 Standard Form of Building Contract. This was subsequently extensively revised in January 1980, to bring it in line with the JCT 80. It is a simplified version of that form of contract and does not envisage the same contractual problems arising from the carrying out of construction works. The simplification inevitably, however, produces a less precise set of conditions. Since its publication in 1980 there have been a number of revisions and reprints of the form, the latest to date being in March 1994.

The major changes have incorporated an additional clause 9 covering the settlement of disputes through arbitration, the abolition of the fair wages clause which coincided with its deletion from JCT 80 and the change in title from supervising officer to contract administrator. This latter amendment is the most significant. Architects have always been unhappy with the title of supervisor, since they claim that this is not a fair description of their activities. Inspector of works would be a preference and a better description Contract administrator is perhaps better terminology since this represents more or less any profession's role within the scope of the contract. Where the term 'architect' is used in this chapter it must also be interpreted to mean contract administrator.

The minor works form is not for use under the following circumstances:
(a)   in Scotland;
(b)   where bills of quantities have been provided;
(c)   where the employer wishes to nominate subcontractors or suppliers;
(d)   on contracts of a duration that require the full labour and materials fluctuations;
(e)   for works of a complex nature;
(f)   for works which involve complex services;
(g)   for works which require more than a short period of time for their execution.

It is intended to be used only on minor building works, although no value has been stated. However, one supposes that in practice it is used on much larger projects. This is due to partially the reluctance of architects to get involved with the complexities of JCT 80. It has sold many thousands of copies indicating its widespread acceptance and suitability for these sorts of works. Its use is restricted to where an employer appoints an architect or any other professional such as a surveyor or engineer, but not the contractor as in the case of design and build. The contract is carried out on an agreed lump sum on the basis of drawings and specifications. It can be an appropriate form for maintenance works where these can be readily defined.

The form of contract follows a similar pattern to JCT 80, but comprises a form of agreement and Conditions of Contract only. The agreement, which needs to be completed by the parties, describes the works, who the contract is between, the contract sum, the name of the architect/contract administrator, provisions for arbitration, and the contract documents. A schedule of rates may be included should the project require remeasurement or the agreement of variations. A quantity surveyor may therefore still be used (possibly holding the title of contract administrator) to prepare the specification or schedule of rates and to agree the final account.

The Conditions of Contract include the clauses under a group of nine headings:

Clause 1   Intention of the parties.
Clause 2   Commencement and completion.
Clause 3   Control of the works.
Clause 4   Payment.
Clause 5   Statutory obligations.
Clause 6   Injury, damage and insurance.
Clause 7   Determination.
Clause 8   Supplementary memorandum.
Clause 9   Settlement of disputes – arbitration.

The contents of these nine main sections are briefly described below.

Clause 1: Intention of the parties

Clause 1.1 states that the contractor's obligations are to carry out the works:
(a)   with due diligence and to complete the works;
(b)   in a good and workmanlike manner;
(c)   in accordance with the contract documents;
(d)   using materials and workmanship of the quality and standard specified;
(e)   to the reasonable satisfaction of the architect or contract administrator.

Clause 1.2 states that the architect/contract administrator's duties include:
(a)   the provision of the necessary information to the contractor to carry out the works;
(b)   issuing certificates;
(c)   confirming all instructions in writing.

Clause 2: Commencement and completion

These clauses state when the works will start on site and when they must be completed. The clauses also cover matters relating to the defects liability period, which is normally 3 months. In the event of the project not being completed on time, separate provisions for an extension of time, or damages for non-completion are included. The damages are assessed on a liquidated basis and the rate per week should therefore be inserted in the contract. The architect or contract administrator shall certify the date when the works have reached practical completion.

Clause 3: Control of the works

These matters deal with assignment and subcontracting, with the general provision that written permission must first be obtained from the architect or contract administrator. The contractor must at all reasonable times keep a competent person-in-charge on site to whom the architect or contract administrator can issue instructions. This is a less onerous position than JCT 80. Any person may be reasonably excluded from the site by the architect, for good reasons.

The architect's instructions to the contractor must be in writing, or confirmed in writing within 2 days. The provisions for covering non-compliance with an instruction are similar to JCT 80. The confirmation within 2 days is the period of time quoted for the confirmation of clerks of works' instructions under JCT 80. There is no provision for a clerk of works under this form of contract.

There are also provisions for variations to the contract. These are to be valued on a fair basis by the architect. Where a quantity surveyor is named in the agreement these duties will be carried out on behalf of the architect. Alternatively, a price can be agreed before the work is carried out, and this seems a sensible course of action to follow. Provisional sums are valued in the same way. Nomination is specifically excluded.

Clause 4: Payment

These clauses deal with payment to the contractor and are as follows:
1. Provision is made for the correction of any inconsistencies in the documents.
2. Progress payments are normally to be made every 4 weeks and include the value of works properly executed and the value of materials and goods which have been reasonably and properly brought to the site. The form does not allow for the payment of materials off site. Retention is normally 5 per cent and payment should be made within 14 days to the contractor.
3. This form of contract provides for a penultimate certificate. This is issued within 14 days after the date of practical completion of the works. Half the retention is released with this certificate.

4.   The contractor shall supply within 3 months from the date of practical completion, all documentation that is necessary to prepare the final account. The final certificate is then issued within 28 days of the receipt of such documentation, provided that all defects have been made good.

5.   Any changes in contributions, levy or tax charges can be recouped. However, these contracts are often of such a short duration that a footnote in the contract suggests that this clause should be deleted from the contract.

6.   The contract is otherwise a fixed price contract, with no allowances being made for changes to labour, materials, plant or other resource costs.

Clause 5: Statutory obligations

Clause 5.1 requires the contractor to comply with all the statutory obligations, notices, fees or charges.

Clauses 5.2 and 5.3 deal with the provisions of VAT and the statutory tax deduction scheme respectively, and these are identical to the provisions of JCT 80.

Clause 5.5 covers corruption, and although this may be incorporated into any contract it usually only applies where the employer is a local authority.

Clause 6: Injury, damage and insurance

These clauses deal with matters of injury and damage and the requirements for appropriate insurance on the part of the contractor. The employer needs to be sure in the first place that if injury or damage occurs the blame and responsibility are that of the contractor. This presumes, of course, that the injury or damage results because of the contractor's negligence, and not because of a fault in the design. The latter may not necessarily provide the contractor with an adequate defence. The employer will therefore need to be satisfied that the contractor is properly insured (clause 6.4). As far as the works are concerned, alternative insurance provisions are available in the case of new works or existing structures. These are similar to clause 22 of JCT 80 and one of the alternatives therefore needs deleting. The contractor, and any subcontractors, will need to produce evidence of insurance if required.

Clause 7: Determination

These clauses cover determination of the contract by either the employer or the contractor. The employer may determine if the contractor:
(a)   fails to proceed diligently with the works (clause 7.1.1);
(b)   suspends the works (clause 7.1.1);
(c)   becomes bankrupt (clause 7.1.2).

The contractor has the option of determining the contract where the employer defaults in respect of:

(a) progress payments (clause 7.2.1);
(b) interference or obstruction of works (clause 7.2.2);
(c) failure to make the premises available (clause 7.2.2);
(d) continuous suspension of the works for one month (clause 7.2.3);
(e) bankruptcy or liquidation (clause 7.2.4).

The procedures for determination are described and this act by either party should be considered as a last resort. This act often requires damages to be paid from one party to the other. Determination must be without prejudice to any other rights or remedies which the parties may possess.

Clause 8: Supplementary memorandum

The supplementary memorandum referred to in this clause is in three parts. The JCT's intention is that it should be used for reference and does not therefore need to be bound in with the executed agreement. The three parts are very similar to the provisions of JCT 80:

Part A   Fluctuations (clause 4.5).
Part B   VAT (clause 5.2).
Part C   Statutory tax deduction scheme (clause 5.3).

Clause 9: Settlement of disputes -- arbitration

This clause provides for disputes or differences which may occur between the contractor and the employer to be referred to arbitration. The provisions are similar to JCT 80 and are to be conducted in accordance with the JCT Arbitration Rules. It should be noted that these rules contain stricter time limits than those prescribed by some arbitration rules which are frequently observed in practice. The parties to the contract should note that a failure to comply with the limits incorporated in the JCT Rules may have adverse consequences.

Comparison with JCT 80

Minor works clause	Clause description	JCT 80 clause
1.1	Contractor's obligations	2, 8
1.2	Architect's/contract administrator's duties	5
2.1	Commencement and completion	17, 23
2.2	Extension of contract period	25
2.3	Damages for non-completion	24
2.4	Completion date	23
2.5	Defects liability	17

Minor works clause	Clause description	JCT 80 clause
3.1	Assignment	19
3.2	Subcontracting	19
3.3	Contractor's representative	10
3.4	Exclusion from the works	8
3.5	Architect's/contract administrator's instructions	4
3.6	Variations	13
3.7	Provisional sums	13
4.1	Correction of inconsistencies	2
4.2	Progress payments and retention	16, 30
4.3	Penultimate certificate	–
4.4	Final certificate	30
4.5	Contribution, levy and tax charges	38
4.6	Fixed price	37
5.1	Statutory obligations, notices, fees and charges	6
5.2	Value added tax	15
5.3	Statutory tax deduction scheme	31
5.4	(Number not used)	
5.5	Prevention of corruption	27
6.1	Injury to or death of persons	20, 21
6.2	Injury or damage to property	20, 21
6.3A	Insurance of the works – fire, etc. – new works	22
6.3B	Insurance of the works – fire, etc. – existing works	22
6.4	Evidence of insurance	22
7.1	Determination by employer	27, 28A
7.2	Determination by contractor	28, 28A
8.1	Supplementary memorandum	15, 31, 37
9.0	Settlement of disputes – arbitration	41

The following conditions from JCT 80 are specifically excluded from the minor works form.

Minor works clause	Clause description	JCT 80 clause
–	Levels and setting out of the works	7
–	Royalties and patent rights	9
–	Clerk of works	12

Minor works clause	Clause description	JCT 80 clause
–	Materials off site	16
–	Partial possession	18
–	Loss and expense	26
–	Works by or on behalf of the employer	29
–	War damage	33
–	Antiquities	34
–	Nominated subcontractors	35
–	Nominated suppliers	36
–	Price adjustment formulae	40

Chapter 27

JCT Intermediate Form of Building Contract

Introduction

Many of the professionals who are employed in the construction industry regard the Standard Form of Building Contract (JCT 80) as too complex, at least for medium-sized projects. Others felt that the gap between this form and the Agreement for Minor Building Works was too great, and that some types of midway conditions were both desirable and essential for the efficient running of construction contracts. The *Intermediate Form* was thus conceived and its first edition was published in 1984. It soon became known as IFC 84.

Whilst it was envisaged that this form would be used on projects at that time worth up to £250,000 (now considerably more) it has been used for projects of much larger values. One of the main differences between IFC 84 and JCT 80 is that there is no provision for nominated subcontractors, as is usually understood. There is provision, however, for the architect to name a subcontractor for whom the main contractor assumes a much greater responsibility. The main concept of naming is as follows. All of the contractors tendering are provided with detailed information regarding the named subcontractor's price and conditions, programme of work and the attendances which the main contractor must provide. The contractor then assumes the same responsibility for the named subcontractor as with any normal domestic subcontractor. If, however, the named subcontractor defaults then there are provisions in the contract to safeguard the main contractor's interest.

IFC 84 generally follows the layout of the minor works form, as the clauses are grouped under similar section headings. The clause content is, however, more detailed and comprehensive although much less so than JCT 80. Unlike JCT 80, IFC 84 is published in only one edition which allows for the differences envisaged in the contractual arrangements. In addition to the drawings, for example, either bills of quantities, a specification or a schedule of works can be used. If the drawings are supported only by a specification then either a schedule of rates or a contract sum analysis must be provided in support of his tender.

The agreement, articles and recitals

Agreement

This is the page in the document which identifies the parties concerned with the contract.

Recitals

These include:

- brief description of the works to be constructed;
- documents which are to be included as contract documents;
- reference to the person under whose direction the works are to be carried out.

Articles

There are five articles as follows:
1. Contractor's obligations.
2. Contract sum.
3. Architect or supervising officer.
4. Quantity surveyor.
5. Settlement of disputes – arbitration.

Intention of the parties

1.1 Contractor's obligations. To carry out and complete the works in accordance with the contract documents which have been identified in the recital above.

1.2 Quality and quantity of work. The quality is as specified in the contract documents, quantities depend upon type of contract documentation which has been prepared.

1.3 Priority of contract documents. A specification, schedule of works or bills of quantities cannot override the Conditions of Contract.

1.4 Instructions as to inconsistencies, errors or omissions. The architect must issue instructions regarding any inconsistencies which may arise in the documents. If these affect the contract sum then they are to be revalued under clause 3.7 (valuation of variations).

1.5 Contract bills and SMM7. Contract bills are assumed to have been prepared under SMM7 unless otherwise stated.

1.6 Custody and copies of contract documents. The contract documents are to remain in the custody of the employer, with the contractor being given one copy of the contract documents certified on behalf of the employer, and two further copies of drawings and other contract documentation, e.g. bills of quantities.

1.7 Further drawings and details. Other drawings and information are likely to be prepared during the course of construction and two copies of these are also to be made available to the contractor.

1.8 Limits to use of documents. The contractor must not use any of these documents for any other purpose than this contract.

1.9 Issue of certificates by architect/supervising officer. Certificates are normally issued to the employer with duplicate copies to the contractor.

1.10 Unfixed materials or goods, passing of property, etc. Goods and materials delivered to the site are not to be removed without the written permission of the architect/supervising officer. Where such items have been paid for by the employer they become the employer's property. The contractor, however, remains responsible for their protection from damage or theft.

1.11 Off-site materials and goods, passing of property. Materials or goods paid for by the employer which are stored off site become the property of the employer. Such items must not be used for purposes other than the works. The contractor is again responsible for their safe keeping.

Possession and completion

2.1 Possession and completion dates. The date of possession is stated in the Appendix and the contractor shall begin and regularly and diligently proceed with the works and complete them before the date stated in the Appendix as the date for completion.

2.2 Deferment of possession. If this clause is to apply, i.e. it is stated in the Appendix as such, then the employer may defer giving possession of the site to the contractor by the period stated. The period is not to exceed 6 weeks. The contractor is then allowed to claim for any direct loss or expense.

2.3 Extensions of time. These are clauses to be followed and interpreted in the event of the works being or likely to be delayed. The contractor must inform the architect/supervising officer that a delay is likely to occur and the cause of such. If the architect/supervising officer feels that there are reasonable grounds for granting the contractor an extension of time then the contractor must estimate the amount of time that is appropriate and inform the contractor in writing of the decision.

2.4 Events referred to in 2.3. This includes the list of events which the contractor may refer to, to support a claim for an extension of time. The list includes similar items referred to in the other JCT contracts.

2.5 Further delay or extension of time. This clause allows for further extensions of time as may be appropriate.

2.6 Certificate of non-completion. The architect/supervising officer must issue a certificate where the contractor has failed to complete the works, either by the date for completion or within any date extended under the terms of the contract.

2.7 Liquidated damages for non-completion. These are stated in the Appendix as a rate of £X per week or month to be paid by the contractor to the employer for delays which are attributed to the fault of the contractor.

2.8 Repayment of liquidated damages. If it is felt at some later date that the delays were not entirely the fault of the contractor then the damages (or a part of them) can be repaid to the contractor.

2.9 Practical completion. When the architect/supervising officer decides that the works are complete a certificate is issued to that effect.

2.10 Defects liability. All defects, which are due to materials or workmanship which are not in accordance with the contract, which are notified to the contractor within 14 days after the expiry of the defects liability periods are to be made good at the contractor's expense.

2.11 Partial possession. This is not a normal part of the contract. Practice Note IN/1 allows for its incorporation if required.

Control of the works

3.1 Assignment. Neither the employer nor the contractor shall without the written consent of the other party assign the contract to someone else.

3.2 Subcontracting. The contractor cannot subcontract any part of the works without the written consent of the architect/supervising officer. The employment of a subcontractor is automatically terminated upon the determination of the main contract. A subcontractor is effectively treated in the same way as if he were the main contractor, so, for example, any materials or goods of a subcontractor which are brought to the site cannot be removed without written permission. If the value of a subcontractor's materials or goods is included in a certificate and this sum is paid by the employer to the main contractor then such items become the property of the employer.

3.3 Named persons as subcontractors. The contract documents may name a person or firm to undertake a section of the works as a subcontractor. Within 21 days of entering into the main contract, the contractor must communicate with the proposed subcontractor using the standard form of tender and agreement NAM/T. If the contractor is unable to enter into a subcontract in this way the architect/supervising officer must be immediately informed of the reasons which prevent this. If the architect/supervising officer is reasonably satisfied that the particulars have prevented a subcontract being made then an instruction is given which may:

1. Change the particulars so as to remove the impediment.
2. Omit the work.
3. Substitute the work with a provisional sum.

In an instruction as to the expenditure of a provisional sum the architect/ supervising officer may require the work to be executed by a named subcontractor. This clause also deals with the situation where the employment of a named subcontractor is determined and the procedures that should then be followed.

IFC 84 is a work and materials contract. It is not a design contract and the contractor is thus not responsible for any design work which may be required. If a named subcontractor has a design element then the main contractor is not responsible for any failures in the design but liability is limited only in respect of the goods, materials and workmanship.

3.4 Contractor's person-in-charge. The contractor has to keep on the works a competent person-in-charge.

3.5 Architect's/supervising officer's instructions. This clause deals with the provision of instructions to the contractor, which must be in writing. There are no provisions for oral instructions. It covers matters of non-compliance and the action the contractor may wish to take in respect of challenging the validity of an instruction.

3.6 Variations. The architect/supervising officer may issue instructions requiring a variation and sanction in writing to those made by the contractor. The term 'variation' is defined to include the alteration or modification of the design, quality or quantity of works as shown on the contract drawings. This may include the addition, omission or substitution of any work, the alteration of the kind or standard of materials or goods to be used, the removal from site of materials or work which are not in accordance with the contract and the addition, alteration or omission of any obligations or restrictions imposed by the employer.

3.7 Valuation of variations and provisional sum work. These broadly follow the provisions laid down in JCT 80 regarding similar work, using the priced schedules as a basis for valuation, fair valuations in the absence of any comparable items of work, dayworks and omitted work. The valuation where appropriate can include the adjustment to the values of preliminary items.

3.8 Instructions to expend provisional sums. The architect/supervising officer must issue instructions regarding the expenditure of provisional sums.

3.9 Levels and setting out. The architect provides the information required for setting out, the contractor is responsible for the actual setting out. Errors are amended in the same manner as JCT 80.

3.10 Clerk of works. The employer may choose to appoint a clerk of works whose sole responsibility is that of inspector.

3.11 Work not forming part of the contract. This allows the employer to employ persons or firms direct and concurrently with the main building work. The contractor must permit this work to be undertaken. Where the contract documents do not allow for this, the contractor must not unreasonably give the employer permission to arrange for the execution of such work.

3.12 Instructions as to inspections and tests. This allows the architect/

supervising officer the authority to open up work for inspection. Where the work is in accordance with the contract then the costs of opening up are added to the contract sum. Where it is not then the costs together with the costs of rectification are borne entirely by the contractor. The substandard work may be allowed to remain, in which case an agreed reduction in cost is made to the contract.

3.13 Instructions following failure of work, etc. See above.

3.14 Instructions as to removal of work, etc. The architect/supervising officer may issue instructions in respect of the removal from site of any goods or work which do not conform with the contract.

3.15 Instructions as to postponement. The architect/supervising officer may issue instructions in regard to the postponement of any work executed under the provisions of the contract.

Payment

4.1 Contract sum. The contract sum is not to be altered in any way, other than within the terms of the contract. Any computation of errors are deemed to have been accepted by the parties.

4.2 Interim payments. Interim payments are to be made monthly unless the contract states otherwise. The employer must pay the contractor within 14 days of the date of the certificate. The majority of the work is subject to 5 per cent retention, i.e. work completed and materials and goods on or off site. Some items of work are not subject to any retention, e.g. tax, insurances.

4.3 Interim payment on practical completion. One-half of the retention fund is released at practical completion and the remainder with the issue of the final certificate.

4.4 Interest in percentage withheld. The employer acts as trustee of the retention fund but without any obligation to invest.

4.5 Computation of adjusted contract sum. Either before or within a reasonable time after practical completion the contractor should provide all the documents which are necessary to adjust the contract sum and to calculate the final account.

4.6 Issue of final certificate. When the contract sum has been agreed the architect/supervising officer must issue the final certificate.

4.7 Effect of final certificate. Only the final certificate is conclusive except for matters which are the subject of proceedings but note recent case law (see JCT 80).

4.8 Effect of certificates other than final. None of the interim certificates are conclusive evidence that any work, materials or goods included in them are in accordance with the contract.

4.9 Fluctuations. These allow for the possibility of fluctuations in cost on the main contract. The JCT fluctuation clauses and formula rules for use with

JCT Intermediate Form of Building Contract IFC 84 should be referred to for the specific details.

4.10 Fluctuations, named persons. This allows for fluctuations in cost in respect of any amounts for named subcontractors.

4.11 Disturbance of regular progress. This clause deals with any direct loss or expense which the contractor may have suffered and which will not be reimbursed by a payment under any other provision of the contract.

4.12 Matters referred to in clause 4.11. This clause identifies the matters which may give rise to a claim for loss and expense. These include delay in receipt of drawings, details, etc., opening up of work for inspection that is found to be in accordance with the contract, execution of work by the employer's own subcontractors, supply by the employer of materials or goods or a failure to supply postponement of the works, failure to provide access to the site, and certain architect's/supervising officer's instructions.

Statutory obligations, etc.

5.1 Statutory obligations, notices, fees and charges. The contractor must comply with all notices which may be required by statute, statutory instrument, by-law, etc., and pay all the fees or charges which may be required. If such charges arise, for example, from a variation then they will be added to the contract sum.

5.2 Notices of divergence from statutory requirements. If the contractor finds any differences between the contract documents or that any of these documents are in conflict with any statutory requirement then a written notice of such divergence should be given to the architect. The contractor is not expected to search for discrepancies, but if they come to the contractor's notice then they should be notified to the architect.

5.3 Extent of contractor's liability for non-compliance. The contractor is not liable for work which does not comply with statutory requirements, if it has been carried out in accordance with the contract documents.

5.4 Emergency compliance. If the contractor is requested urgently to comply with a statutory obligation, before receiving appropriate instructions from the architect, then the minimum that is necessary should be carried out. The architect must then be informed and the work treated as a variation.

5.5 Value Added Tax, Supplemental condition A. The contract sum is exclusive of any value added tax and this is dealt with in the same way as in JCT 80.

5.6 Statutory tax deduction scheme, Supplemental condition B. This clause is also comparable to the similar clause in JCT 80.

Injury, damage and insurance

6.1 Injury to persons and property and employer's indemnity. The contractor is liable for and must indemnify the employer, against any action including costs and damages, in respect of injury or death of anyone. The contractor's only real defence is to show that such an occurrence was due to the neglect of the employer or of someone for whom the employer was responsible. The employer does have the option of accepting some of these risks and there is provision for such in clause 6.3.

6.2 Insurance against injury to persons and property. The provisions are broadly the same as JCT 80 in this respect, i.e. the contractor is responsible for the works and that of all subcontractors, the contractor should therefore seek to ensure that these subcontractors maintain relevant insurance and if there is a default in this respect then the employer can insure on their behalf and deduct the premiums from the contract sum.

6.3 Insurance in the joint names of the employer and contractor. The insurance will be taken out in the joint names of the employer and the contractor. There are three mutually exclusive clauses 6.3A, 6.3B and 6.3C and the Appendix must indicate which is to apply. These provisions broadly follow the principles described in JCT 80.

Determination

7.1 Determination by employer. The employer may determine the contract if the contractor:
   1. Unreasonably suspends the works.
   2. Fails to proceed regularly and diligently with the works.
   3. Persistently refuses to comply with an architect's instruction to remove defective work, and this results in further damage to the works.
   4. Fails to comply with the provisions of subcontracting and named persons.

7.2 Contractor becoming bankrupt. If the contractor becomes bankrupt or makes a composition or arrangement with creditors or has a winding up order made against the company that is either voluntary or otherwise, then the contract is automatically determined. This may be reinstated and continued where the employer and liquidator or receiver agree.

7.3 Corruption, determination by employer. Where the employer is a local authority then determination of the contractor's employment can occur where a gift or inducement to seek favours has been made by the contractor. Certain of these would no doubt cause any employer to determine a contract.

7.4 Consequences of determination under clauses 7.1–7.3. The consequences of determination can be summarized as follows:
   1. The contractor relinquishes the possession of the site.

2. If the architect so instructs then the contractor must remove from the works goods, materials, plant, etc.
3. The employer may engage others to complete the works and to use the goods, materials and plant. The benefits of these in practice may be limited, e.g. the right does not apply to hired plant, the goods and materials may be the subject of a retention of title clause and materials or goods used will form a part of the final account.

7.5 Determination by contractor. The contractor under some circumstances is also able to determine the contract. These are as follows:
1. The employer does not honour a certificate.
2. The employer interferes with or obstructs the issue of a certificate.
3. If the works are suspended for a period of at least one month due to inconsistencies, variations, postponement, late instructions, delays or failure by the employer or those engaged direct by the employer or failure on the part of the employer in respect of site access.

7.6 Employer becoming bankrupt, etc. If the employer becomes bankrupt then the contractor can terminate the contract. This is similar to clause 7.2.

7.7 Consequences of determination under clause 7.5 or 7.6. These are as follows:
1. The contractor removes temporary buildings, plant, tools, equipment, goods and materials and gives the subcontractors the same facilities.
2. The contractor is paid in respect of the following:
    (a) value of work done but not yet paid;
    (b) loss and expense ascertained;
    (c) cost of goods and materials properly ordered and paid for;
    (d) reasonable costs of removal under (a) above;
    (e) direct loss and expense caused by the determination.

7.8 Determination by employer or contractor. This clause is now the same as appears in JCT 80 as clause 28A.

7.9 Consequences of determination under clause 7.8. These are the same as where the contractor determines under clause 7.7.

Interpretation of the contract

8.1 References to clauses. These are the clauses of IFC 84.
8.2 Articles, etc. to be read as a whole. This makes it clear that articles, clauses and items in the Appendix are to be read as a whole.
8.3 Definitions. This clause contains a number of pertinent definitions, e.g. Appendix, clause 6.3 perils, contract sum analysis, etc.
8.4 The architect/supervising officer. If the person identified in article 3 is

ineligible to be described as an architect under the Architect's (Registration) Acts 1931 to 1969 then the term 'supervising officer' is to be used.

8.5 Priced specification or priced schedules of work. This refers to the documentation in the second recital of the Conditions of Contract.

Settlement of disputes

9.1–9.7 These clauses refer to the arbitration agreement outlined in article 5.1.

Chapter 28

ICE Conditions of Contract

These Conditions of Contract are used on projects that can broadly be described as civil engineering works. The sponsoring authorities for the sixth edition, which was revised in 1991, are:
1. The Institution of Civil Engineers.
2. The Association of Consulting Engineers.
3. The Federation of Civil Engineering Contractors.

A permanent joint committee of these bodies keeps the document under review, and will consider any suggestions or amendments.

Civil Engineering Procedure (published by the Institution of Civil Engineers) lists the following documents that are normally used in connection with a civil engineering contract:
1. Conditions of Contract.
2. Form of tender.
3. Form of agreement.
4. Instructions to tenderers.
5. Drawings.
6. Bills of quantities.
7. Specification.

The last three of the above documents are similar to those used on a building contract, but with a distinctly engineering emphasis. The bills of quantities, for example, will have been prepared in accordance with the rules of the Civil Engineering Standard Method of Measurement (CESMM), or alternatively the Method of Measurement for Roads and Bridgeworks (MMRB). Civil engineering contracts on the basis of measurement include a bill and a specification. As the specification will not identify the work sufficiently for pricing purposes, it more aligns with the trade preambles found in a bill for a building project. The specification will include:
(a) character and quality of materials and workmanship;
(b) special responsibilities imposed upon the contractor that are not covered by the conditions of contract;
(c) order for executing the works where necessary;
(d) methods of construction to be adopted where required by the engineer;
(e) particulars of facilities afforded to other contractors on the site;
(f) requirement on the part of the contractor to submit a programme for the works;

(g)   request the contractor to describe the proposed method of working and any temporary works.

The drawings for a civil engineering project are more likely to have been prepared within the procedures of engineering drawing, rather than the way an architect would produce drawings for a building project.

The purpose of the instructions to tenderers is to assist the tenderers in the preparation of their tenders, and to ensure that they are presented in a form required by the promoter and the engineer.

The remaining three documents, along with the form of bond, are all included in the document known as the ICE Conditions of Contract.

Form of tender

The form of tender is the tenderer's written offer to execute the work in accordance with the other contract documents. The form of tender should state:
(a)   the contractor's price;
(b)   commencement date and time for completion;
(c)   salient particulars of the offer.

The form of tender also includes the Appendix to the form of contract, which includes:
(a)   defects correction period;
(b)   contract agreement;
(c)   performance bond;
(d)   insurance;
(e)   liquidated damages;
(f)   venting materials not on site;
(g)   method of measurement;
(h)   percentage of value of materials; to be included in interim certificates;
(j)   minimum amount of interim certificates;
(k)   rate and limit of retention;
(l)   bank base rate.

Form of agreement

This is the legal undertaking entered into between the promoter and the contractor, for the execution of the work in accordance with the contract documents and which each party signs.

Form of bond

A security bond may be required by the promoter, and this is executed by the contractor at the time of signing the contract. The amount of the bond is often in the order of 10 per cent of the contract sum. Clause 10 of the conditions of contract deals with sureties.

Conditions of Contract

The Conditions of Contract are subdivided into 23 sections which contain in total 71 clauses. In addition, a separate clause on contract price fluctuations and arbitration procedure may be included where the contract is on that basis. The conditions also include a very useful index to the clauses. The clause contents are similar to the JCT Standard Form of Building Contract, but have been written with civil engineering projects in mind. Space does not permit a detailed treatment of these clauses. The major differences between this and JCT 80 are therefore only highlighted. Students who require a more detailed exposition should refer to a text dedicated to the engineering contract.

Definition and intepretation (clause 1)

This clause provides the reader with several important definitions in a like manner to JCT 80.

Engineer and engineer's representative (clause 2)

The engineer is defined in clause 1 by name. The nature of civil engineering works is that they are often large and cumbersome, and may be constructed on extended sites such as roads and railway projects. The engineer may therefore be assisted by a representative on site, who in turn may require the assistance of several other engineers. Each of these is able to issue instructions to the contractor; the 'other engineers' largely on points of detail for the particular area of work for which they are responsible. There are restrictions over which only the engineer may issue instructions. These include delays, extension of time, certificates of completion, agreement of the final account, maintenance certificate, forfeiture and assignment and the settlement of disputes.

Assignment and subcontracting (clauses 3 and 4)

The interpretation of these clauses is similar to JCT 80.

Contract documents (clauses 5–7)

These clauses fail to identify precisely what the contract documents comprise. Clause 1 includes a definition of the contract, and this has a wider interpretation than might be expected under JCT 80. Clause 6 identifies those documents which the contractor will receive at the start of the project. In other respects there is a great deal of similarity with JCT 80 regarding matters such as copyright, return of documents, delay in the issue of drawings and the general availability of the documents on the site.

General obligations (clauses 8–35)

The general obligations contain a wide range of matters which are covered by this group of clauses. Many of the clauses are self-explanatory. Clause 8 describes the contractor's general responsibilities to 'construct and complete the works', which, although in different words, is in essence the same as the building contractor under JCT 80. A performance bond (clause 10) may be required, and although this is absent from JCT 80 it can be incorporated, resulting in basically the same requirement.

Amongst this group, clause 12 is an important clause that really does not have anything comparable in JCT 80. This clause covers adverse physical conditions and artificial obstructions that may be encountered during the execution of the works. It specifically excludes bad weather conditions or conditions which may be the direct result of bad weather. Where, however, bad weather makes these adverse difficulties worse, this would have to be taken into account in this clause. It is worth remembering that a large amount of civil engineering works is carried out at or below ground level, and the possibility of this clause being used is therefore quite common. Even where adequate boreholes and a site investigation has been carried out, such problems still occur.

When such a problem occurs the contractor must attempt as soon as possible to give details of the cause and the likely effect upon the works. The contractor must also give details of the countermeasures he intends to take. The engineer may also:

(a)   require an estimate of the contractor's costs and time;
(b)   approve the proposed measures with or without modification;
(c)   give instructions on how the physical conditions are to be dealt with;
(d)   order a suspension of the works.

It should be noted that the contractor's estimate is a guide only for the engineer. The contractor will be paid for this work in accordance with the terms of the contract.

Clause 13 requires the work to be to the satisfaction of the engineer, and has its comparable equivalent in JCT 80. It should, however, be noted that the powers of the engineer are wider than those of the architect under JCT. The contractor's mode, manner and speed of construction are to be to the approval of the engineer.

Clause 14 requires the contractor to provide a programme for the works. This has only become a requirement in the JCT 80 form. In addition, the contractor must also describe how the works are intended to be carried out, and the methods to be used. This can be of particular significance on a civil engineering project where construction method is more varied than on building works. A variation to the permanent works may cause severe repercussions in the construction of the temporary works. The engineer may require details of the contractor's temporary works and the construction plant that is intended to be used. The safety of the permanent works may be affected by these, and the engineer will therefore need to establish that no detriment occurs to the finished project. If the engineer delays in approval of the proposed methods to be used by the contractor, then this may provide the basis for an extension of time. It should be noted that all these approvals by the engineer will not relieve the contractor of any duties or responsibilities under the contract (clause 14.9).

Clause 18 includes a specific clause requiring the contractor to undertake any exploratory excavation work if directed to do so by the engineer. Since civil engineering is often predominantly at or below ground level, this could be a common instruction in practice. The contractor will, of course, be paid for this work as it is actually carried out, even if different quantities had been assumed for the bill of quantities.

Clause 20 deals with the contractor's care of the works. The contractor remains fully responsible for the project until the date of issue of the certificate of completion. This clause places the responsibility for making good defects with the contractor other than the usual excepted risk items.

Clause 21 is the clause describing the contractor's responsibility for insuring the works. There are no alternatives, or allowance for the fact that the employer may already have a current insurance in existence. The scope of this clause is also much wider than the JCT counterpart. The contractor must insure in the joint names of the employer and contractor to cover:

(a)   the temporary and permanent works;
(b)   the plant and equipment materials;
(c)   an additional 10 per cent to cover any additional costs that may arise including professional fees and demolition.

JCT 80, as far as the client is concerned, only relates to permanent works. The ICE conditions, therefore, take account of and make a greater allowance for the fact that it is often more plant intensive and can also incorporate substantial temporary works which the employer may have already paid for in an interim certificate.

Clause 27 clarifies to the contractor the often complex position that can arise where the project involves a certain amount of street works. The relationship between the contractor, the Public Utilities Street Works Act 1950 and the project are described. For a detailed understanding of this clause a study of the appropriate Act is necessary.

Clause 29 is concerned with limiting the amount of interference to the public, access to other roads or properties by the public, reducing noise, disturbance and pollution.

Clause 30 covers the avoidance of damage to highways, and the possible claims that may arise where extraordinary traffic within the meaning of the Highway Act 1980 can occur. This clause further identifies the different nature between building and civil engineering works. The costs of any precautions or temporary works will be borne by the employer. Where the contractor fails to carry out the works with reasonable care, and where, because of this, damage occurs, then the responsibility for its repair is entirely that of the contractor.

Clause 31 requires the contractor to afford all reasonable facilities for other contractors or statutory bodies whom the employer has contracted with independently. Some of these firms, who may be working beyond the limits of the site, could be undertaking extensive projects. These activities should be identified precisely in the contract documents in order to allow for the contractor to price them adequately. Where such contractors, whether known or unknown, cause a delay to the works, the contractor is entitled to a delay and extra cost claim.

Workmanship and materials (clauses 36–40)

Clauses 36–39 are very similar in content to those used in JCT 80. They cover the quality of materials and the standard of workmanship and tests as defined by the engineer. They include matters relating to:

quality of materials and workmanship and tests;
cost of samples;
cost of tests;
access to site;
examination of work before covering up;
uncovering and making openings;
removal of unsatisfactory work and materials.

The effects regarding responsibility and costs are similar to JCT 80. The contractor can also not assume that the work is satisfactory until it has been accepted. The engineer has the option at any time to disapprove of any workmanship or materials, within the terms of the contract.

Clause 40, dealing with the suspension of the works, has a similar effect to the JCT clause of postponement.

Commencement time and delays (clauses 41–46)

Clause 41. The works commencement date, if known, is stated on the Appendix. If unspecified then it is within 28 days of the award of the contract or such other date as agreed by the parties. The engineer will notify the contractor, after the tender has been accepted, of a start date, and the work should then proceed reasonably soon after that date.

Clause 42. Due to the nature of civil engineering works, particularly the extended sites, provision of the site may be made progressively. This clause does not afford to the contractor the exclusive possession of the site. If the employer fails to give possession of the site in accordance with the contract provisions then the contractor will be entitled to a delay and cost claim. The contractor is also responsible for any access (rights of way) that may be necessary in the execution of the works. Temporary access roads, where these are required, will have to be provided and paid for by the contractor.

Clause 43. Sectional completion is an optional clause that can be incorporated into JCT 80. The ICE Conditions, however, intend that phased completion would generally be considered as the norm (see Appendix). The completion dates would need to be considered in respect of the somewhat flexible date for commencement.

Clause 44. This refers to extension of time caused by: variations, increased quantities, delays referred to in the conditions, exceptionally adverse weather conditions and other special circumstances.

Clause 45. This clause deals with night and Sunday work, which are both generally forbidden unless one or other is either unavoidable or absolutely necessary in the context of saving life or property or for safety reasons. If the type of work envisaged is normally carried out beyond the usual working hours, then this clause will not apply. In any case the contractor should always inform the engineer of his specific intentions.

Clause 46. The engineer may serve a notice on the contractor where reasonable progress is not being maintained. Clause 23 of JCT 80 includes a similar provision. The engineer will be able to measure the progress against the contractor's intentions shown on the programme for the works. The contractor may request to be allowed to carry out work beyond the normal working hours. The engineer's permission on this matter is not to be reasonably refused. Night or Sunday work is entirely at the expense of the contractor. The engineer's refusal to this request, if the project was close to a hospital for example, would not necessarily imply that the contractor should be given an extension of time. A claim would have to be supported by one of the reasons mentioned in clause 44, which was not known at the time of tender.

Liquidated damages for delay (clause 47)

This clause seeks in its overall aims the same achievements as the one used in JCT 80. If the contractor is late in completing the works for reasons that were within the contractor's control, then damages become due to the employer accordingly. The damages are determined on the basis of loss and cannot become a penalty for late completion. Since the project is expected to be completed in sections, the appropriate and individual liquidated damages relevant to the section of the works concerned is stated (see Appendix). The complex arrangement regarding this item could result in unfortunate consequences in practice. This might result in inadequate recovery by the employer or the claim that the sum is really a penalty (even though the contract explicitly states that it is not), by the contractor. It is not clear whether some of the delays could result in overlapping damages for the sections of work that must be somewhere related.

Certificate of substantial completion (clause 48)

The main difference between this clause and the certificate of practical completion, issued under JCT 80, is in the wording and its concept. When the contractor considers that the civil engineering works are substantially complete a request may be made to the engineer to issue the completion certificate. Practical completion on JCT 80 means virtually complete with only very minor items remaining to be carried out. Substantially complete on civil engineering projects may mean that the largest amount of work to be done has been finished. In each contract, however, they probably both imply that this certificate will be issued at the handover date to the client.

Outstanding work and defects (clauses 49–50)

Clause 49 describes the term 'defects correction period' which largely has the same meaning as the more commonly named defects liability period under the JCT forms. The length of this period must be stated in the Appendix, but no recommendation on the time-scale is given. The defects liability period under JCT 80 is the time allowed to remedy all of the contractor's defective work. The period of maintenance mentioned here allows for the rectification of any defective work. The contractor will, of course, be suitably reimbursed for repair work, due to an inappropriate design. The engineer is also entitled to expect the contractor to search or carry out tests in order to discover the reason for any inspections or faults which may arise.

Alterations, additions and omissions (clauses 51–52)

These clauses represent the equivalent of clause 13 in the JCT 80 form. They do, however, offer the engineer a wider scope in the issue of variations, and in addition he does not have to justify the instruction. Variations are defined as:
    additions/omissions/substitutions/alterations;
    changes in quality/form/character/position/dimension/line/level;
    changes in any specified sequence/method/timing.
They may be ordered during the defects correction period. Although variations must be in writing to be of any monetary effect, the procedure for the confirmation of verbal instructions does not place the same time restraints on the contract. Since this type of contract is of a remeasurement type, no instructions are required to vary the quantities of work involved.

The valuation of variations follows a similar pattern to the JCT forms. If the contractor and engineer cannot agree upon the rate to be used, even after a 'fair' valuation has been made, then the engineer will have the final say. Where the contractor does not believe that the rate used is reasonable and proper, the opinion of an arbitrator can be sought. The engineer decides which work is to be for a daywork basis, and the 'Schedules of Daywork carried out Incidental to

Contract Work' are then used. These have some similarity to those used on building projects.

Clause 52(4) describes the procedure to be followed where the contractor intends to claim a higher rate than one previously notified to the engineer. The contractor must notify the engineer in due time, keep appropriate records available and present the accounts at various stages. Where the contractor does not follow this procedure, then there may be difficulties of getting the claim accepted by the engineer. Once the claim has been agreed it will be included as an interim payment.

Property in materials and contractor's equipment (clauses 53–54)

Clause 53 seeks to provide the same sort of position regarding the ownership of materials, but the case of *Dawber Williamson* v. *Humberside County Council* is also relevant here. The employer's title to the materials or goods must not be defective. It is, however, doubtful whether this clause gives any enforceable rights in respect of subcontractors. In the event of insolvency, the employer may use the contractor's plant and materials, but the plant must be returned when no longer required. Hired plant is generally excluded from this provision. The vesting of certain items of plant and goods is listed in the contract Appendix.

Measurement (clauses 55–57)

The only basis of tendering considered under these conditions is based upon approximate quantities and remeasurement upon completion. The method of measurement envisaged on both occasions is the latest edition of the *Civil Engineering Standard Method of Measurement* (CESMM). The Appendix to the conditions does, however, allow the use of other methods of measurement, for example, the *Method of Measurement of Road and Bridgeworks* produced by the then Ministry of Transport. Whichever method of measurement is used, this must be clear to those tendering for the project. The use of two different methods on a single project has happened in extreme cases but this is not to be recommended.

Errors in the documents are treated in much the same way as JCT 80, and the rules for valuing variations, described in clause 52, allow for new rates to be used where the quantities of work actually carried out differ considerably from those in the bills.

Provisional and prime cost sums and nominated subcontracts (clauses 58–59)

The contents of these clauses follow, in principle, the relevant conditions of JCT 80. There is, however, a refreshing absence of the procedures required for nomination that has become so cumbersome on JCT 80. Nominated suppliers do not exist in name, but are included within the definition of nominated subcontractors. The clauses adequately define prime cost sum and a provisional sum, and when these should be used on a civil engineering contract. The contractor may object to the nomination of a subcontractor, although the reasons listed are very limited in scope. In practice, where a contractor was sufficiently forceful in an objection an engineer would be unwise to proceed along those lines. The procedure to be adopted by the engineer where a contractor does object to a particular nomination are fully detailed in clause 59. The main contractor's cash discount is limited to any amount that is obtainable by the contractor. The contractor must carefully check the bills of quantities in this respect and price the work accordingly.

Certificates and payments (clauses 60--61)

The provisions relating to the above follow a similar pattern to JCT 80, on the basis of payments on account. Each month the contractor submits a detailed statement to the engineer which might include:
(a)   value of permanent works;
(b)   lists of goods and materials on site;
(c)   list of identified goods and materials not yet on site;
(d)   value of temporary works or contractor's equipment;
(e)   amount of nominated subcontractors.
The engineer's certificate must be honoured within 28 days rather than the more customary 14 days used on other contracts. There is also a provision for a minimum amount of interim certificates, and this amount is stated in the Appendix. This means that unless the valuation achieves this amount each month any payment is deferred for another month. The purpose is to offer added incentive for regular progress of the works. Retention is recommended at 5 per cent of the monthly valuation, but a limit of 3 per cent of the contract sum is also applied. This form recognizes, therefore, that once a sufficient amount in a retention fund has been achieved there is no necessity to continue to deduct retention monies. Release of retention follows a similar pattern to JCT 80. Deductions for liquidated damages or for direct payments to nominated subcontractors can also be made from interim certificates. Another important difference between these provisions and JCT 80 is that the contractor is automatically entitled to add interest charges at 2 per cent per annum above the base lending rate specified in the appendix. This applies on both interim and final accounts. In connection with the latter, the onus of preparing the final account is on the contractor and should be done within 3 months of the defects correction certificate. Once it has been prepared the engineer must, of course, be allowed a reasonable period of time to check it – in this case 3 months. It is now commonplace for the quantity surveyor to be employed on civil engineering works, and it is the quantity surveyor who generally prepares certificates and accounts in a similar manner to building contracts.

Clause 61 deals with the maintenance certificate, and the engineer's satisfaction that the works are now free from any defects. The remainder of the retention is released 28 days after the issue of this certificate, and the contractor's obligation to remedy any defective work now ends.

Remedies and powers (clauses 62–63)

Clause 62 covers the carrying out of urgent works. If the contractor fails to do this, then the engineer may employ others to do so, and adjust the contractor's account accordingly.

Clause 63 covers the causes leading to determination of the contract. These are similar to those of determination in JCT 80.

Miscellaneous clauses (clauses 64–71)

Clause 64 deals with frustration of contracts and clause 65 war and its associated damages. Clause 66 is the arbitration clause, with the minor difference that, prior to arbitration, both parties should discuss the matter with the engineer. One presumes, however, that even on a building contract a similar process will be carried out with the architect, prior to instigating formal arbitration proceedings.

Clause 67 applies the contract to Scotland, noting that Scottish law is different from English law. The location of the site will determine which law prevails.

Clause 71 allows additional clauses to be written into the form of contract where this is considered to be desirable.

Where the contract is on the basis of fluctuations, an additional clause covering contract price fluctuations is added. This follows a similar pattern to the appropriate clauses of JCT 80. The Baxter indices are, of course, used where the formula method is applied.

Clause comparision between JCT 80 and ICE conditions of contract

JCT 80	ICE	
1. Interpretation, definition	1.	Definitions and interpretation
2. Contractor's obligation	8/9.	Contractor's general responsibilities
	55/56.	Measurement
	57.	Method of measurement
3. Contract sum		
4. Architect's instructions	2.	Engineer and engineer's representative
	68.	Notices
5. Contract documents	5–7.	Contract documents

JCT 80	*ICE*	
	14.	Programme to be furnished
6. Statutory obligations, notices, fees and charges	26.	Giving notices and paying fees
7. Levels and setting out the works	17.	Setting out
8. Work, materials and goods	13.	Work to be to the satisfaction of the engineer
	16.	Removal of contractor's employees
	33.	Clearance of site on completion
	36.	Quality of materials and workmanship and tests
	38.	Examination of work before covering up
	39.	Removal of unsatisfactory work and materials
9. Royalties and patent rights	28.	Patent rights, royalties
10. Person-in-charge	15.	Contractor's superintendence
11. Access for architect to works	37.	Access to site
12. Clerk of works		
13. Variations and provisional sums	51/52.	Alterations, additions and omissions
	58.	Provisional sums
14. Contract sum		
15. Value added tax	70.	Value added tax
16. Materials and goods unfixed or off site	53/54.	Vesting of contractors, equipment, goods and materials
17. Practical completion and defects liability	48.	Certificate of substantial completion
	49.	Outstanding work and defects
	61.	Defects correction certificate
18. Partial possession by employer		
19. Assignment and subcontracts	3/4.	Assignment and subcontracting
20. Injury to persons and property and employer's indemnity	19.	Safety and security
	20.	Care of the works
	22.	Damage to persons and property
21. Insurance against injury to persons and property	23.	Third party insurance
	24.	Accident or injury to workmen
	25.	Evidence and terms of insurance
22. Insurance of the works against clause 22 perils	21.	Insurance of works
23. Date of possession, completion and postponement	40.	Suspension of works
	41.	Works commencement date

JCT 80	ICE	
	42.	Possession of site and access
	43.	Time for completion
	46.	Rate of progress
24. Damages for non-completion	47.	Liquidated damages
25. Extension of time	44.	Extension of time for completion
26. Loss and expense		
27. Determination by employer	63.	Determination of the contractors employment
28. Determination by contractor	64.	Frustration
29. Works by employer or persons employed or engaged by employer	31.	Facilities for other contractors
30. Certificates and payments	60.	Certificates and payments
31. Finance – tax deduction scheme		
32. Outbreak of hostilities		
33. War damage	65.	War clause
34. Antiquities	32.	Fossils
35. Nominated subcontractors	59.	Nominated subcontractors
36. Nominated suppliers	59.	Nominated subcontractors
37. Fluctuations	69.	Tax fluctuations
38. Contributions, levy and tax fluctuations		
39. Labour and materials cost and tax fluctuations		
40. Use of price adjustment formulae		
41. Settlement of disputes – arbitration	10.	Securities
	11.	Provision and interpretation of information and inspection of site
	12.	Adverse physical conditions and artificial obstructions
	18.	Boreholes and exploratory excavation
	27.	Public Utilities Street Works Act
	29.	Interference with traffic and adjoining properties
	30.	Avoidance of damage to highways, etc.
	35.	Return of labour and contractor's equipment

JCT 80

ICE

45.   Night and Sunday work
50.   Contractor to search
62.   Urgent repairs
66.   Settlement of disputes
67.   Application to Scotland
71.   Special condition

Chapter 29

General Conditions of Contract for building and civil engineering

Public works projects represent a significant sector of the construction industry. The various types of projects are undertaken by a variety of organizations both locally and centrally. Local authorities have a preference for JCT 80 for building works and the ICE Conditions for civil engineering works. Construction projects administered by central government agencies, however, prefer to use their own forms of contract, i.e. General Conditions of Contract for Building and Civil Engineering Works. The latest edition was published in 1990 and revised in 1991. The forms which are currently in use are:

1. GC/Works/1/ – third edition which is for use on major projects. There are different versions depending upon whether the quantities are firm, subject to remeasurement or without quantities, and single stage design and build

2. GC/Works/2/ – for use on minor works.

In addition a further form is in use for the measured-term type contracts, which are an important feature of maintenance projects carried out for government establishments within a specified contract period. Central government pioneered this type of contractual arrangement which is now used by other types of client.

The forms are now prepared under the auspices of the Department of the Environment and published by Her Majesty's Stationery Office. The Conditions do not include a form of tender or agreement but these are provided for separately. This latest edition of the Conditions envisages the use of a PM or project manager replacing the term architect on JCT 80 (although on some JCT forms supervising officer may be used) and engineer on the ICE form. The PM is defined as being the manager and superintendent of the works. If the works have been fully designed (the implication in most of the forms in use!) then there is no necessity for the PM to be restricted to a designer. The appointment to this key position during the construction phase can then be given to the individual who is most suited to such a role. The names of the various parties associated with the project are given in the Abstract of Particulars.

The clauses are numbered consecutively from 1 to 65 and are grouped together under eight major sections. Conditions, such as a variation of price condition, may be added to supplement the printed General Conditions according to circumstances. They are incorporated into the Contract Conditions by listing in the Abstract of Particulars which is included with the invitation to tender. The clauses, known as conditions, under this form of contract, contain the usual amalgam of items that are to be found in the other forms. It is generally accepted that they are, however, more legally precise than the other forms and that they include more matters of a procedural nature. Some of the conditions are similar in their effect to JCT clauses, e.g. setting out, patents, antiquities. Other conditions have no parallel in JCT 80. Some of these cover matters more to do with procedures and include, for example, the provision of daily returns by the contractor, passes which are now a standard security measure of all government agencies, racial discrimination, photographs and emergency powers. Some clauses included in JCT 80 have no equivalent in this form, for example, the war damage clause. This matter should it occur is dealt with independently by the government department concerned.

The following is a brief résumé of some of these contract conditions, from GC/Works/1.

Contract, documentation, information and staff

Condition 1 lists a number of definitions which are referred to throughout the form of contract. Many other forms of contract now adopt this approach in order to clarify matters which are relevant to the execution of the project.

Conditions 2 and 3 are concerned with the contract documents and their relationship with each other. The documents are listed in the definitions under 'contract' and include:

- Contract Conditions
- Abstract of Particulars
- specification
- drawings
- bills of quantities
- the tender
- authority's written acceptance

In common with the ICE form both a specification and bills of quantities are contract documents. The conditions of the contract are the most important followed by the specification and then the drawings. The PM can reverse the importance of these last two documents should this be desired. Condition 3 refers to bills of quantities and deals with the method of measurement (which needs to be identified). It also describes how errors and omissions should be dealt with and the use of approximate quantities.

Conditions 4–6 deal with staff matters, and include the delegation and representation of the authority's powers, the requirement of the contractor to keep a competent agent on site to supervise the execution of the works, and the removal from site of anyone whom the PM thinks is undesirable. On this last matter, there is little scope for negotiation since the PM's view is final and conclusive.

General obligations

Condition 7 requires the contractor to be fully satisfied on the following points regarding the site:
(a)   communications and access to it;
(b)   its contours and boundaries;
(c)   the risks associated with adjacent property and its occupiers;
(d)   the ground conditions;
(e)   conditions under which the work will be executed and the precautions necessary to prevent nuisance and pollution;
(f)   availability of labour;
(g)   availability of goods, materials, etc.;
(h)   any other factors which will influence the execution of the works or the tender price.
No claim for additional payments will be allowed if the contractor misunderstands or misinterprets any of the above. If, however, the contractor encounters unforeseeable ground conditions during the execution of the works the PM may agree to the contract sum being increased or decreased accordingly.

Condition 8 covers matters of insurance and specifically:
(a)   employers' liability insurance;
(b)   insurance against loss or damage;
(c)   insurance against personal injury and loss or damage to property.

Condition 9 outlines the various responsibilities in respect of setting out. The PM provides the information for setting out the works. It is the contractor's responsibility to do the setting out including providing all the necessary instruments, profiles, templates, etc.

Condition 10 allows for some of the design to be done by the contractor or subcontractor should this be required. The contractor's liability in this respect is the same as if the design work had been provided by an architect.

Conditions 11–12 describe the need to comply with statutory provisions and pay the charges involved and to make the necessary payments for royalties or patent rights.

Conditions 13–14 require the contractor to protect the works and goods and material on site from damage, and to protect workmen and the public from any danger. The conditions also require the contractor to prevent nuisances and inconvenience to anyone from occurring.

Conditions 15–17 require the contractor to inform the PM of the number and type of workmen employed on the site each day, that the excavations are ready to receive the foundations and that work which should be inspected by the PM is ready for being covered up with earth or other materials.

Conditions 18 and 25 cover the joint meeting of the quantity surveyor and the contractor's representative to agree measurements on site, and the keeping of contract records which may be needed by the quantity surveyor for the preparation of the final account. In the absence of the contractor's representative then the quantity surveyor can proceed to take measurements and to use these as if they had been agreed.

Condition 19 is concerned with loss and damage to:
(a)   property;
(b)   personal injury to, or sickness or death of, any person;
(c)   the works including materials on site;
(d)   loss of profits or loss suffered because of any loss or damage.

Contractors must take steps at their own expense to reinstate, replace or make good to the satisfaction of the authority any loss or damage to the works. If this also results in a claim against the authority by third persons, then the contractor has to refund the authority for any costs or expense that may be incurred. The contractor is able to be reimbursed if the loss or damage was the fault of the authority, due to unforeseen ground conditions, an accepted risk or circumstances outside the control of the contractor.

Conditions 20, 22 and 23 are conditions not found in other forms of contract. Condition 20 outlines the contractor's position in respect of the loss, destruction, disclosure and access to 'personal data' as defined in the Data Protection Act 1984.

Condition 22 deals with contractors working within the boundaries of existing government premises and condition 23 covers the scope of the Race Relations Act 1976.

Condition 21 deals with the making good of defects during the maintenance period, the contractor's responsibility is for the costs involved and in the case of his default, the recovering of costs by the authority.

Condition 24 deals with corruption and the receiving of gifts, considerations, inducements or rewards for doing nothing or for showing favour. The authority need be only reasonably satisfied that a breach has occurred, rather than needing to rely on the provisions of the Prevention of Corruption Acts 1889–1916 in order to determine the contractor's employment.

Security

Conditions 26–29 cover matters of a government–security nature, which are naturally not to be found in the other forms of contract. These include unauthorized admittance to the site, the need for passes in some site locations, limitations on photographs of the site and a general awareness of the Official Secrets Act 1911 to 1939.

Materials and workmanship

Condition 30 deals with the vesting of 'things' which have been defined in condition 1 of the form of contract. *'Things'* has two different meanings:
- 'Things for incorporation' means goods and materials intended to form part of the completed work.

- 'Things not for incorporation' means good or materials provided or used to facilitate execution of the works but not for incorporation in them.

The contractor is responsible for the protection, preservation, and replacement of things that are lost, stolen, damaged, destroyed or unfit or unsuitable for their intended purpose. Nothing shall be removed from the site without the written consent of the PM.

Condition 31 is the main condition which deals with quality. It states that the contractor shall execute the works:

(a)   with diligence;
(b)   in accordance with the programme;
(c)   with all proper skill and care;
(d)   in a workmanlike manner.

The contractor must use the necessary skill and care to ensure that the works and anything that is due for incorporation conforms to the requirements of the specification, bills of quantities and drawings. The PM has the power at any time to inspect, examine or test on site at a factory or in a workshop. The PM can arrange for an independent expert to do the testing in order to ensure that there is conformity with the contract requirements. In the event of a failure then the contractor has to bear the costs of the test and any retesting that may ensue.

Condition 32 refers to excavations, which in this context means antiquities such as fossils and other items of interest or value found on the site. Such findings remain the property of the employer.

Commencement, programme, delays and completion

Conditions 33 and 35 deal with the programme and progress of the works. The contractor must submit a programme to show the sequence of operations, details of temporary work, method of working, labour and plant requirements and the critical events which might influence the progress and completion of the works. Progress meetings are normally held once a month where the contractor is required to provide a written report showing any or all of the following:

(a)   the relationship between progress of the works and the contract programme;
(b)   information required by the contractor;
(c)   delays and possible delays;
(d)   requests for an extension of time;
(e)   proposals to bring the project back on schedule.

The PM then within 7 days of this meeting must provide a written statement in response to these points.

Conditions 34 and 36–38 describe commencement, completion, extensions of time, early possession and acceleration. The authority will notify the contractor of when possession can be effected and completion is then calculated from this time in accordance with the contract. Condition 36 identifies the reasons for granting an extension of time to the contractor. This is only done after first receiving a request for such from the contractor. Early possession of the project is covered in condition 37 and referred to as a completed part, where a section or a part of the works is completed to the PM's satisfaction and the authority wishes to take possession. This has the effect of starting the maintenance period for that part of the works, restricting any further liquidated damages and releasing part of the reserve, i.e. one-half of the retention money which is held on that part of the project. Condition 38 allows for achieving an accelerated completion date. If this is required then the contractor is asked to price specified proposals and indicate how early completion might be achieved.

Condition 39 covers matters relating to the issue of certificates at completion and at the end of the maintenance period.

Instructions and payments

Condition 40 lists the procedures dealing with the PM's instructions. The provisions allow for the issue of further drawings, details, instructions, directions and explanations. Instructions must be in writing or confirmed in writing within 7 days. Instructions which alter, add, omit or change the design, quality or quantity of works are known as variation instructions (VIs). Instructions may be given in respect of the following:

(a)   the variation/modification of the specification drawings, bills of quantities, or the design, quality or quantity of works;
(b)   discrepancy between specification, drawings and bills of quantities;
(c)   removal from site of any things for incorporation and their substitution with any other things;
(d)   removal/re-execution of work;
(e)   order of execution of the works;
(f)   hours of work and overtime;
(g)   suspension of the works;
(h)   replacement of any person employed in connection with the contract;
(i)   opening up for inspection;
(j)   making good of defects;
(k)   execution of emergency work;
(l)   use/disposal of materials from the excavations;
(m)   action to be followed on the discovery of fossils, etc.;
(n)   measures to avoid nuisance/pollution;
(o)   any other matter which the PM considers is expedient.

Conditions 41–43 cover matters dealing with the valuation of work. The valuation of a VI can be determined in one of two ways:

(a)   the acceptance by the PM of a lump-sum quotation;
(b)   valuation by the quantity surveyor using the following principles:
    (i)   use of bill rates;
    (ii)   use of rates which are pro-rata to rates in the bills;
    (iii) fair valuation or agreement;

(iv)   daywork rates;

(v)   adjustment to these rates for any disruption.

If circumstances arise where as a result of an instruction, not being a VI, the contractor properly incurs expense beyond that provided for, or makes a saving in the cost of executing the works then such costs can also be adjusted.

Condition 44 covers labour tax, i.e. any tax, levy or contribution which by law has to be paid by the contractor. If these vary during the course of the contract then the appropriate sum is added to or deducted from the contract sum.

Condition 45 consists of the usual conditions describing VAT.

Condition 46 covers prolongation and disruption to the works and the associated costs which might be involved.

Condition 47 deals with the honouring of payments due to the contractor. If the authority withholds payments then the contractor is allowed to add finance charges to those amounts at a rate of 1 per cent above the Bank of England's lending rate.

Condition 48 deals with interim monthly payments as follows:

(a)   95 per cent of the relevant amount from a stage payment chart assuming that the project is on schedule. The remaining 5 per cent is defined as a reserve;

(b)   100 per cent of variations;

(c)   100 per cent of prolongation and disruption;

(d)   100 per cent of finance charges.

Condition 49 covers the preparation of the final account. Upon completion of the works half of the reserve fund is paid to the contractor. The final account should normally be prepared within 6 months from this date, and any difference between this and the amount paid at completion will be paid to the contractor as soon as possible. The remainder of the reserve fund is paid at the end of the maintenance period.

Conditions 50–52 cover the issue of certificates by the PM and the ability to be able to recover sums owing by the contractor against these certificates, even from other projects. Condition 52 deals with suggestions which the contractor may have for effecting cost savings either of the works or in the costs of its future maintenance of the project.

Particular powers and remedies

Condition 53 states that if the main contractor fails within a reasonable period of time to comply with an instruction then the contract may be terminated.

Condition 54 provides for emergency work to be undertaken as required by the PM.

Condition 55 outlines the procedures to be adopted in the case of a delay in completing the works and the application of liquidated damages. These are included in the Abstract of Particulars, and the appropriate amounts may be deducted from advances paid under interim certificates.

Conditions 56–58 cover determination by the authority (there is no comparable provision for determination by the contractor) and the procedures to be followed in terms of contract completion and financial arrangements. There are circumstances, however, where the contractor may suffer unavoidable loss due to the determination and the contract makes provision for reimbursement where this is thought to be reasonable.

Conditions 59 and 60 describe the procedures to be followed in response to disputes arising between the parties. Initially matters are referred to the adjudicator who has been named in the Abstract of Particulars. If the matter cannot be satisfactorily resolved at this stage then the dispute can be referred to arbitration.

Assignment, subletting, subcontracting, suppliers and others

Conditions 61–65 deal with those employed on the site other than the main contractor. Condition 61 forbids assigning the contract without authority. Condition 62 covers subletting and the need to obtain authority to do so and to ensure that the main contract conditions are fully covered in each subcontract. Condition 63 describes the procedure to be used in the case of nominated suppliers and subcontractors. These include the usual provisions of the authority paying for the work direct and the reasonable objection that a main contractor may have in entering a contract with a particular firm. The conditions make no references to either any main contractor's attendance or to cash discounts. Condition 64 refers to provisional sums, the need for instructions from the PM prior to their execution and their subsequent valuation under condition 42. Condition 65 gives the authority powers to execute other work on site at the same time that the works are being executed.

Chapter 30

Building with contractor's design

Anyone wishing to have a building constructed has the choice of either commissioning an architect to produce the design, or approaching a building contractor to carry out the design work in addition to the normal construction work. The latter refers to a D&B project, and the use of the Standard Form of Building Contract with Contractor's Design, 1981 edition, in preference to the usual JCT 80 Standard Form of Building Contract. The above form superseded the NFBTE Design and Building Form of Contract, which had been in use since 1970. The contractor's duties under these forms are wider than usual, since greater responsibility has to be taken for a much wider service. There is also now a wide variation of different arrangements available.

The JCT form with contractor's design is based upon JCT 80, but incorporates significant differences due to the nature of the work envisaged. There are 38 clauses in this form compared with 41 in JCT 80. Some of the clauses are a direct reproduction of JCT 80, whereas others incorporate minor amendments or a completely new clause. All references to 'the architect' have been deleted, and these now become 'the employer'. There is no specific provision for a clerk of works, although such a person may well come within the definition of one of the employer's agents. The intention is, however, broadly the same. The following are some of the significant differences from the standard form.

Articles of Agreement

The employer in the first recital in lieu of supplying the contractor with drawings and bills of quantities has issued the contractor with basic requirements. These requirements will broadly be the same as the information that would have been provided to the architect. In the second recital the contractor's proposals are identified. These include details of the contract sum analysis that will be required for the execution of these proposals. The third recital states that the employer has accepted these proposals and the contract sum analysis and that the employer is satisfied that they meet the requirements for the project. The employer's requirements, contractor's proposals and the contract sum analysis are described in detail in Appendix 3 to the conditions. Article 3 names the employer's agent. Since there is no independent designer or supervisor for the works envisaged, provision is made for someone to act on behalf of the employer. The duties of this person may include:

(a) receiving or issuing applications, consents, instructions, notices, requests or statements;

(b) acting on behalf of the employer.

The conditions

Clause 2

Clause 2 includes the provisions of the counterpart clause of the standard form, but in addition covers matters appropriate to the contractor's design and his liability for it. The contractor in clause 2.1 shall carry out and complete the works, including the selection of any specifications of materials and workmanship in order to meet the employer's requirements. Clause 2.5 indicates that the contractor must carry out the design work in an equal manner to that of an independent architect or professional designer. The contractor's responsibility to the employer for any inadequacy of the design work includes the exclusion of defects or any insufficiency in the design work. Where the work includes the design and construction of dwellings, reference is made to the liability under the Defective Premises Act 1972. If the Act does not apply, the contractor's design liability for loss of use or profit or consequential loss is limited to the amount, if any, set out in Appendix 1. The contractor's design under this clause includes that which may have been prepared by others on behalf of the contractor.

Clause 4

The contractor must comply with all instructions issued by the employer, as long as the employer has the contractual power to issue such instructions. Variations are referred to as change instructions in clause 12, and where the contractor makes a reasonable objection in writing to a change instruction there is no need to comply with it. The provisions relating to employer's instructions generally are similar to those dealing with architect's instructions under the standard form.

Clause 5

This clause requires that both the employer's requirements and the contractor's proposals are to remain in the custody of the employer. The contractor is to be allowed access to them at all reasonable times. When the contract has been signed by the parties the employer will provide the contractor, free of charge, with:

(a)   a copy of the certified Articles of Agreement, Conditions and Appendices;
(b)   a copy of the employer's requirements;
(c)   a copy of the contractor's proposals which includes the contract sum analysis.

The contractor must then provide the employer with two copies of the drawings, specifications, details, levels and setting out dimensions which are proposed to be used on the works. All this information largely represents the equivalent of the contract documents of the standard form, but is not described as such in this form. A copy of all the above information is to be kept on site and available to the employer's agent at all reasonable times.

Prior to the commencement of the defects liability period the employer is to be provided with copies of the 'as built' drawings and other relevant information. This information may include details of the maintenance and operation of the building works, including any installations comprised in the works. The information provided by either party is for the use of this contract only. It would appear, therefore, that copyright of the documents is vested in the party who actually prepared them.

Clause 7

The employer is required to define the boundaries of the site, and this information is to be written into the conditions of contract at this point.

Clause 12

Variations are referred to as changes in the employer's requirements. The alteration in wording from the standard form may lead one to suspect that changes are intended to be of a minor nature only, the employer's requirements in the first instance being comprehensive and complete. A change in the contractor's proposals is not envisaged, but where the contractor considers these to be necessary the employer's permission will need to be obtained; the contractor will possibly incur extra cost where this occurs. In other respects this clause is very similar to clause 13 of the standard form which deals with variations and provisional sums.

Clause 16

Upon practical completion of the works, the contractor will receive a written statement from the employer to that effect. The defects liability will operate from that date, and the employer must provide the contractor with a schedule of defects within 14 days. Practical completion marks the end of the contract, and no further new instructions from the employer are permissible. A notice of completion of making good defects is issued when the work has been properly rectified.

Clause 26

Clause 26.2 includes the normal grounds for claiming loss and expense. In addition, it also includes the provision for dealing with a delay in receipt of any permission or approval for the purposes of development control requirements necessary for the works to proceed. The contractor must have taken all practicable steps to avoid or reduce this delay. This can also give rise to an extension of time under clause 25.4.7 as a relevant event. It is also considered to be an important factor that could result in the determination by the contractor under clause 28.1.2.8.

Clause 27

The employer may terminate the employment of the contractor for one of the reasons suggested under clause 27.1. In the event of this occurring, the contractor must provide the employer with two copies of all the current drawings, details, schedules, etc., in order that another contractor may be engaged to complete the works. A similar condition will still apply where the contractor has terminated the contract for one of the reasons listed in clause 28.1.

Clause 30

The processes to be used for interim payments follow those of normal practice. Two alternatives are, however, specifically suggested, and these are described in Appendix 2. Alternative A is on a stage payment basis. The stages are predetermined and the appropriate amounts set against them, the total of which adds up to the contract sum. Any adjustments to the employer's requirements or for fluctuations and claims must be properly documented. Alternative B describes the periodic payment basis which is the more usual method used with the standard form. Payment on this basis must be supported by the appropriate information. The other matters of retention, and when the payments are due to be paid by the employer, are in accordance with the standard form.

The final account must be presented to the employer within 3 months of practical completion of the works (clause 30.5.1). The employer must then agree to this within a maximum period of 4 months from the time of submission. Thereafter the account is conclusive evidence of the amount due. It is also conclusive evidence that the employer is fully satisfied that the project is in accordance with the terms of the contract and the employer's requirements.

Generally

The role of the building contractor in the design of any project is valid. Criticism has often been levelled at the absence of any contractor input, and the fragmentation of the design and construction process. There is no doubt, therefore, that this method of contracting plays a very vital role and function within the industry today. It does not include all the advantages over the more traditional methods, since if it did, these methods would now be moving nearer towards extinction. The more one can involve the contractor in both the constructional detailing and method, the more satisfactory buildings are likely to be. An employer, however, considering embarking upon this contractual option for a proposed project, is well advised to retain in some form professional advice of an architect and quantity surveyor. The normal building employer is unlikely to be familiar with building contracts or the processes involved. An independent adviser is therefore likely to be able to offer both constructive comments on the contractor's proposals, and also assistance during the building's erection.

The JCT have produced a number of amendments (six up to 1995) to coincide generally with revisions to JCT 80. There are also two practice notes which provide an introduction and commentary on this form.

Part 7

Appendix

Appendix

Cases of interest

Cases law relating to building

In some instances where the form of contract is thought to be either lacking or unclear, it is common practice to bring the matter before the courts for learned opinion. This may mean bringing the matter first to arbitration, then to the High Court, the Court of Appeal and finally the House of Lords, where leave to appeal along the way has been granted. The principles upon which these courts base their decisions are stated, and will then in future affect similar cases. This achieves a measure of consistency on matters on which the various parties to a contract may then rely. Where the higher courts reverse the decisions of lower courts, it is the higher opinions that will count in the future. The resulting body of opinion is then established as case law. It is published in the various law reports of the legal journals and, where relevant to the construction industry, in trade and professional journals. There are now also a number of construction law journals and other sources that record the considerable case law of this industry.

The following cases represent just a sample of some of the disagreements that have reached the courts over a number of years. The complete list would form several books alone. Some of the cases described have become household names for the student of building contracts.

Amalgamated Building Contractors v.
Waltham Holy Cross UDC – 1952
A contractor had applied for an extension of time because of labour and material difficulties. The architect acknowledged the request but did not at this time grant an extension to the contract period. Some time after the completion of the works the architect granted the contractor an extension in retrospect. It was held that this was valid on the grounds that it was a continuing cause of delay. The architect was unable to determine the length of extension until after completion. The parties must therefore have envisaged the retrospective application of the extension clause. The Court of Appeal held that granting of an extension of time after completion would therefore seem to be an explicit possibility.

AMF International Ltd v.
Magnet Bowling Ltd and Another – 1968

Bowling equipment had been installed for Magnet Bowling Ltd by AMF International Ltd. This equipment was damaged after a flood had been caused by exceptionally heavy rain. The bowling centre was only partially completed at this time. AMF therefore claimed £21,000 in damages against Magnet Bowling Ltd and the main contractor. The point at issue in this case was whether the indemnity clause included in the contract would protect the employer and enable him to claim successfully against the contractor. Held:

1.   The employer was liable in tort due to his negligence in failing to check that the site had been made safe for AMF.
2.   The contractor was liable under the Occupiers Liability Act for failing to take reasonable care.

The damages were apportioned on a 60/40 basis between the main contractor and the employer.

The question of whether the employer could recover from the contractor then arose. Held:

1.   The employer, because he had been found guilty of negligence, could not therefore claim under the indemnity clause. This is based upon a legal principle that the indemnity clause will not protect negligence on the part of the one who relies upon it.
2.   The employer was able to recover on contractual grounds since the contract included a clause requesting the contractor to protect the works from damage by water.

Anns v.
London Borough of Merton – 1978

It was alleged that in 1962 a builder had erected a block of maisonettes with defective foundations. It was further suggested that the defendant local authority had, through its inspector, either failed to inspect the foundations or had inspected them carelessly. The plaintiffs had taken long leases on some of the maisonettes. In February 1972, the plaintiffs issued writs against the builder and against the local authority. This action was brought to decide whether the proceedings against the local authority were barred under the Limitation Act of 1939, which was then in use. Obviously the plaintiffs' cause of action against the council accrued in 1962. It was therefore too late, under this Act, to start an action in 1972. In fact although the appeal was nominally on the limitation issue, the speeches in the House of Lords were mainly concerned with the more fundamental question of whether an action would lie against the local authority at all on such facts. In the House of Lords it was held that such an action would lie, and it would thus not be statute barred.

If the fact that the defects to the maisonettes first appeared in 1970, and the writs were issued in 1972, then the consequences must be that none of these actions were barred by this Act.

Architectural Installation Services Ltd v.
James Gibbons Windows Ltd – 1989
The plaintiffs were a specialist labour-only subcontractor installing window units to the defendants as main contractors. The subcontract included a clause for termination by notice on specified grounds, including default of the subcontractor for wholly suspending the works or failing to proceed with them expeditiously and then remaining in default for 7 days after being given written notice of the default by the main contractor. The plaintiffs sued the defendants for moneys alleged due and for wrongful determination of the contract. The defendants counterclaimed stating that they were entitled to determine the contract and to seek damages for defective work. It was ordered that two preliminary issues be tried, each of which assumed that the plaintiffs had wholly suspended or failed to proceed with the works in breach of clause 20 of the subcontract. It was held that:
1. On the assumptions set out in the preliminary issues it was agreed that it was not a rightful termination of the subcontract, because there was no sensible connection between the defendants' notice of default and the notice of determination.
2. However, the defendants' telex was a rightful termination of the subcontract at common law since clause 8 did not exclude common law rights expressly or by implication, but existed side by side with the common law right to terminate.

Bacal Construction v.
Northampton Development Corporation – 1975
This was a contract for a housing development. The development corporation had provided borehole data on which the contractor had based his substructure design. During the course of the work tufa was discovered in several areas and this required a redesign of the foundation. It was held that there should be an implied term that the ground conditions would accord with the hypotheses upon which the contractor had been instructed to design the foundation. Because the client had provided the borehole data that were now shown to be inaccurate, the differing costs were to be borne by the employer.

Percy Bilton v.
Greater London Council (GLC) – 1982
Bilton contracted with the GLC to erect a housing estate. The contract was dated 25 October 1976, and was substantially JCT 63. The original completion date was January 1979. The nominated subcontractor for the mechanical services went into liquidation on July 1978. By this time the contract was already running 40 weeks behind the programme. A new subcontractor was nominated, but subsequently withdrew before starting work. A new nominated subcontractor was not appointed until December 1978. The programme for this meant that the work would not now be completed until January 1980. Various

extensions of time were granted and the extended completion date became February 1980. However, the contract was not completed by that date and thereafter the GLC deducted liquidated damages. The House of Lords held that the withdrawal of a subcontractor is not a fault or breach of contract on the part of the employer, nor is it covered by JCT 63, clause 23. The architect's clause 22 certificate was valid and the GLC was entitled to deduct liquidated damages.

Bottoms v.
Lord Mayor of York – 1812

The contractor in carrying out work for a sewage works had intended to use poling boards to support the excavations. However, the nature of the soil turned out to be different from that which was expected and necessitated extra works. The engineer refused to authorize this has a variation. The contractor then abandoned the works and sued the client for the value of the work completed. Neither party had sunk boreholes. Before the signing of the contract, the defendants had been advised that the contractor's price was such that he was bound to lose money on the type of soil conditions that were anticipated. It was held that the plaintiff's claim must fail. He was not entitled to abandon the works on discovering the nature of the soil or because the engineer declined to authorize extra payments.

Bower v.
Chapel-en-le-Frith Rural District Council – 1911

The plaintiffs were the successful tenderers for the erection of a waterworks for the council. The contract was for a lump sum, based on specifications and bills of quantities. The plaintiffs were required by the council to purchase a windmill tower and pump from a named supplier and to fix them. The windmill did not work as expected. It was not argued that the default was in any way due to defective installation by the contractor. The council then requested the plaintiffs to replace it with one that would work efficiently. The plaintiffs argued that they were not responsible, as they had played no part in the choice of the windmill. It was held that the plaintiffs were not liable.

Brightside Kilpatrick Engineering Services v.
Mitchell Construction (1973) Ltd –1975

The plaintiffs were nominated as subcontractors under JCT 63. The subcontract was placed by the defendants which stipulated that the subcontract documents should consist of a 'Standard Form of Tender, a Specification, Conditions of Contract and a Schedule of Facilities'. The order continued that, 'The Form of Contract with the employer is the RIBA 1963 Edition', and concluded 'The Conditions applicable to the subcontract shall be those embodied in the RIBA as the above agreement.' Printed references to the 'green form' of subcontract had been deleted. In the Court of Appeal it was held that the words should be read as referring to those clauses in the main contract which referred to matters concerning nominated subcontractors. Clause 27 of JCT 63 regulated the nominated subcontract relationship, and the only way to give a sensible meaning to the relationship was to read into it the terms of the 'green form'.

British Crane Hire Corporation Ltd v.
Ipswich Plant Hire Ltd – 1974
Both of these parties were involved in the plant hire business. A drag line crane was hired over the telephone. The hire charges were agreed, but nothing was discussed about the terms and conditions of hire. After delivery, the plaintiff owners sent to the defendants the then current 'General Conditions for Hiring Plant'. The defendants failed to sign and return the acceptance note. In the Court of Appeal it was stated that, since both parties were in the plant hire business, and that both used the same standard conditions when hiring plant, it must be assumed that the contract was made on those terms.

Courtney v.
Fairbairn Ltd v.
Tolaini Brothers (Hotels) Ltd and Another – 1975
In 1969 Mr Tolaini, a hotel owner, decided to develop a site in Hertfordshire. He contacted Mr Courtney who was both a property developer and a building contractor. Mr Courtney wrote to Mr Tolaini stating that if he (Mr Courtney) found suitable sponsors for the scheme, he would undertake the building work. Mr Courtney found sponsors who were able to reach a satisfactory financial arrangement with Mr Tolaini. Mr Tolaini then instructed his quantity surveyor to negotiate a building contract for the project based upon cost plus 5 per cent. The financial aspects were quickly concluded, but negotiations between the quantity surveyor and the building contractor broke down. Mr Tolaini therefore decided to let the contract to another firm, and was promptly sued for breach of contract by Mr Courtney.

It was held, on appeal, that the exchange of letters did not constitute a contract. Because price was of such fundamental importance to the contract, no contract could be formulated until this was agreed, or there was an agreed method of ascertaining it.

Crowshaw v.
Pritchard and Renwick – 1899
The plaintiff wrote to the defendant enclosing a drawing and specification, and inviting a tender for some alteration work. The defendant replied, 'Our estimate to carry out the sundry alterations to the above premises, according to the drawings and specification, amounts to £1,230.' The plaintiff wrote next day accepting the defendant's 'offer to execute' the works. Later the defendant refused to go ahead. He contended that by using the word 'estimate', he did not intend it as an offer to do the work, and that there was a trade custom that a letter in this form was not to be treated as an offer. It was held that the estimate

was an offer which had been accepted by the plaintiff and the defendant was liable in contract. The judge in the Queen's Bench Division stated, 'It has been suggested that there is some custom or well known understanding that a letter in this form is not to be treated as an offer. There is no such custom, and, if there is, it is contrary to law.'

Davies & Co. Shopfitters Ltd v.
William Old – 1969

A nominated subcontractor submitted a tender which was accepted by the architect. In placing the order for the work the main contractor added new terms that had been absent from the earlier documentation. One of those terms stated that no payment would be made to the subcontractor until the main contractor had been paid. In spite of this the nominated subcontractor started work. It was held that the order from the main contractor constituted a counter-offer which had been accepted by the subcontractor prior to starting work.

Davies Contractors Ltd v.
Fareham UDC – 1956

A contractor undertook to build 78 houses in 8 months for a fixed price sum. He attached a letter to his tender with the proviso that the price was on the basis of adequate supplies of labour being available. The unexpected shortages of labour on a national scale increased the contract period to 22 months. The letter, however, failed to be incorporated into the contract. The courts held, therefore, that the employer must suffer the delay, but that the contractor must bear the expense.

Dawber Williamson Roofing v.
Humberside County Council – 1979

A main contractor had, with approval, sublet the roofing part of the project to a domestic subcontractor. The slates were delivered to the site and their value included in an interim certificate as materials on site. The certificate was honoured with the sum for these materials being paid to the main contractor. Prior to paying this domestic subcontractor the main contractor went into liquidation. The subcontractor therefore sought permission from the council to remove the slates, but this was refused. The subcontractor sued for the value of the slates on the grounds that they remained his property until fixed. It was held that the title rested with the subcontractor. This resulted in the employer paying twice for these materials.

Dawneys v.
F.G. Minter Ltd and Another – 1971

This case involved certified payments to a nominated subcontractor being withheld by the main contractor as set-off against damages. Lord Denning summed up this case as follows:

When the main contractor has received sums due to the subcontractor – as certified or contained in the architect's certificate – the main contractor must pay those sums to the subcontractor. He cannot hold them up so as to satisfy his cross claims. Those must be dealt with separately in appropriate proceedings for the purpose. This is in accord with the needs of business. There must be a cash flow in the building trade. It is the very lifeblood of the enterprise. The subcontractor has to expend money on steel work and labour. He is out of pocket. He probably has an overdraft at the bank. He cannot go on unless he is paid for what he does as he does it. The main contractor is in a like position. He has to pay his men and buy his materials. He has to pay the subcontractors. He has to have cash from the employers, otherwise he will not be able to carry on. So, once the architect gives his certificates, they must be honoured all down the line. The employer must pay the main contractor; the main contractor must pay the subcontractor; and so forth. Cross claims must be settled later.

Dodd v. *Churton* – 1897

A contract provided for the whole of the works to be completed by June 1892. Liquidated damages were included in the contract. There was a provision in the contract that any authority given by the architect for additional work would not vitiate the contract. There were thus no provisions for an extension of time. However, additional works were ordered that delayed the works beyond the completion date. The employer decided on a reasonable amount of time for doing the additional works and then claimed the amount of liquidated damages mentioned in the contract. The Court of Appeal held that by giving the order for additional works the employer had waived the stipulation for liquidated damages in respect of non-compliance of the works by the stipulated time. It was stated that where one party to a contract is prevented from performing it by the act of another, he is not liable in law for that default.

Dodd Properties v. *Canterbury City Council* – 1980

Canterbury City Council built a multi-storey car park next to a building owned by Dodd Properties. Piling operations caused damage to the building and Dodd Properties claimed damages for both the cost of necessary repairs and for the loss of business during the carrying out of the repairs. When the case came to court the work had not been done, since they were awaiting the damages to pay for the repairs. Dodd Properties claimed current rates, whereas the council suggested that these should be based upon rates relevant at the time the damage was done. It was held that there had been no failure on the part of Dodd Properties to investigate the loss and their claim was therefore upheld.

Dutton v.

Bognor Regis UDC – 1971

The foundations of a house were built upon land that had been used as a refuse disposal tip. The foundations were passed and approved by the local authority building inspector. Some time later the plaintiff purchased the house from the original owner, and cracks that began to appear in the wall were discovered to be due to settlement. The builder settled the matter for an agreed sum. The local authority, however, were held to be liable for negligence, since they owed a duty of care and this had not been reasonably given. Lord Denning expressed the view that the cause of action arose when the defective foundations were laid.

East Ham Corporation v.

Bernard Sunley and Sons Ltd – 1965

The corporation claimed damages for defective work in the construction of a school in East Ham. The building contract was in the RIBA form (revision of 1950). The contractor had completed the work and the architect had issued his final certificate 3 years after practical completion. This final certificate issued by the architect at the end of the job was conclusive evidence of the adequacy of the works. Two years later some cladding panels fell down due to faults in the fixings. The courts had to consider two questions:

1. On the true construction of the contract, was the final certificate issued by the architect conclusive evidence as to the sufficiency of the works subject to the exceptions mentioned in clause 24(f)?
2. Did the words 'reasonable examination' mean that carried out during progress or at the end of the defects liability period?

It was held by the courts that the final certificate was conclusive evidence that the works had been properly carried out, subject to the provisions of the final certificate clause.

The stone panels fell off as a result of the careless and incompetent fashion in which they had been attached. It was extremely fortunate that no one was killed or injured. Many contractors would have been not only too willing but anxious to remedy such defects. Not these contractors. They had relied on an escape clause in the contract and sought to throw the whole of their defective work on to the council. The Court of Appeal concluded that the contractors escaped liability under the contract provision. However, on leave to appeal to the House of Lords the decision was reversed. The employer was therefore awarded damages based upon the costs at the time of performing it.

English Industrial Estates Corporation v.

George Wimpey and Co. Ltd – 1972

This case was based upon the JCT conditions relevant at the time. In addition, a special condition allowed for the employer's tenant to install machinery and store materials during the construction of the works. The contractor was, however, to be responsible for insuring the works. During the construction period an extensive fire damaged the works with a loss of approximately £250,000. The issue then arose as to whether this loss should be borne by the contractor's insurers or by those of the employer. The contractor claimed that clause 12 of the Conditions of Contract excluded the possibility of special provisions, particularly where they were in conflict with standard conditions, in this instance clause 16 (clauses 18 and 2 of JCT 80, respectively).

The courts held in favour of the employer, because they were not satisfied that there had been a sufficient taking of possession for clause 16 to apply. It would appear that since, at the outset, both parties envisaged this early occupation by the employer, the insurance risk would remain with the employer.

A.E. Farr v.
The Admiralty – 1953
The plaintiffs contracted to construct a jetty at a naval base. Clause 26 (2) of the contract stated, 'The works and all materials and things whatsoever including such as may have been provided by the Authority on the site in connection with and for the purpose of the contract shall stand at the risk and be the sole charge of the contractor, and the contractor shall be responsible for, and with all possible speed make good, any loss or damage thereto arising from any cause whatsoever other than the accepted risks ...' After the plaintiffs had done a substantial part of the work, the jetty was damaged by a destroyer (owned by the employer) which collided with it. The plaintiffs claimed the costs of repairing the jetty. It was held because of the clause that the plaintiffs were liable for the repairs to the jetty.

A.E. Farr Ltd v.
Ministry of Transport – 1965
This was an appeal by A.E. Farr Ltd to the House of Lords which reversed a decision of the Court of Appeal. The case related to the payment of working space on a civil engineering contract using the relevant documents. The method of measurement at the time allowed for separate bill items to be measured for working space which would include their consequent refilling. Although the ICE Conditions of Contract at the time included a clause, 'The contractor shall be deemed to have satisfied himself before tendering as to the correctness and sufficiency of tender for the works', this could not be extended to include errors made by the client's advisers. The court therefore accepted that separate items should have been measured in accordance with the appropriate method of measurement. All bills of quantities are prepared in accordance with a method of measurement and strict compliance with this should be made, or specific amendments stated where necessary.

Re Fox ex parte Oundle & Thrapston RDC v.
Trustee – 1948
A building contractor became bankrupt and the question the courts had to

decide was whether the materials not incorporated into the works were vested in the contractor's trustee. The basis for this was the reputed ownership clause contained in the Bankruptcy Act. This stated, 'All goods being at the commencement of the bankruptcy in the possession, order or disposition of the bankrupt in his trade or business by consent or permission of the true owner, he is the reputed owner thereof and his ownership passes to the trustee.' It was held that the trustee had no claim to materials on site which had been paid for in interim certificate. He did, however, have a good claim to materials paid for, but retained in the contractor's yard.

Gilbert Ash (Northern) Ltd v. Modern Engineering (Bristol) Ltd – 1973

This case involved a contractor who had deducted sums due to a nominated subcontractor for set-off, because of a breach of warranty by the subcontractor. The Gilbert Ash form of subcontract had been used, which included a set-off clause. A sentence in this clause allowed for set-off for any breach of the subcontract, however minor, and unrelated to the actual damages actually suffered. This was held to be quite outside any rights which the courts will enforce and declared to be a penalty. Another sentence did, however, allow set-off for *bona-fide* claims of the contractor, and the court held that these sums were capable of being deducted.

M.J. Gleeson (Contractors) Ltd v. London Borough of Hillingdon – 1970

Gleeson's contract for the erection of 300 houses and associated buildings was based upon drawings and bills of quantities. The bills allowed for the completion of works in various stages, but the Appendix to the Conditions of Contract provided for a single completion date only. It was held that liquidated damages could not be deducted until the date for completion shown in the Appendix was exceeded. The decision was based upon the wording of the clause: 'Nothing contained in the Contract Bills shall override, modify or affect in any way whatsoever the application or interpretation of that which is contained in these conditions.' The court expressed the view that it would have been an easy matter to add words to that clause, to the effect that it was subject to conditions included in the bills. This, however, is contrary to recommended practice and could lead to confusion and uncertainty.

M.J. Gleeson v. Taylor Woodrow Construction Co. Ltd – 1989

This case concerned a management contract for building works on the Imperial War Museum. Taylor Woodrow were to organize, manage and supervise the works and Gleeson were to carry out their portion of the subcontract works. The subcontract works were delayed. Gleeson were awarded 39 days against a claim for 73 days. Taylor Woodrow argued that because of this delay, they had been subjected to claims from other subcontractors and they therefore deducted 'set-off claims' from Gleeson and in addition liquidated damages. Gleeson accepted that the dispute concerning the extension of time and the liquidated damages aspect would be dealt with under the arbitration procedures. However, they considered that the set-off sums had been wrongfully deducted. Taylor Woodrow argued that these should also be dealt with under arbitration. The court held that a prerequisite of setting-off was to quantify it precisely. This had not been done. The court also believed that the set-off and the liquidated damages might involve some duplication, since both were concerned with the alleged delay by the subcontractor.

Accordingly, the court found that there was no defence to Gleeson's claim and no dispute that could be referred to arbitration as far as the set-off amount was concerned. Judgment was therefore given for the plaintiffs, with the remaining matters of liquidated damages and the extension of time being referred to arbitration.

Gloucester County Council v. *Richardson* – 1968

This contract was based upon the 1939 form of contract, which is considerably different from that in use. It illustrates the problems of warranty agreements which the new form seeks to overcome. The main contractor was instructed by the architect to accept a contract from a nominated supplier. This was for the supply of precast concrete columns, on terms and at a price agreed by the employer. After erection, cracks appeared in the units and the question of the contractor's liability arose. It was held that the contractor was not liable since he had been directed to enter into a contract which severely restricted his right of recourse against the supplier in the event of defects. It should be noted that the 1939 form did not give the contractor the right to object to nomination of a supplier or to insist upon indemnity.

Gold v. *Patman & Fotheringham Ltd* – 1958

This contract contained a provision whereby the contractor sought to indemnify the employer against claims in respect of damage to property arising out of the works. The indemnity only occurred where it could be shown that the contractor had been negligent in carrying out the works. He had furthermore only insured the works in his own name, and not that of the employer since this was not a requirement of the contract. (N.B. The current JCT form of contract requires a joint insurance in the names of the contractor and the employer.) During construction piling operations damaged adjoining property, but no question of negligence arose since he was carrying this out correctly within the terms of the contract. The owners of the adjoining property therefore sued the employer, and he attempted to bring an action against the contractor for failure to safeguard the employer's interest. It was held that the contractor's obligation was only to insure himself and not the employer as well.

Martin Grant & Co. Ltd v.
Sir Lindsay Parkinson & Co. Ltd – 1985

Grants were subcontractors for formwork on a large number of local authority housing projects. The subcontract was in non-standard form and contained no provisions for the risk of delay. Substantial delays arose in the performance of the main contracts. Grants suffered considerable loss, since they had to carry out their work several years later than they anticipated. Grants contended that the main contractor would make sufficient work available for them in order that they might maintain a reasonable progress of the works in an economic and efficient manner.

The trial judge decided that the express terms of the subcontract left no room for the kind of implied term for which Grants contended. The case went to the Court of Appeal, who dismissed Grants' case. The express terms of the subcontract left no room for the term contended for to be implied. There is no general rule of law implying such a term in a building subcontract, either because of the relationship of the parties or otherwise.

Greaves & Co. (Contractors) Ltd v.
Baynham Meikle and Partners – 1976

A firm of consulting engineers were responsible for the design of a warehouse. The two-storey building would be used for the storage of oil drums, and forklift trucks would be used for transporting these around the building. Within a matter of a few weeks cracks occurred in the building. The engineers were sued for the costs of the remedial work that was necessary, on the basis that the design was unsuitable for the purpose intended. It was held by the Court of Appeal that because the engineers knew of the building's proposed use beforehand, they were liable for the costs of the remedial work.

Hadley v.
Baxendale – 1854

The principles for assessing damages resulting from a breach of contract were stated in this case as:
(a)   that arising naturally from the breach;
(b)   that which may reasonably be supported to have been in the minds of the parties at the time they entered into contract.

Hedley Byrne & Co. Ltd v.
Heller and Partners Ltd – 1964

A firm of advertising agents gave credit to a client in reliance upon a banker's reference, and suffered loss when the client became insolvent. The reference had been given carelessly but, since the bank had expressly disclaimed liability when giving it, the action failed. Nevertheless the House of Lords stated that, contrary to what had previously been believed, liability for negligence may extend to careless words as well as to careless deeds and that damages may be awarded for financial loss as well as for physical injury to persons and property.

W. Higgins Ltd v.
Northampton Corporation – 1927

Higgins contracted with the local authority to erect 58 houses. However, Higgins had completed his tender incorrectly. He thought that he was tendering for the erection of the houses at £1,670 a pair, when in fact it was £1,613, because of the way in which Higgins had made up the bills. It was held that Higgins was bound by his mistake and could not claim to have the contract set aside or rectified.

Howard Marine v.
Ogden and Sons – 1978

Ogdens, a firm of contractors, were one of the tenderers for the construction of a sewage works for the Northumbrian Water Authority. Surplus excavation material was to be loaded into barges, shipped downstream and dumped at sea. Howards were a firm who owned barges that were capable of doing this work. A quotation for the hire of the barges specified the volume of material that each barge could carry, and this was 850 cubic metres. On this basis the contractor could establish the number of trips necessary and this effect upon the programme. But one fact was overlooked. Each vessel travelling on water has a safe loading line which depends upon the weight of the material. The amount carried was therefore at the most 850 cubic metres, but because the spoil was clay this in practice turned out to be considerably less. Various telephone conversations took place between Howards and Ogdens, but misunderstandings occurred. To further complicate matters the payload figure in Lloyd's register was incorrect. This was stated as 1,600 tonnes but was in actual fact only 1,055 tonnes. Although Ogdens had prudently based their calculations on a lower figure than that agreed of 850 cubic metres, the barges failed to carry even this volume. Ogdens then refused to pay for any more barges, and Howards withdrew their transport. Howards claimed for their outstanding hire, and Ogdens counterclaimed for misrepresentation and damages.

The moral of the story is that when making enquiries it is unsafe to rely upon telephone conversations alone. Such answers may be too casual and of little legal consequence. Either independent advice should be sought or, preferably, the salient facts should be in writing.

The principle of *Hedley Byrne* v. *Heller and Partners* (1964) came up for consideration by the Court of Appeal. This stated: 'When an enquirer consults a businessman in the course of his business and makes it clear to him that he is seeking considered advice and intends to act on it in a particular way, a duty to take care in giving such advice arises and the adviser may be liable in negligence if the advice he gives turns out to be bad.'

IBA v.
EMI and BICC – 1980

EMI were the main contractors for a project for the IBA. BICC were nominated subcontractors for an aerial mast. The mast collapsed because of BICC's failure to consider the effects of asymmetric ice loading on the struts. Although EMI took no part in the design process they had accepted the contractual responsibility for the adequacy of the design. It was stated that one who contracts to design and supply an article for a known purpose, must ensure that it is fit for that purpose.

Owing to the complexity of modern buildings, it is often necessary for the architect to employ specialists. Some of these may be independent consultants or subcontractors. One of the functions of the architect is to co-ordinate the design to ensure that it is compatible with the overall scheme and is reasonably fit for the purpose intended. (See *Moresk Cleaners Ltd* v. *Hicks* 1966.)

Ibmac Ltd v.
Marshall (Homes) Ltd – 1968

The defendants, who were building a council housing estate, employed the plaintiffs to build a roadway to serve it. The plaintiffs quoted a price for the work, supplying a bill of quantities with rates for the work. The plaintiffs found that the work was more difficult than they had envisaged, since the site lay at the bottom of a steep hill. There were also serious difficulties with water. The plaintiffs abandoned the works and claimed payment for the work that they had done. Their claim failed in the Court of Appeal.

Killby & Gayford Ltd v.
Selincourt Ltd – 1973

In a letter, the architects asked a firm of contractors to price alteration work. The letter concluded, 'Assuming that we can agree a satisfactory contract price between us, the general conditions and terms will be subject to the normal standard form of RIBA contract.' The contractors submitted a written estimate. The architect replied that he was accepting the estimate on behalf of the client and shall be obliged if you will accept this letter as your formal instruction to proceed with the work. No JCT contract was ever signed, but the contractors proceeded with work. In the Court of Appeal it was held that the exchange of letters incorporated the current JCT form.

William Lacey (Hounslow) v.
Davis – 1957

The plaintiff tendered for the reconstruction of war-damaged premises belonging to the defendant, who led the plaintiff to believe that it would receive the contract. At the defendant's request, the plaintiff calculated the timber and steel requirements for the building, and prepared various further schedules and estimates which the defendant made use of in negotiations with the War Damage Commission. Eventually the plaintiff was informed that the defendant intended to employ another builder to do the work. In fact, the defendant sold the premises. The plaintiff claimed damages for breach of contract, and alternatively, remuneration on a *quantum meruit* basis in respect of the work done by it in connection with the reconstruction scheme. It was held that although no binding contract had been concluded between the parties, a promise should be implied that the defendant would pay a reasonable sum to the plaintiff in respect of the services rendered. Judgment was entered for the plaintiff.

Lewis and Brass – 1877

An architect invited tenders for building works. The defendant's tender read, 'I hereby agree to execute complete, within the space of 26 weeks from the day receiving the instructions to commence, the whole of the work required to be done ... for the sum of £4,193.' The architect replied that he had been instructed to accept the tender and a contract would be prepared, ready for signature within a few days. The defendant had made a mistake in his tender and tried to withdraw from the contract. In the Court of Appeal it was held that the tender and acceptance formed a contract. A tender and its acceptance may therefore amount to a contract, even though the acceptance refers to a formal contract to be drawn up afterwards.

Sir Lindsay Parkinson & Co. Ltd v.
Commissioners for Work – 1949

A construction contract was agreed on the basis that the contract price would be the cost of the works, plus a net profit not exceeding £300,000. The project was typical cost plus contract carried out at this time. Additional works were ordered which extensively increased the size of the project. The court held that the contractor was entitled to a *quantum meruit* payment for this additional work, since this work could not have been envisaged at the start of the project.

London Borough of Newham v.
Taylor Woodrow (Anglian) Ltd – 1980

This infamous case was for a contract for the erection of a 22-storey block of flats, known as Ronan Point. The building was of a prefabricated concrete construction. One morning, gas caused an explosion in a flat on the eighteenth floor. This resulted in the collapse of the south-east corner. The local authority claimed for the cost of repairing and strengthening a number of similar blocks. The court acquitted the contractor of negligence, largely on the basis that several other local authorities had approved and accepted the design. The court held, however, that the contractor was liable for a breach of contract, on the basis that the flats should have been designed and constructed so that they would be safe and fit for their purpose. In addition, the building contract included a provision that the contractor would be responsible for any faults and repair work at his own expense. This case was again reopened in 1984 but the final decision on liability has still to be resolved.

London County Council v.
Wilkins (Valuation Officer) – 1956
This case established that the provision of temporary accommodation on site by a contractor was rateable if erected for a sufficient period of time.

London School Board v.
Northcroft – 1889
The quantity surveyor was responsible for measuring buildings up to a value of £12,000. The employers brought an action for negligence resulting from two clerical errors in the quantity surveyor's calculations. This involved over-payments to the builder of £118 and £15, respectively. It was held that the quantity surveyor, who had employed a skilled clerk who had carried out hundreds of intricate calculations correctly, was not liable, since he had done what was reasonably necessary.

Marston v.
Kigrass Ltd – 1989
The plaintiffs claimed for preparatory works over and above the costs and work of preparing their tender for a design and build contract to provide a factory to replace one that had burnt down. The contract was never placed since the funds from the insurance company were insufficient to cover the costs of rebuilding. The plaintiffs' tender was the best value for money but because of the tight time-scale it needed to be supplemented with further details. The tender was followed by a vital meeting when the plaintiffs were the only tenderers invited to discuss their tender. The chairman of the company said that no contract could be entered into without the insurance money for rebuilding. Nothing was suggested that any preparatory work would be at the contractor's own risk, in the event that the insurance money did not materialize. The defendants were well aware that the plaintiffs would need to start the preparatory work before the contract was signed. It was also made plain that subject to this work being satisfactory the contract would be given to the plaintiffs.

It was held that there was an express request made by the defendants to the plaintiffs to carry out a small quantity of design work and there was an implied request to carry out preparatory works in general. Both express and implied requests gave rise to a right to payment of a reasonable sum.

Minter v.
Welsh Health Technical Services – 1980
This case was based upon a claim for loss and expense, the equivalent of clause

26, but on the 1963 form. The amounts paid were challenged on the basis that they had not been certified and paid until long after the contractor had incurred the loss. The courts held that direct loss and/or expense were to be read as conferring a right to recover sums on the same principle as common law damages. In essence, therefore, this might include compensation for the loss of the use of capital.

Molloy v. *Liebe* – 1910

A contract provided that no works beyond those that were included in the contract would be paid for by the employer, unless it was in writing from the employer and the architect. During the progress of the works, the employer required certain work to be carried out. The employer insisted that these were within the terms of the contract. The contractor insisted that they represented extra works and must be paid for separately. It was held that it was open to the arbitrator to decide. If the arbitrator concluded that the works were not part of the original contract, then the employer by implication agreed to pay for them.

Re Newman ex parte Capper – 1876

This contract included a provision of a large fixed amount of liquidated damages payable by the contractor in the event of any breach occurring. The court held that this was in effect a penalty since it could not relate with all of the varying amounts of loss which might arise. It was not, therefore, enforceable. The courts did, however, fix an appropriate amount that was upheld as being damages sustained.

North West Metropolitan Regional Hospital Board v. *T.A. Bickerton Ltd* – 1976

This case placed the responsibility of renomination with the architect rather than the contractor, after a nominated subcontractor had defaulted. A nominated subcontractor failed to complete his work due to his liquidation. The main contractor then requested the architect under the terms of the contract (1963 edition) to appoint a new firm as a successor to this nominated subcontractor. Because a new price was required, and that this was likely to be a higher price, the employer suggested that the contractor was responsible for completing this work in any way, but to the approval of the architect. This may result in the contractor doing the work himself or subletting with approval, but that any extra in cost must be borne by the main contractor.

The 1963 edition of the form of contract is unclear on this point, but the case was decided in the contractor's favour. It was the architect's responsibility, therefore, to renominate in the event of default, and the employer is therefore obliged to pay the additional cost of the new firm employed. JCT 80 has clarified this point along the lines of this decision.

Oram Builders Ltd v.
M.J. Pemberton and C. Pemberton – 1985
This project was on the Minor Works Agreement (JCT 1980 edition). Article 4
is an arbitration agreement in general terms. The supervising officer issued
instructions to the plaintiffs which constituted a substantial variation to the
contract. The plaintiffs claimed to have done the extra work and so required a
certificate for its payment. This was not forthcoming and the plaintiffs claimed
extra costs for the work or alternatively damages. The defendants disputed the
plaintiffs' claim and counterclaimed for alleged breaches of contract. The
preliminary issue, with which this judgment is concerned, was whether the
courts had powers to review the exercise of the supervising officer's
discretionary powers under the contract and open up certificates. It was held
that the courts had no jurisdiction to go behind a certificate of the architect or
supervising officer. Where there is an arbitration clause in general terms
referring any dispute or difference between the parties concerning the contract
to the arbitrator ... then even on a narrow interpretation of the reasoning of the
Court of Appeal in *Northern Health Authority* v. *Derek Crouch Construction
Co. Ltd* (1984), the High Court has no jurisdiction to go behind an architect's
certificate.

Peak Construction Ltd v.
McKinney Foundations Ltd – 1970
This case considered two separate matters concerning a project that overran its
contract period. The first problem was concerned with an extension of time.
McKinney Foundations Ltd were the nominated subcontractors for piling work.
Upon completion of this work defects were found, but there was a prolonged
delay on the part of the employer in both obtaining an engineer's advice and
deciding upon the remedial work to be carried out. When the project overran
the employer levied liquidated damages on the main contractor. The main
contractor then attempted to recover these from the subcontractor. Furthermore,
the above was not a reasonable cause for granting an extension of time within
the terms of the contract. It was held, however, that because the delay was due
largely to the employer's default, liquidated damages could not be deducted.
This was the case if the extension of time clause did not make provision for
such a delay, or even if there was failure to extend the time.
    The second matter was concerned with the price fluctuation clause. The court
held that this clause continued to operate after the time for completion was past.
This matter has been clarified in JCT 80.

Porter v.
Tottenham Urban District Council – 1915
The plaintiff contracted to build a school for the council upon land belonging to
them. The contract provided that he should be entitled to enter the site
immediately, and that the works should be completed by a specified date. The

only access to the site was from an adjoining road and to lay a temporary sleeper road and then subsequently a permanent pathway. The plaintiff began work but was forced to abandon it because of a threatened injunction from an adjoining owner, who claimed that the road was his property. The third party's claims were held to be unfounded. The plaintiff then resumed and completed the works. He claimed damages against the council in respect of the delay caused by the third party's action. In the Court of Appeal, the plaintiff's claim failed. It was stated that there was no implied warranty by the council against wrongful interference by third parties with free access to the site.

Roberts & Co. Ltd v. *Leicestershire County Council* – 1961

A contractor submitted a tender which specified a completion of 18 months. The county architect, unknown to the contractor, decided that 30 months was a more appropriate contract period. Prior to the signing of the contract, there were two meetings at which the contractor referred to his plans to complete the work according to a progress schedule in 18 months. It was held that the contractor was entitled to rectification on the grounds that the defendants were estopped by their conduct from saying that there was no mistake.

Scott v. *Avery* – 1856

This case concerned an insurance policy which indicated that only arbitration proceedings were permissible in the event of a dispute occurring. It therefore sought to prohibit direct legal actions in the courts. It was held that this provision was valid. The majority of the standard forms of building contract contain arbitration provisions. This course of action is agreed to between the parties, who may consider arbitration more appropriate. If one of the parties wishes to hold to arbitration, he may apply for a stay of proceedings on the basis that the contract follows the *Scott* v. *Avery* principle. In practice, the courts in deciding whether to grant this are likely to take into consideration any hardship that may be caused.

Sutcliffe v. *Thackrah and Others* – 1974

The facts of this case were that Mr Sutcliffe employed Thackrah and Others, a firm of architects, to design and supervise the construction of a house. During construction two certificates (Nos 9 and 10) were issued and duly paid by Mr Sutcliffe. Shortly afterwards the contract with the builders ended when the builders became insolvent and another firm completed the work.

It was then discovered that the two above-mentioned certificates had included defective work. Because it could not be recovered from the builders, Mr Sutcliffe sued the architects for his loss because of their negligence in issuing the certificates. The negligence was not due to a failure to detect the defective work, since one of the architects was aware of this; it was due to a failure to pass the information to the quantity surveyor who had valued it, assuming that it was in accordance with the contract.

The official referee who tried the case in arbitration, held that the architect was negligent and awarded damages to Mr Sutcliffe. The Court of Appeal reversed this decision but this was finally overruled by the House of Lords. It was held that the architect was discharging a duty under the contract between the parties, but that there was no dispute over the subject matter and so it could not be contended that he was acting in arbitration.

In order for quantity surveyors to safeguard themselves from possible repercussions in the future, they now include on their valuations words to the following effect: 'That the valuation assumes that the work is in accordance with the specification of materials and workmanship.' A quantity surveyor would clearly not include in a valuation work that was obviously defective, but the matter of quality control is more rightly the responsibility of the architect. The case of *Chambers* v. *Goldthorpe* was cited, but this was overruled by the House of Lords.

George E. Taylor & Co. Ltd v.
G. Percy Trentham – 1980

Taylor were nominated subcontractors to Trentham. They also had a contract with the employer whereby they warranted due performance of the subcontract works so that the main contractors should not become entitled to an extension of time. The employer paid Trentham only £7,526 against an interim certificate of £22,101. The amount withheld was the balance payable to the subcontractors after deduction of the main contractor's claim against them for delay. It was held that the employer was not entitled to withhold the money, the contract between the employer and the subcontractor being *res inter alios acta*.

Trollope & Colls and *Holland and Hannan and Cubitts Ltd* v.
Atomic Power Construction – 1962

The contractor tendered for work under a contract which included provisions for variations and fluctuations. After a delay of 4 months the contractor was requested to commence work upon the site. This request included a letter of intent to enter into a formal contract when the terms of the contract were settled. Substantial changes to the scheme had been notified to the contractor and this continued to occur until the terms of the contract were agreed 10 months later. The contractor therefore claimed that he should be paid on a *quantum meruit* basis for the work that had already been completed prior to the signing of the formal agreement. This he claimed was more equitable than on the basis of his original tender adjusted by variations, since at that time no contract was in existence.

It was held, however, that both parties had contemplated entering into a contract which would affect all the work associated with the contract. The contract was formulated in the light of the work going on at the time and it had therefore a retrospective effect.

Trollope & Colls Ltd v.
North Western Metropolitan Regional Hospital Board – 1973
This was a very large building contract where the Court of Appeal reversed the ⌇⌇sion of the trial judge; but the House of Lords confirmed the trial judge's opinion. The Hospital Board wanted the project completed in three phases, using three largely similar sets of conditions. Phase 1 was delayed by 59 weeks and the architect granted an extension of time by 47 weeks. Phase 3 was to start contractually 6 months after Phase 1 had received its certificate of practical completion. Phase 3 did, however, still retain its original completion date which then envisaged a 16-month contract rather than the previously accepted 30-month contract period.

In these circumstances, could the time for completion of Phase 3 be extended by the period of 47 weeks granted on Phase 1? Unexpectedly it was the contractor who suggested that it could not, but for his own advantage. The contractor professed to being able to complete in time, and they therefore called upon the Hospital Board to nominate their appropriate subcontractors. This they were unable to do. In this situation the contractors would require new prices to be agreed relevant to the prevailing date. The contractors therefore sought a declaration in the High Court that the date for completion of Phase 3 was unaffected by Phase 1 being behind schedule.

The decision was made in favour of the contractor on the basis that the business efficacy of this large contract did not necessitate implying the kind of term the board required. The House of Lords was not satisfied that the parties had overlooked the effect of delays on earlier phases, in fixing the completion date for Phase 3.

Tyrer v.
District Auditor for Monmouthshire – 1974
A firm of contractors who went into liquidation had been employed upon several contracts by a local authority. The local authority found that this firm had been overpaid on interim certificates. The district auditor established that overpayment was due to the negligence of the quantity surveyor, in accepting excessively high rates for work carried out and failing to check simple arithmetic. The auditor then surcharged the quantity surveyor for the sums that he was unable to recover from the liquidator. The quantity surveyor appealed on the grounds that he had undertaken his duties in the capacity of an arbitrator. The court, however, rejected this appeal stating that 'there was nothing to show that the appellant was in quasi-judicial position when carrying out his duties here'.

Victoria Laundry Ltd v.
Newman Ltd – 1948
This case provides an interesting contrast with the case of *Hadley* v. *Baxendale* above. The plaintiffs were launderers and dyers and required a large boiler to

extend their plant and to help them win some lucrative contracts. A firm of engineers contracted to sell them such a boiler, but because of certain faults arising the delivery of the boiler was seriously delayed. The plaintiffs claimed damages. First, equivalent to the estimated loss of the increased profits the use of the boiler would have acquired for them; and second, the amount that they would have earned from dyeing contracts during the same period. The court held that the engineers were liable for the ordinary losses which they must have known from the particular circumstances. They were not liable in the second instance since this would have required special knowledge which they did not have.

University of Warwick v. *Sir Robert McAlpine* – 1989

The buildings at the university had ceramic tile cladding on a concrete frame. The cladding which had been carried out by subcontractors began to fail. The architects blamed bad workmanship and, McAlpine, the main contractors, blamed the design. The university decided to remedy the defects by a resin injection process that was an innovation. The sole licensees of the process were a firm known as CCL. These were recommended by the architect and employed by McAlpine to carry out the remedial works. The main contract conditions were varied, and whilst CCL were technically not nominated subcontractors they were employed by McAlpine.

McAlpines had considerable reservations about the use of this new process. The remedial works were not successful and the university alleged that McAlpine were in breach of an implied fitness for purpose. It was held that a term that resin be fit for its purpose could only be implied in the main contract if the university had relied on McAlpine. As they had not done so, no such term was to be implied.

City of Westminster v. *J. Jarvis & Sons Ltd* and *Peter Lind* – 1970

Jarvis contracted with Westminster for the erection of a multi-storey car park, with flats, offices, showrooms and ancillary works. The contract was in JCT 63 form. Lind were nominated subcontractors for the piling work. Lind carried out the work and purported to complete by the subcontract completion date. Lind left the site. Some weeks later, it was discovered that many of the piles were defective, either as a result of bad workmanship or poor materials. Lind carried out the remedial works. The main contract works were delayed for some 21.5 weeks. Jarvis, the main contractor, claimed an extension of time under clause 23(g). In the House of Lords it was held that Jarvis was not entitled to an extension of time since the works had apparently been completed by the due date. 'Delay' within the meaning of the clause occurs only if, by the subcontract completion date, the subcontractor had failed to achieve such completion of his work that he cannot hand it over to the main contractor.

Re Wilkinson ex parte Fowler – 1905

This contract allowed for the right to make direct payment to certain firms, where the main contractor defaulted or delayed in proper payment to them. The contractor became bankrupt and the employer decided to make payments out of the retentions owing to the contractor. It was held by the courts that such payments were valid against the trustee.

William Sindall v.
North West Thames Regional Health Authority – 1977

The main contractor introduced a bonus incentive scheme on a site in accordance with the principles recommended by the National Joint Council for the Building Industry. The contract was on a fluctuations basis incorporating clause 31A. An increase in the basic rates of wages occurred and this, in a bonus scheme, was a voluntary decision and not as an unavoidable consequence of following the obligatory rules or decisions, and the cost of its operation was therefore outside of the scope of clause 31A. This was in spite of the fact that once the contractor had introduced his bonus scheme on the basis of the NJCBI rules, he had to also pay the eventual increase.

Williams v.
Firzmaurice – 1859

This involved the contractor in building a house in accordance with the drawings and specification supplied by the architect. The specification included a clause, 'that the contractor undertook to provide the whole of the materials necessary for the completion of the works and to perform all the works of every kind mentioned'. Floor boarding, although shown on the drawings, was not included in the specification. The contractor therefore refused to carry out this work unless it was paid for as extra works. It was held that the boarding was necessary and was therefore included in the contract price, even though it had been omitted from the specification.

INDEX